M000266121

STATA USER'S GUIDE
RELEASE 11

A Stata Press Publication
StataCorp LP
College Station, Texas

Copyright © 1985–2009 by StataCorp LP
All rights reserved
Version 11

Published by Stata Press, 4905 Lakeway Drive, College Station, Texas 77845
Typeset in TEX
Printed in the United States of America

10 9 8 7 6 5 4 3 2 1

ISBN-10: 1-59718-064-5
ISBN-13: 978-1-59718-064-1

This manual is protected by copyright. All rights are reserved. No part of this manual may be reproduced, stored in a retrieval system, or transcribed, in any form or by any means—electronic, mechanical, photocopy, recording, or otherwise—without the prior written permission of StataCorp LP unless permitted by the license granted to you by StataCorp LP to use the software and documentation. No license, express or implied, by estoppel or otherwise, to any intellectual property rights is granted by this document.

StataCorp provides this manual "as is" without warranty of any kind, either expressed or implied, including, but not limited to, the implied warranties of merchantability and fitness for a particular purpose. StataCorp may make improvements and/or changes in the product(s) and the program(s) described in this manual at any time and without notice.

The software described in this manual is furnished under a license agreement or nondisclosure agreement. The software may be copied only in accordance with the terms of the agreement. It is against the law to copy the software onto DVD, CD, disk, diskette, tape, or any other medium for any purpose other than backup or archival purposes.

The automobile dataset appearing on the accompanying media is Copyright © 1979 by Consumers Union of U.S., Inc., Yonkers, NY 10703-1057 and is reproduced by permission from CONSUMER REPORTS, April 1979.

Stata and Mata are registered trademarks and NetCourse is a trademark of StataCorp LP.

Other brand and product names are registered trademarks or trademarks of their respective companies.

For copyright information about the software, type help copyright within Stata.

The suggested citation for this software is

StataCorp. 2009. *Stata: Release 11*. Statistical Software. College Station, TX: StataCorp LP.

Table of contents

Stata basics

Elements of Stata

Advice

Stata basics

1 Read this—it will help

Contents

(Continued on next page)

A Complete Stata Documentation Set contains more than 8,000 pages of information in the following manuals:

[GS]	*Getting Started with Stata* (Mac, Unix, or Windows)
[U]	*Stata User's Guide*
[R]	*Stata Base Reference Manual*
	Volume 1, A–H
	Volume 2, I–P
	Volume 3, Q–Z
[D]	*Stata Data-Management Reference Manual*
[G]	*Stata Graphics Reference Manual*
[XT]	*Stata Longitudinal-Data/Panel-Data Reference Manual*
[MI]	*Stata Multiple-Imputation Reference Manual*
[MV]	*Stata Multivariate Statistics Reference Manual*
[P]	*Stata Programming Reference Manual*
[SVY]	*Stata Survey Data Reference Manual*
[ST]	*Stata Survival Analysis and Epidemiological Tables Reference Manual*
[TS]	*Stata Time-Series Reference Manual*
[I]	*Stata Quick Reference and Index*
[M]	*Mata Reference Manual*
	Volume 1, [M-1]–[M-3]
	Volume 2, [M-4]–[M-6]

Detailed information about each of these manuals and the other Stata manuals may be found online at

http://www.stata-press.com/manuals/

In addition, installation instructions are found in the *Installation Guide*, which comes in the DVD case.

1.1   Getting Started with Stata

There are three *Getting Started* manuals:

[GSM] *Getting Started with Stata for Mac*
[GSU] *Getting Started with Stata for Unix*
[GSW] *Getting Started with Stata for Windows*

1. Learn how to use Stata—read the *Getting Started* (GSM, GSU, or GSW). manual.

2. Now turn to the other manuals; see [U] **1.2 The User's Guide and the Reference manuals**.

1.2   The User's Guide and the Reference manuals

The *User's Guide* is divided into three sections: *Stata basics*, *Elements of Stata*, and *Advice*. At the beginning of each section is a list of the chapters found in that section. In addition to helping you explore the fundamentals of Stata—information that all users should know—this manual will guide you to other sources for Stata information.

The other manuals are the *Reference* manuals. The Stata *Reference* manuals are each arranged like an encyclopedia—alphabetically. Look at the *Base Reference Manual*. Look under the name of a command. If you do not find the command, look in the index. A few commands are so closely related that they are documented together, such as `ranksum` and `median`, which are both documented in [R] **ranksum**.

Not all the entries in the *Base Reference Manual* are Stata commands; some contain technical information, such as [R] **maximize**, which details Stata's iterative maximization process, or [R] **error messages**, which provides information on error messages and return codes.

Like an encyclopedia, the *Reference* manuals are not designed to be read from cover to cover. When you want to know what a command does, complete with all the details, qualifications, and pitfalls, or when a command produces an unexpected result, read its description. Each entry is written at the level of the command. The descriptions assume that you have little knowledge of Stata's features when they are explaining simple commands, such as those for using and saving data. For more complicated commands, they assume that you have a firm grasp of Stata's other features.

If a Stata command is not in the *Base Reference Manual*, you can find it in one of the other *Reference* manuals. The titles of the manuals indicate the types of commands that they contain. The *Programming Reference Manual*, however, contains commands not only for programming Stata but also for manipulating matrices (not to be confused with the matrix programming language described in the *Mata Reference Manual*).

1.2.1   PDF manuals

Every copy of Stata comes with a PDF version of Stata's complete documentation. Of course, printed manuals are also available.

The PDF documentation may be accessed from within Stata by selecting **Help** > **PDF Documentation**. Even more convenient, every help file in Stata links to the equivalent manual entry. If you are reading **help regress**, simply click on [R] `regress` in the `Title` section of the help file to go directly to the [R] **regress** manual entry.

We provide recommended settings for your PDF viewer to optimize it for Stata's documentation at http://www.stata.com/support/faqs/res/documentation.html.

1.2.2   Example datasets

Various examples in this manual use what is referred to as the automobile dataset, `auto.dta`. We previously created a dataset on the prices, mileages, weights, and other characteristics of 74 automobiles and saved it in a file called `auto.dta`. (These data originally came from the April 1979 issue of *Consumer Reports* and from the United States Government EPA statistics on fuel consumption; they were compiled and published by Chambers et al. [1983].)

In our examples, you will often see us type

```
. use http://www.stata-press.com/data/r11/auto
```

We include the `auto.dta` file with Stata. If you want to use it from your own computer rather than via the Internet, you can type

>   . sysuse auto

See [D] **sysuse**.

You can also access the `auto` dataset by selecting **File > Example Datasets...**, clicking on *Example datasets installed with Stata*, and clicking on use beside the `auto.dta` filename.

There are many other example datasets that ship with Stata or are available over the web. Here is a partial list of the example datasets included with Stata:

auto.dta	1978 Automobile Data
autornd.dta	Subset of 1978 Automobile Data
bplong.dta	fictional blood pressure data
bpwide.dta	fictional blood pressure data
cancer.dta	Patient Survival in Drug Trial
census.dta	1980 Census data by state
citytemp.dta	City Temperature Data
citytemp4.dta	City Temperature Data
educ99gdp.dta	Education and GDP
gnp96.dta	U.S. GNP, 1967–2002
lifeexp.dta	Life expectancy, 1978
nlsw88.dta	U.S. National Longitudinal Study of Young Women (NLSW, 1988 extract)
pop2000.dta	U.S. Census, 2000, extract
sp500.dta	S&P 500
uslifeexp.dta	U.S. life expectancy, 1900–1999
uslifeexp2.dta	U.S. life expectancy, 1900–1940
voter.dta	1992 presidential voter data

All these datasets may be used or described from the **Example Datasets...** help file.

Even more example datasets, including most of the datasets used in the reference manuals, are available at the Stata Press web site (http://www.stata-press.com/data/). You can download the datasets with your browser, or you can use them directly from the Stata command line:

>   . use http://www.stata-press.com/data/r11/nlswork

An alternative to the use command for these example datasets is webuse. For example, typing

>   . webuse nlswork

is equivalent to the above use command. For more information, see [D] **webuse**.

1.2.3 Cross-referencing

The *Getting Started* manual, the *User's Guide*, and the *Reference* manuals cross-reference each other.

>   [R]   **regress**
>   [D]   **reshape**
>   [XT]   **xtmixed**

The first is a reference to the `regress` entry in the *Base Reference Manual*, the second is a reference to the `reshape` entry in the *Data-Management Reference Manual*, and the third is a reference to the `xtmixed` entry in the *Longitudinal-Data/Panel-Data Reference Manual*.

[GSW] **C Advanced Stata usage**
[GSM] **C Advanced Stata usage**
[GSU] **C Advanced Stata usage**

are instructions to see the appropriate section of the *Getting Started with Stata for Windows, Getting Started with Stata for Mac,* or *Getting Started with Stata for Unix* manual.

1.2.4   The index

At the end of each manual is an index for that manual. The index for the *Base Reference Manual* is found at the end of the third volume. The index for the *Mata Reference Manual* is found at the end of the second volume.

The *Quick Reference and Index* contains a combined index for the *Getting Started* manuals, the *User's Guide,* and all the *Reference* manuals except the *Mata Reference Manual.* It also contains quick reference information on subjects such as the estimation commands.

To find information and commands quickly, you can use Stata's search or hsearch commands; see [R] **search** and [R] **hsearch**. At the Stata command prompt, try typing search geometric mean. search searches Stata's keyword database and, optionally, will search the Internet, too. Try typing search geometric mean, all. Searching the Internet lets you find more commands and extensions for Stata written by Stata users. hsearch, on the other hand, searches the text of all the Stata help files on your computer, including help files that you have written and help files from user-written extensions that you have installed, and orders the outcome by relevancy. Try typing hsearch geometric mean. Between these two commands, if a capability exists, you should be able to find it.

1.2.5   The subject table of contents

A subject table of contents for the *User's Guide* and all the *Reference* manuals except the *Mata Reference Manual* is located in the *Quick Reference and Index.* This subject table of contents may also be accessed by clicking on **Contents** in the PDF bookmarks.

If you look under "Functions and expressions", you will see

[U]   Chapter 13 . . . . Functions and expressions
[D]   dates and times . . . . Date and time (%t) values and variables
[D]   egen . . . . Extensions to generate
[D]   functions . . . . Functions

1.2.6   Typography

We mix the ordinary typeface that you are reading now with a typewriter-style typeface that looks like this. When something is printed in the typewriter-style typeface, it means that something is a command or an option—it is something that Stata understands and something that you might actually type into your computer. Differences in typeface are important. If a sentence reads, "You could list the result ...", it is just an English sentence—you *could* list the result, but the sentence provides no clue as to how you might actually do that. On the other hand, if the sentence reads, "You could list the result ...", it is telling you much more—you could list the result, and you could do that by using the list command.

We will occasionally lapse into periods of inordinate cuteness and write, "We `described` the data and then `listed` the data." You get the idea. `describe` and `list` are Stata commands. We purposely began the previous sentence with a lowercase letter. Because `describe` is a Stata command, it must be typed in lowercase letters. The ordinary rules of capitalization are temporarily suspended in favor of preciseness.

We also mix in words printed in italic type, such as "To perform the rank-sum test, type `ranksum` *varname* `, by(`*groupvar*`)`". Italicized words are not supposed to be typed; instead, you are to substitute another word for them.

We would also like users to note our rule for punctuation of quotes. We follow a rule that is often used in mathematics books and British literature. The punctuation mark at the end of the quote is included in the quote only if it is a part of the quote. For instance, the pleased Stata user said she thought that Stata was a "very powerful program". Another user simply said, "I love Stata."

In this manual, however, there is little dialogue, and we follow this rule to precisely clarify what you are to type, as in, type "`cd c:`". The period is outside the quotation mark because you should not type the period. If we had wanted you to type the period, we would have included two periods at the end of the sentence: one inside the quotation and one outside, as in, type "`use myfile.`".

We have tried not to violate the other rules of English. If you find such violations, they were unintentional and resulted from our own ignorance or carelessness. We would appreciate hearing about them.

We have heard from Nicholas J. Cox of the Department of Geography at Durham University in the United Kingdom and express our appreciation. His efforts have gone far beyond dropping us a note, and there is no way with words that we can fully express our gratitude.

1.2.7   Vignettes

If you look, for example, at the entry [R] **brier**, you will see a brief biographical vignette of Glenn Wilson Brier (1913–1998), who did pioneering work on the measures described in that entry. A few such vignettes were added without fanfare in the Stata 8 manuals, just for interest, and many more were added in Stata 9, and even more have been added in Stata 10 and Stata 11. A vignette could often appropriately go in several entries. For example, George E. P. Box deserves to be mentioned in entries other than [TS] **arima**, such as [R] **boxcox**. However, to save space, each vignette is given once only, and an index of all vignettes is given in the *Quick Reference Manual and Index*.

All the vignettes were written by Nicholas J. Cox, Durham University, and were compiled using a wide range of reference books, articles in the literature, Internet sources, and information from individuals. Especially useful were the dictionaries of Upton and Cook (2006) and Everitt (2006) and the compilations of statistical biographies edited by Heyde and Seneta (2001) and Johnson and Kotz (1997). Of these, only the first provides information on people living at the time of publication.

1.3   What's new

This section is intended for previous Stata users. If you are new to Stata, you may as well skip to [U] **1.3.13 What's more**.

As always, Stata 11 is 100% compatible with the previous releases, but we remind programmers that it is important to put `version 10` or `version 9`, etc., at the top of old do- and ado-files so that they continue to work as you expect. You were supposed to do that when you wrote them, but if you did not, go back and do it now.

If you use user-written postestimation commands, you might need to use version control even when working interactively. There is a new feature of Stata 11, factor variables, that these commands may know nothing about if they were written before Stata 11. Until they are updated, you obviously will have to avoid using factor variables with them. In our testing, these older commands mostly worked fine even without specifying version 10 before running them. There is, however, a technical issue related to how estimation results are stored and sometimes an older program would stumble on this. If the user-written postestimation command you are using acts up, run both the estimation command and the postestimation command under version control. Then the user-written command will work because specifying version 10 really does make Stata 11 act like Stata 10.

We will list all the changes, item by item, but first, here are the highlights:

1. Stata now allows factor variables! In estimation, you can now fit models by typing, for example,

```
. regress y i.sex i.group i.sex#i.group age              (1)
. regress y i.sex##i.group age                           (same as 1)
. regress y i.sex i.group i.region
          i.sex#i.group i.sex#i.region i.group#i.region  (2)
          i.sex#i.group#i.region
          age
. regress y i.sex##i.group##i.region age                 (same as 2)
```

and Stata will form for itself the indicator variables for sex, group, and region, and their interactions. You do not use the old xi command, and no new variables will be created in your data. You can form interactions of factor variables with continuous variables, and continuous variables with continuous variables by using the c. prefix:

```
. regress y i.sex##i.group##i.region
          age c.age#c.age                                (3)
. regress y i.sex##i.group##i.region
          age i.sex##i.group##i.region#c.age             (4)
          c.age#c.age i.sex##i.group##i.region#c.age#c.age
. regress y i.sex##i.group##i.region##c.age              (same as 4)
          i.sex##i.group##i.region##c.age#c.age
```

This new factor-variable notation is understood by nearly every Stata estimation command, so you can type, for example,

```
. logistic outcome i.treatment##i.sex age bp c.age#c.bp
```

Factor variables work with summarize and list, too:

```
. list outcome i.treatment##i.sex
```

Factor variables have lots of additional features; see [U] **11.4.3 Factor variables**.

2. Stata 11's new postestimation command margins estimates margins and marginal effects. Included are estimated marginal means, least-squares means, average and conditional marginal and partial effects, average and conditional adjusted predictions, predictive margins, and more. There are few users who will not find margins useful. It will be well worth your time to read [R] **margins**.

3. Stata's new mi suite of commands performs multiple imputation. There is so much to say that mi gets its own manual.

mi provides methods for the analysis of incomplete data, data for which some values are missing, and provides both the imputation and estimation steps. mi's estimation step combines the estimation and pooling steps. Multivariate normal imputation is provided, along with five univariate methods that can be used alone or as building blocks for multivariate imputation.

mi can import already imputed data, including data from NHANES and ice. mi solves the problem of keeping multiple datasets in sync. You can create or drop variables or observations just as if you were working with one dataset. You can merge, append, and reshape data, all of which is to say that you can perform data management either before or even after forming the imputations.

Included is an interactive control panel that provides access to almost all of mi's capabilities and guides you through the steps of analysis.

See [MI] **intro**.

4. The new Variables Manager is the one-stop place to go to manage your variables. Click on the Variables Manager button or type varmanage. You can change names, labels, display formats, and storage types. You can define and edit notes, and define and edit value labels. The Variables Manager is useful even for those who have thousands of variables in their data; just type part of the name in the filter at the top left. See [D] **varmanage** and [GS] **7 Using the Variables Manager** (GSM, GSU, or GSW).

5. The Data Editor is all new. It is now a live view onto your data, which means that you can run a Stata command and see the changes reflected immediately. You can apply filters to view subsets of your data, take snapshots so that you can undo changes, and enter dates and times the natural way. See [D] **edit** and [GS] **6 Using the Data Editor** (GSM, GSU, or GSW).

6. The Do-file Editor under Windows is all new, too. Syntax highlighting and code folding are provided. There is no limit to file size. See [R] **doedit**.

7. You can now put bold and italic text, Greek letters, symbols, superscripts, and subscripts on graphs! See [G] *text*.

8. If you are not reading this on your computer, you could be. Stata now has PDF manuals—[GS], [U], [D], [G], [MI], [MV], [R], [ST], [SVY], [TS], [XT], [P], [M], and [I]—and they are shipped with every copy of Stata. Select **Help > PDF Documentation**. Even better, the manuals are integrated into the help system. From a help file, you can jump directly to the relevant page just by clicking on the reference. There is nothing more to know.

There are other exciting new features in this release depending on who you are and what interests you. These include

- competing-risks regression models; see [ST] **stcrreg**
- GMM estimation; see [R] **gmm**
- state-space (Kalman filtering) modeling; see [TS] **sspace**
- multivariate GARCH; see [TS] **dvech**
- dynamic-factor models; see [TS] **dfactor**
- unit-root tests for panel data; see [XT] **xtunitroot**
- error structures for linear mixed models; see [XT] **xtmixed**
- standard errors for BLUPs in linear mixed models; see [XT] **xtmixed**
- object-oriented programming in Mata; see [M-2] **class**
- full model-based optimization in Mata; see [M-5] **moptimize( )**
- numerical derivative function in Mata; see [M-5] **deriv( )**

Each of these, and more, is covered in the sections that follow.

1.3.1   What's new in the GUI and command interface

1. As mentioned in the highlights, the new Variables Manager is the one-stop place to go to manage your variables. See [D] **varmanage** and [GS] **7 Using the Variables Manager** (GSM, GSU, or GSW).

2. Also a highlight is the new Data Editor, a live view onto your data. See [D] **edit** and [GS] **6 Using the Data Editor** (GSM, GSU, or GSW).

3. The Do-file Editor is all new under Windows and provides syntax highlighting and code folding. See [R] **doedit**.

4. You doubtlessly have already noticed that Stata's Results window now has a white background. Stata has several new color schemes, and the one you are seeing is called **Standard**. What was the default scheme in Stata 10 is called **Classic**, so if you want it back, select **Edit > Preferences > General Preferences...** and change the scheme for the Results window to it. You can try the other schemes or make your own and save it in **Custom 1**, **Custom 2**, or **Custom 3**.

5. In Stata for Windows, you can now choose from among five different default layouts for the overall size and position of Stata's windows or, just as previously, you can make your own. Select **Edit > Preferences > Load Preference Set** and pick a layout. In addition to **Factory Settings**, available are **Compact Window Layout** and three **Presentation** layouts optimized for different projector resolutions.

6. Output scrolling in the Results window is now significantly faster. Also, the upper limit of set scrollbufsize has been increased to 2,000,000. See [R] **set**.

7. In Stata for Windows, Graph windows no longer float.

8. In Stata for Windows, existing command windows manage has new subcommand prefs for loading and saving named preference sets; type help window manage for details.

9. Stata for Unix(GUI) now supports copying graphs to the Clipboard in bitmap format.

10. Stata for Mac now supports copying graphs to the Clipboard in PDF format.

11. Stata for Mac's graphical user interface (GUI) has been completely rewritten in Apple's Cocoa programming interface.

12. Stata for Mac is now available as a universal binary that runs natively on 32-bit Intel- or PowerPC-based Macs and 64-bit Intel-based Macs to deliver optimal performance for all three architectures in a single package.

1.3.2   What's new in data management

1. Existing command merge has all new syntax. It is easier to use, easier to read, and makes it less likely that you will make a mistake. Merges are classified as 1:1, 1:m, m:1, and m:m. When you type merge 1:1, you are saying that you expect the observations to match one-to-one. merge 1:m specifies a 1-to-many merge; m:1, a many-to-1 merge; and m:m, a many-to-many merge. New options assert() and keep() allow you to specify what you expect the outcome to be and what you want to keep from it. For instance,

        . merge 1:1 subjid using *filename*, assert(match)

   means that you expect all the observations in both datasets to match each other, whereas

        . merge 1:1 subjid using *filename*, assert(match using) keep(match)

   specifies that you expect each observation to either match or be solely from the using data and, assuming that is true, you want to keep only the matches.

   Sorting of both the master and the using datasets is now automatic.

The new `merge` does not support merging multiple files in one step. Merge the first two datasets, then merge that result with the next dataset, and so on.

`merge` now aborts with error if variables are string in one dataset and numeric in the other unless new option `force` is specified.

See [D] **merge**. The old `merge` syntax continues to work.

2. Existing command `append` has several new features: 1) it will work even if there are no data in memory; 2) multiple files can be appended in one step; and 3) new option `generate(newvar)` creates a variable indicating the source of the observations, numbered 0, 1, ... `append` now aborts with error if variables are string in one dataset and numeric in the other unless new option `force` is specified. See [D] **append**. Old behavior is preserved under version control.

3. Stata's default memory allocations have changed:

   a. Stata/SE and Stata/MP now default to allocating 50 M of memory rather than 10 M. Stata/IC now defaults to 10 M rather than 1 M. Stata's required footprint has not grown; we reset these defaults because users were resetting to larger numbers anyway.

   b. Stata/IC now defaults `matsize` to 400 rather than 200; the default for Stata/SE and Stata/MP remains 400. The default for Small Stata is now 100 rather than 40.

4. Existing command `order` now does what `order`, `move`, and `aorder` did; see [D] **order**. Old commands `aorder` and `move` continue to work but are no longer documented.

5. New commands `zipfile` and `unzipfile` compress and uncompress files and directories in zip archive format. See [D] **zipfile**.

6. New command `changeeol` converts text from one operating system's end-of-line format to another's. Stata does not care about end-of-line format, but some editors and other programs do. See [D] **changeeol**.

7. New command `snapshot` saves to disk and restores from disk copies of the data in memory. `snapshot` is used by the new Data Editor. An important feature of the Data Editor is that it can log all the changes you make interactively. `snapshot` will show up in those logs. `snapshot` really is a command of Stata, so you can replay logs to duplicate past efforts. For your own use, however, it is better if you continue using `preserve` and `restore`. See [D] **snapshot**.

8. You can now copy-and-paste commands from logs and execute them without editing out the period (the dot prompt) in front! Stata 11 ignores leading periods.

9. Existing command `notes` has new options `search`, `replace`, and `renumber`. See [D] **notes**.

10. Concerning value labels:

    a. Existing command `label define` has new option `replace` so that you do not have to drop the value label before redefining it.

    b. New command `label copy` copies value labels.

    c. Existing command `label values` now allows a varlist, so you can label (or unlabel) a group of variables at the same time.

    See [D] **label**.

11. Existing command `expand` has new option `generate(newvar)` that makes it easier to distinguish original from duplicated observations. See [D] **expand**.

12. Concerning `egen`:

    a. New function `rowmedian(varlist)` returns, observation by observation, the median of the values in *varlist*.

   b. New function rowpctile(*varlist*), p(#) returns, observation by observation, the #th row percentile of the values within *varlist*.

   c. Existing function mode(*varname*) with option missing treats missing values as a category. When version is set to 10 or less, missing does not treat missing as a category.

   d. Existing functions total(*exp*) and rowtotal(*varlist*) have new option missing. If all values of *exp* or *varlist* for an observation are missing, then that observation in *newvar* will be set to missing.

   See [D] **egen**.

13. Existing command copy now allows copying a file to a directory without having to type the filename twice; see [D] **copy**.

14. Existing command clear now allows clear matrix to clear all Stata matrices (as distinguished from Mata matrices) from memory; see [D] **clear**.

15. Existing command outfile now exports date variables as strings rather than their underlying numeric value. Under version control, old behavior is restored. See [D] **outfile**.

16. Existing command reshape now preserves variable and value labels when converting from long to wide and restores variable and value labels when converting from wide to long. Thus the value and variable labels for the i variable, which exists in long form but not in wide form, are restored when converting back from wide to long. The value labels of the xij variables are similarly restored. Prior behavior is preserved when version is 10 or earlier. See [D] **reshape**.

17. Existing command collapse now allows new statistics semean, sebinomial, and sepoisson for obtaining the standard error of the mean. See [D] **collapse**.

18. Existing command destring allows new option dpcomma to convert to numeric form string representation of numbers using commas as the decimal point. See [D] **destring**.

19. Concerning existing command odbc:

   a. odbc insert now uses parameterized inserts, which are faster.

   b. The dialogs for odbc load and odbc insert can now store a data-source user ID and password for a Stata session.

   c. odbc query has new options verbose and schema. verbose lists any data source alias, nickname, typed table, typed view, and view along with tables so that data from these table types can be loaded. schema lists schema names with the table names if the data source returns schema information.

   d. odbc insert has a new dialog.

   e. Existing option dsn() now allows the data source to be up to 499 characters.

   f. odbc now reports driver errors directly. Previously, odbc would issue the error "ODBC error; type -set debug on- and rerun command to see extended error information" when an ODBC driver issued an error.

   g. odbc, with set debug on, for security reasons no longer displays the data source name, user ID, and password used for connecting to your data source.

   See [D] **odbc**.

20. New function strtoname() converts a general string to a string meeting Stata's naming conventions. Also, existing functions lower(), ltrim(), proper(), reverse(), rtrim(), and upper() now have synonyms strlower(), strltrim(), ..., and strupper(). Both sets of names work equally well. See [D] **functions**.

21. New function `soundex()` returns the soundex code for a name, consisting of a letter followed by three numbers. New function `soundex_nara()` returns the U.S. Census soundex for a name, also consisting of a letter followed by three numbers, but produced by a different algorithm. See [D] **functions**.

22. New functions `sinh()`, `cosh()`, `asinh()`, and `acosh()` join existing functions `tanh()` and `atanh()` to provide the hyperbolic functions. See [D] **functions**.

23. New functions `binomialp()`; `hypergeometric()` and `hypergeometricp()`; `nbinomial()`, `nbinomialp()`, and `nbinomialtail()`; and `poisson()`, `poissonp()`, and `poissontail()` provide distribution and probability mass for the binomial, hypergeometric, negative binomial, and Poisson distributions. See [D] **functions**.

24. New functions `invnbinomial()` and `invnbinomialtail()`, and `invpoisson()` and `invpoissontail()` provide inverses for the negative binomial and Poisson distributions. See [D] **functions**.

25. Algorithms for the existing functions `normal()` and `lnnormal()` have been improved to operate in 60% and 75% of the time, respectively, while giving equivalent double-precision results.

26. New functions `rbeta()`, `rbinomial()`, `rchi2()`, `rgamma()`, `rhypergeometric()`, `rnbinomial()`, `rnormal()`, `rpoisson()`, and `rt()` produce random variates for the beta, binomial, chi-squared, gamma, hypergeometric, negative binomial, normal, Poisson, and Student's t distributions, respectively.

    Old function `uniform()` has been renamed to `runiform()`, but `uniform()` continues to work.

    Thus all random-variate functions start with `r`.

    See [D] **functions**.

27. Existing command `drawnorm` now uses new function `rnormal()` to generate random variates. When `version` is set to 10 or earlier, `drawnorm` reverts to using `invnormal(uniform())`. See [D] **functions**.

28. Existing command `describe` now respects the width of the Results window when formatting output; see [D] **describe**.

29. Existing command `renpfix` now returns the list of variables changed in `r(varlist)`; see [D] **rename**.

30. Previously existing command `impute` still works but is now undocumented. It is replaced by the new multiple-imputation command `mi`. See the *Multiple-Imputation Reference Manual.*

1.3.3   What's new in statistics (general)

1. The highlight of this release is statistics related, namely, factor variables. We have already said a lot about them. You will not be able to avoid them. You will not want to avoid them. See [U] **11.4.3 Factor variables**.

2. The new postestimation command `margins` is also a highlight of this release. `margins` estimates margins and marginal effects. Included are estimated marginal means, least-squares means, average and conditional marginal and partial effects, average and conditional adjusted predictions, predictive margins, and more. We urge you to read [R] **margins**.

    `margins` replaces old commands `mfx` and `adjust`. `mfx` and `adjust` are no longer documented but continue to work under version control.

3. New command `mi` performs multiple imputation; see [MI] **intro**.

4. New command `misstable` makes tables that help you understand the pattern of missing values in your data; see [R] **misstable**.

5. New command `gmm` implements the generalized method of moments estimator. `gmm` allows linear and nonlinear models; allows one-step, two-step, and iterative estimators; works with cross-sectional, time-series, and panel data; and allows panel-style instruments. To fit a model, you need only write the expressions of the moments. See [R] **gmm**.

6. Concerning factor variables:

   a. Factor variables may be specified with almost all estimation commands (see item 6g below).

   b. If an estimation command works with factor variables, so do its postestimation commands. If the postestimation command accepts or requires a varlist, factor variables may be specified.

   c. Factor variables may be specified with existing commands `list` and `summarize`.

   d. Commands that allow factor variables also allow new options affecting how output appears: `vsquish`, `baselevels`, `allbaselevels`, `noemptycells`, and `noomitted`. Many commands that work with factor variables, such as `estat summarize`, `estat vce`, and the like, also allow the above options. Estimation commands also allow new option `coeflegend`. See [R] **estimation options**.

   `coeflegend` is useful when you wish to access the coefficients or standard errors individually using `_b[]` or `_se[]`, such as when you are using `lincom`, `nlcom`, or `test`. `coeflegend` provides what you need to type.

   `vsquish` reduces the amount of white space used vertically to display results.

   Stata used to drop covariates because of collinearity before performing estimation. This is now handled differently. Stata dropped variables for three reasons: because they were 1) base levels of factors, 2) levels corresponding to interactions where there were no data, and 3) truly collinear. These are now identified separately.

   New option `baselevels` says to report reason 1 in main effects.

   New option `allbaselevels` says to report reason 1 in all terms.

   New option `noemptycells` says not to report reason 2.

   New option `noomitted` says not to report reason 3.

   e. New command `fvset` allows you to specify default base levels and design settings for variables that can be recorded in the dataset and so remembered from one session to the next; see [R] **fvset**.

   f. New command `set emptycells drop` specifies that all estimation commands drop covariates associated with empty cells from estimation. The default is `set emptycells keep`. If you have sufficient memory, it is better to keep the covariates because then new postestimation command `margins` can better identify nonestimability.

   g. Factor variables are allowed with the following estimation commands: anova, areg, binreg, biprobit, blogit, bootstrap, bprobit, clogit, cloglog, dfactor, dvech, eivreg, frontier, glm, glogit, gnbreg, gprobit, heckman, heckprob, hetprob, intreg, ivprobit, ivregress, ivtobit, jackknife, logistic, logit, manova, mlogit, mprobit, mvreg, nbreg, newey, ologit, oprobit, poisson, prais, probit, reg3, regress, rologit, rreg, scobit, slogit, sspace, stcox, streg, sureg, svy, tobit, treatreg, truncreg, xtcloglog, xtfrontier, xtgee, xtgls, xtintreg, xtivreg, xtlogit, xtmelogit, xtmepoisson, xtmixed, xtnbreg, xtpcse, xtpoisson, xtprobit, xtrc, xtreg, xtregar, xttobit, zinb, zip, ztnb, and ztp.

7. `anova` and `manova` now use Stata's new factor-variable syntax, which means new estimation and postestimation features and a few changes to what you type.

   a. In other estimation commands, covariates are assumed to be continuous unless `i.` is specified in front of variable names. In `anova` and `manova`, covariates are assumed to be factors unless `c.` is specified.

   b. To form an interaction, you now use *varname#varname* rather than *varname*varname*. A * now means variable-name expansion. A | continues to be used to indicate nesting.

   c. *varname1##varname2* can now be specified to indicate full factorial layout, i.e, *varname1 varname2 varname1#varname2*. You can use *varname1##varname2##varname3* to form 3-way factorial layouts, and so on.

   d. No longer allowed are negative and noninteger levels for categorical variables. Options `category()`, `class()`, and `continuous()` are no longer allowed; instead, factor-variable notations `i.` and `c.` are used where there might be ambiguity.

   e. Reporting option `regress` is no longer allowed. To redisplay results, use the `regress` command after `anova`, or the `mvreg` command after `manova`.

   f. Option `detail` is no longer allowed nor necessary. Output produced by `anova` and `manova` is self explanatory, and you can use `regress` or `mvreg` if you want factor-level information.

   g. Option `noanova` is no longer allowed. To suppress output, type `quietly` in front of the command just as you would with any other estimation command.

   h. New option `dropemptycells` makes `anova` and `manova` more space efficient by dropping from `e(b)` and `e(V)` any interactions for which there are no observations. The disadvantage is that new postestimation command `margins` then cannot identify nonestimability and issue the appropriate warnings; see [R] **margins**.

   i. The following postestimation commands now work after `anova` just as they do after `regress`: `dfbeta`, `estat imtest`, `estat szroeter`, `estat vif`, `hausman`, `lrtest`, `margins`, `predictnl`, `nlcom`, `suest`, `testnl`, and `testparm`. Full `estat hettest` syntax is now allowed, too.

   j. The following postestimation commands now work after `manova` just as they do after `mvreg`: `margins`, `nlcom`, `predictnl`, and `testnl`.

   k. Existing command `test` used after `anova` now allows all the syntaxes allowed after `regress` while continuing to allow the special syntaxes for `anova`.

   l. Existing command `test` used after `manova` now allows all the syntaxes allowed after `mvreg` while continuing to allow the special syntaxes for `manova`.

   Old `anova` and `manova` syntaxes continue to work under version control. See [R] **anova** and [MV] **manova**.

8. Concerning the `bootstrap` and `jackknife` prefix commands:

   a. They may now be used with `anova` and `manova`.

   b. `bootstrap`'s new option `jackknifeopts()` allows options to be passed to `jackknife` for computing acceleration values for BCa confidence intervals.

   c. `bootstrap` no longer overwrites the macro `e(version)`, which the command being prefixed saved.

9. Concerning fractional polynomial regression:

   a. Existing commands `fracpoly` and `mfp` have a new syntax. They are now prefix commands, so you type `fracpoly`, ...: *estimation_command* and `mfp`, ...: *estimation_command*. Old syntax continues to be understood.

   b. Option `adjust()` used by `fracpoly`, `mfp`, and `fracgen` is renamed `center()`. The old option continues to be understood.

   c. `fracpoly` now works with `intreg`; see [R] **intreg**.

   d. `mfp` now works with `intreg`; see [R] **intreg**.

   See [R] **fracpoly** and [R] **mfp**.

10. Concerning the existing `estimates` command:

    a. `estimates save` has new option `append`, which allows results to be appended to an existing file. See [R] **estimates save**.

    b. `estimates use` and `estimates describe` using have new option `number(#)`, which specifies the results to be used or described. See [R] **estimates save** and [R] **estimates describe**.

    c. `estimates table` now supports factor variables and time-series–operated variables and so supports the new options `vsquish`, `noomitted`, `baselevels`, `allbaselevels`, and `noemptycells`; see [R] **estimates table**.

11. Concerning existing estimation command `ivregress`:

    a. New postestimation command `estat endogenous` for use with `ivregress 2sls` and `ivregress gmm` performs tests of whether endogenous regressors can be treated as exogenous; see [R] **ivregress postestimation**.

    b. New option `perfect` for use with `ivregress 2sls` and `ivregress gmm` allows perfect instruments; it skips checking whether endogenous regressors are collinear with excluded instruments (see [R] **ivregress**).

12. Concerning `regress`:

    a. Existing postestimation command `dfbeta` now names the variables it creates differently. Variables are now named `_dfbeta_#` rather than DF*name*. The old naming convention is restored under version control.

    b. New option `notable` suppresses display of the coefficient table.

    See [R] **regress**.

13. Constraints are now allowed by existing estimation commands `blogit`, `bprobit`, `logistic`, `logit`, `ologit`, `oprobit`, and `probit`. New option `collinear` specifies not to omit collinear variables from the model.

14. New option `nocnsreport` for use on estimation commands suppresses display of constraints. See [R] **estimation options**.

15. Existing command `pcorr` can now calculate semipartial correlation coefficients; see [R] **pcorr**.

16. Existing command `pwcorr` has new option `listwise` to omit observations in which any of the variables contain missing and thus mimic `correlate`'s treatment of missing values, while maintaining access to all of `pwcorr`'s other features; see [R] **correlate**.

17. Existing estimation command `glm` now allows option `ml` in `family(nbinomial ml)` to allow estimation via maximum likelihood; see [R] **glm**.

18. Existing estimation commands `asmprobit` and `asroprobit` have several new features:

   a. New option `factor(#)` specifies that a factor covariance structure with dimension # be used.

   b. New option `favor(speed|space)` allows you to set the speed/memory tradeoff. `favor(speed)` is the default.

   c. New option `nopivot` specifies that interval pivoting not be used in integration. By default, the programs pivot the wider of the integration intervals into the interior of the multivariate integration. Although this improves the accuracy of the quadrature estimate, discontinuities may result in the computation of numerical second-order derivatives.

   d. New postestimation command `estat facweights` specifies that the covariance factor weights be displayed in matrix form.

   e. Existing postestimation command `estat correlation` now uses a default output format of `%9.4f` instead of the previous `%6.3f`.

   See [R] **asmprobit**, [R] **asroprobit**, [R] **asmprobit postestimation**, and [R] **asroprobit postestimation**.

19. `biprobit` with option `constraints()` specified now applies these constraints when fitting the comparison models. As such, we can now report a likelihood-ratio (LR) test of the comparison model test instead of a Wald test. To obtain a Wald comparison test, type `test [athrho]_cons` after fitting the model.

20. Existing quality-control commands `cchart`, `pchart`, `rchart`, `xchart`, and `shewhart` have new option `nograph`, which suppresses the display of the graph. These commands also now return in `r()` the relevant values displayed in the charts. Also, `pchart` has new option `generate()`, which saves the variables plotted in the chart. See [R] **qc**.

21. `predict` used after `mlogit`, `mprobit`, `ologit`, `oprobit`, and `slogit` now defaults to predicting the probability of observing the first outcome. Previously, the `outcome()` option was required.

22. Existing estimation command `reg3` now reports large-sample statistics by default when constraints are specified, regardless of the estimator used.

23. Several estimation commands now accept existing convergence-criterion options `nrtolerance(#)` and `nonrtolerance`. Commands include `blogit`, `factor`, `logit`, `mlogit`, `ologit`, `oprobit`, `probit`, `rologit`, `stcox`, and `tobit`. The default is `nrtolerance(1e-5)`.

24. Existing estimation commands `exlogistic` and `expoisson` allow option `memory()` to be more than 512 MB; see [R] **exlogistic** and [R] **expoisson**.

25. Existing command `ssc`, which obtains user-written software from the Statistical Software Components archive, has new syntax `ssc hot` to list the most-downloaded submissions; see [R] **ssc**.

1.3.4 What's new in statistics (longitudinal data/panel data)

1. New command `xtunitroot` performs the Levin–Lin–Chu, Harris–Tzavalis, Breitung's, Im–Pesaran–Shin, Fisher-type, and Hadri Lagrange multiplier tests for unit roots on panel data. See [XT] **xtunitroot**.

2. Concerning existing estimation command `xtmixed`:

   a. `xtmixed` now allows modeling of the residual-error structure of the linear mixed models. Five structures are available: independent, exchangeable, autoregressive (AR), moving average (MA), and unstructured. Use new option `residuals()`. Within `residuals()`, you may also specify suboption `by(varname)` to obtain heteroskedastic versions of the above structures. For example, specifying `residuals(independent, by(sex))` will estimate distinct residual variances for both males and females.

    b. `xtmixed` has new options `matlog` and `matsqrt`, which specify the matrix square root and matrix logarithm variance-component parameterizations, respectively. Previously, `xtmixed` supported the matrix logarithm parameterization only. Now `xtmixed` supports both parameterizations and the default has changed to `matsqrt`. Previous default behavior is preserved under version control.

    c. `xtmixed` now supports time-series operators.

    See [XT] **xtmixed**.

3. `predict` after `xtmixed` now allows new option `reses` for obtaining standard errors of predicted random effects (best linear unbiased predictions). See [XT] **xtmixed postestimation**.

4. Concerning existing estimation command `xtreg`:

    a. Specifying `xtreg, re vce(robust)` now means the same as `xtreg, re vce(cluster` *panelvar*`)`. The new interpretation is robust to a broader class of deviations. The old interpretation is available under version control.

    b. Similarly, specifying `xtreg, fe vce(robust)` now means the same as `xtreg, fe vce(cluster` *panelvar*`)` in light of the new results by Stock and Watson (2008).

    c. `xtreg` now allows the `in` *range* qualifier.

    See [XT] **xtreg**.

5. All xt estimation commands now allow Stata's new factor-variable varlist notation, with the exception of commands `xtabond`, `xtdpd`, `xtdpdsys`, and `xthtaylor`. See [U] **11.4.3 Factor variables**. Also, estimation commands allow the standard set of factor-variable–related reporting options; see [R] **estimation options**.

6. New postestimation command `margins` is available after all xt estimation commands; see [R] **margins**.

7. Concerning existing estimation commands `xtmelogit` and `xtmepoisson`:

    a. They have new option `matsqrt`, which allows you to explicitly specify the default matrix square-root parameterization.

    b. They now support time-series operators.

    See [XT] **xtmelogit** and [XT] **xtmepoisson**.

8. As of Stata 10.1, existing estimation commands `xtmixed`, `xtmelogit`, and `xtmepoisson` require that random-effects specifications contain an explicit level variable (or `_all`) followed by a colon. Previously, if these were omitted, a level specification of `_all:` was assumed, leading to confusion when only the colon was omitted. To avoid this confusion, omitting the colon now produces an error, with previous behavior preserved under control.

9. Existing command `xttab` now returns the matrix of results in `r(results)` and the number of panels in `r(n)`. See [XT] **xttab**.

1.3.5   What's new in statistics (time series)

1. New estimation command `sspace` fits linear state-space models by maximum likelihood. In state-space models, the dependent variables are linear functions of unobserved states and observed exogenous variables. This includes VARMA, structural time-series, some linear dynamic, and some

stochastic general-equilibrium models. sspace can estimate stationary and nonstationary models. See [TS] **sspace**.

2. New estimation command dvech estimates diagonal vech multivariate GARCH models. These models allow the conditional variance matrix of the dependent variables to follow a flexible dynamic structure in which each element of the current conditional variance matrix depends on its own past and on past shocks. See [TS] **dvech**.

3. New estimation command dfactor estimates dynamic-factor models. These models allow the dependent variables and the unobserved factor variables to have vector autoregressive (VAR) structures and to be linear functions of exogenous variables. See [TS] **dfactor**.

4. Estimation commands newey, prais, sspace, dvech, and dfactor allow Stata's new factor-variable varlist notation; see [U] **11.4.3 Factor variables**. Also, these estimation commands allow the standard set of factor-variable–related reporting options; see [R] **estimation options**.

5. New postestimation command margins, which calculates marginal means, predictive margins, marginal effects, and average marginal effects, is available after arch, arima, newey, prais, sspace, dvech, and dfactor. See [R] **margins**.

6. New display option vsquish for estimation commands, which allows you to control the spacing in output containing time-series operators or factor variables, is available after all time-series estimation commands. See [R] **estimation options**.

7. New display option coeflegend for estimation commands, which displays the coefficients' legend showing how to specify them in an expression, is available after all time-series estimation commands. See [R] **estimation options**.

8. predict after regress now allows time-series operators in option dfbeta(); see [R] **regress postestimation**. Also allowing time-series operators are regress postestimation commands estat szroeter, estat hettest, avplot, and avplots. See [R] **regress postestimation**.

9. Existing estimation commands mlogit, ologit, and oprobit now allow time-series operators; see [R] **mlogit**, [R] **ologit**, and [R] **oprobit**.

10. Existing estimation commands arch and arima now accept maximization option showtolerance; see [R] **maximize**.

11. Existing estimation command arch now allows you to fit models assuming that the disturbances follow Student's t distribution or the generalized error distribution, as well as the Gaussian (normal) distribution. Specify which distribution to use with option distribution(). You can specify the shape or degree-of-freedom parameter, or you can let arch estimate it along with the other parameters of the model. See [TS] **arch**.

12. Existing command tsappend is now faster. See [TS] **tsappend**.

1.3.6   What's new in statistics (survival analysis)

1. Stata's new stcrreg command fits competing-risks regression models. In a competing-risks model, subjects are at risk of failure because of two or more separate and possibly correlated causes. See [ST] **stcrreg**. Existing command stcurve will now graph cumulative incidence functions after stcrreg; see [ST] **stcurve**.

2. Stata's new multiple-imputation features may be used with stcox, streg, and stcrreg; see [MI] **intro**.

3. Factor variables may now be used with stcox, streg, and stcrreg. See [U] **11.4.3 Factor variables**.

4. New postestimation command `margins`, which calculates marginal means, predictive margins, marginal effects, and average marginal effects, is available after `stcox`, `streg`, and `stcrreg`. See [R] **margins**.

5. New reporting options `baselevels` and `allbaselevels` control how base levels of factor variables are displayed in output tables. New reporting option `noemptycells` controls whether missing cells in interactions are displayed.

   These new options are supported by estimation commands `stcox`, `streg`, and `stcrreg`, and by existing postestimation commands `estat summarize` and `estat vce`. See [R] **estimation options**.

6. New reporting option `noomitted` controls whether covariates that are dropped because of collinearity are reported in output tables. By default, Stata now includes a line in estimation and related output tables for collinear covariates and marks those covariates as "(omitted)". `noomitted` suppresses those lines.

   `noomitted` is supported by estimation commands `stcox`, `streg`, and `stcrreg`, and by existing postestimation commands `estat summarize` and `estat vce`. See [R] **estimation options**.

7. New option `vsquish` eliminates blank lines in estimation and related tables. Many output tables now set off factor variables and time-series–operated variables with a blank line. `vsquish` removes these lines.

   `vsquish` is supported by estimation commands `stcox`, `streg`, and `stcrreg`, and by existing postestimation command `estat summarize`. See [R] **estimation options**.

8. Estimation commands `stcox`, `streg`, and `stcrreg` support new option `coeflegend` to display the coefficients' legend rather than the coefficient table. The legend shows how you would type a coefficient in an expression, in a test command, or in a constraint definition. See [R] **estimation options**.

9. Estimation commands `streg` and `stcrreg` support new option `nocnsreport` to suppress reporting constraints; see [R] **estimation options**.

10. Concerning `predict`:

    a. `predict` after `stcox` offers three new diagnostic measures of influence: DFBETAs, likelihood displacement values, and LMAX statistics. See [ST] **stcox postestimation**.

    b. `predict` after `stcox` can now calculate diagnostic statistics `basesurv()`, `basechazard()`, `basehc()`, `mgale()`, `effects()`, `esr()`, `schoenfeld()`, and `scaledsch()`. Previously, you had to request these statistics when you fit the model by specifying the option with the `stcox` command. Now you obtain them by using `predict` after estimation. The options continue to work with `stcox` directly but are no longer documented. See [ST] **stcox postestimation**.

    c. `predict` after `stcox` and `streg` now produces subject-level residuals by default. Previously, record-level or partial results were produced, although there was an inconsistency. This affects multiple-record data only because there is no difference between subject-level and partial residuals in single-record data. This change affects `predict`'s options `mgale`, `csnell`, `deviance`, and `scores` after `stcox` (and new options `ldisplace`, `lmax`, and `dfbeta`, of course); and it affects `mgale` and `deviance` after `streg`. `predict, deviance` was the inconsistency; it always produced subject-level results.

       For instance, in previous Stata versions you typed

       ```
       . predict cs, csnell
       ```

       to obtain partial Cox–Snell residuals. One statistic per record was produced. To obtain subject-level residuals, for which there is one per subject and which `predict` stored on each subject's last record, you typed

```
. predict ccs, ccsnell
```

In Stata 11, when you type

```
. predict cs, csnell
```

you obtain the subject-level residual. To obtain the partial, you use the new `partial` option:

```
. predict cs, csnell partial
```

The same applies to all the other residuals. Concerning the inconsistency, partial deviances are now available.

Not affected is `predict, scores` after `streg`. Log-likelihood scores in parametric models are mathematically defined at the record level and are meaningful only if evaluated at that level.

Prior behavior is restored under version control. See [ST] **stcox postestimation**, [ST] **streg postestimation**, and [ST] **stcrreg postestimation**.

11. `stcox` now allows up to 100 time-varying covariates as specified in option `tvc()`. The previous limit was 10. See [ST] **stcox**.

12. Existing commands `stcurve` and `estat phtest` no longer require that you specify the appropriate options to `stcox` before using them. The commands automatically generate the statistics they require. See [ST] **stcurve** and [ST] **stcox PH-assumption tests**.

13. Existing epitab commands `ir`, `cs`, `cc`, and `mhodds` now treat missing categories of variables in `by()` consistently. By default, missing categories are now excluded from the computation. This may be overridden by specifying `by()`'s new option `missing`. See [ST] **epitab**.

14. Existing command `sts list` has new option `saving()`, which creates a dataset containing the results. See [ST] **sts list**.

1.3.7 What's new in statistics (multivariate)

1. New command `mvtest` performs multivariate tests on means, covariances, and correlations (both one-sample and multiple-sample), and it performs tests of univariate, bivariate, and multivariate normality. Included are Box's M test for covariances, and for tests of normality, the Doornik–Hansen omnibus test, Henze–Zirkler test, Mardia's multivariate kurtosis test, and Mardia's multivariate skewness test. See [MV] **mvtest**.

2. The new factor-variable syntax allowed throughout Stata affects `manova` even though `manova` always allowed factor variables. See [MV] **manova**.

   a. `manova` has an all-new syntax. The old syntax continues to work under version control.

   b. `manova`, just like `anova`, adopts the new factor-variable syntax, but with a twist. In other Stata commands, continuous is assumed and you use `i.`*varname* to indicate a categorical variable. In `manova` and `anova`, categorical is assumed and you use `c.`*varname* to indicate continuous. Thus the options `category()`, `class()`, and `continuous()` are no longer used.

   c. To form an interaction, you use *varname1*#*varname2*. Previously, you used *varname1**varname2. A * now means variable-name expansion, just as it does on other commands, so you could type manova y* = a b* a#b*. The | symbol continues to be used for nesting.

   d. You can now use *varname1*##*varname2* as a shorthand for full factorial, meaning *varname1* *varname2* *varname1*#*varname2*. You can use *varname1*##*varname2*##*varname3* for 3-way factorial, and so on.

3. Existing command `mvreg` may now be used after `manova` to show results in regression-style format, just as `regress` can be used after `anova`. See [MV] **manova**.

4. Existing command `test` after `manova`, in addition to allowing the special syntax previously provided, now allows all the standard `test` syntax, too. See [MV] **manova postestimation**.

5. Existing commands `predictnl`, `nlcom`, `testnl`, and `testparm` may now be used after `manova`; see [R] **predictnl**, [R] **nlcom**, [R] **testnl**, and [R] **test**.

6. New postestimation command `margins` may be used after `manova`. See [R] **margins**.

7. `manova` now requires that categorical variables take on nonnegative integer values. Previously, a categorical variable could take on values -1, 2.5, 3.14159, etc., although few did. Arbitrary values are still allowed under version control. See [MV] **manova**.

8. `manova`'s new option `dropemptycells` removes unobserved levels from the model rather than setting their coefficients to zero. Statistically, the approaches are equivalent. Computationally, a larger `matsize` is required when empty cells are retained. In models with many interactions, you may need to specify this option. See [MV] **manova** and see [R] **set emptycells**.

9. Programmers: The row and column names on `e(b)`, `e(V)`, etc., after `manova` are now meaningful and follow standard factor-variable notation. See *What's new* in [P] **intro**.

10. Existing command `biplot` has several improvements:

    a. `biplot` can now be used with larger datasets. Previously, the row dimension was limited by Stata's maximum `matsize`.

    b. `biplot` has new option `generate()`, which saves the coordinates of observations in variables.

    c. `biplot` has new options `rowover()` and `row#opts()`, which allow highlighting groups of observations on the graph and customizing the look of the graph.

    d. New option `rowlabel()` makes customizing rows easier.

    e. `biplot` now drops constant variables from the computation.

    f. `biplot` now uses an improved version of the singular value decomposition, which may result in sign differences and slight differences in values.

    g. `rowopts()`, `colopts()`, and `negcolopts()` now allow names to contain simple and compound quotes.

    h. `biplot` did not honor option `scheme(economist)` for separate graphs (option `separate`). This has been fixed.

11. Existing command `canon`'s default output has changed. It previously displayed something that looked like estimation output but was not because standard errors were conditional. The output now looks like you would expect. The conditional output can be obtained by specifying new option `stderr` or under version control (set `version` to 10 or earlier).

12. The manual now includes a glossary; see [MV] **Glossary**.

1.3.8 What's new in statistics (survey)

1. New command `margins`, a highlight of the release, may be used after estimation, whether survey or not, but will be of special interest to those doing survey estimation. One aspect of `margins`—predictive margins—was developed by survey statisticians for reporting survey results.

   `margins` lets you explore the response surface of a fitted model in any metric of interest—means, linear predictions, probabilities, marginal effects, risk differences, and so on. `margins` can evaluate responses for fixed values of the covariates or for observations in a sample or subsample. Average responses can be obtained, not just responses that are conditional on fixed values of the covariates. Survey-adjusted standard errors and confidence intervals are reported based on a linearized variance estimator of the response that accounts for the sampling distribution of the covariates. Thus inferences can be made about the population. See [R] **margins**.

2. Survey estimators may be used with Stata's new multiple-imputation features. Either `svyset` your data before you `mi set` your data or use `mi svyset` afterward. See [MI] **intro**.

3. Survey commands now report population and subpopulation sizes with a larger number of digits, reserving scientific notation only for sizes greater than 99 trillion.

4. Survey estimation commands may now be used with factor variables; see [U] **11.4.3 Factor variables**.

5. New reporting options `baselevels` and `allbaselevels` control how base levels of factor variables are displayed in output tables. New reporting option `noemptycells` controls whether missing cells in interactions are displayed. These new options are supported by existing prefix command `svy` and existing postestimation commands `estat effects` and `estat vce`. See [R] **estimation options**.

6. New reporting option `noomitted` controls whether covariates that are dropped because of collinearity are reported in output tables. By default, Stata now includes a line in estimation and related output tables for collinear covariates and marks those covariates as "(omitted)". `noomitted` suppresses those lines.

   `noomitted` is supported by prefix command `svy` and postestimation commands `estat effects` and `estat vce`. See [R] **estimation options**.

7. New option `vsquish` eliminates blank lines in estimation and related tables. Many output tables now set off factor variables and time-series–operated variables with a blank line. `vsquish` removes these lines.

   `vsquish` is supported by prefix command `svy` and postestimation command `estat effects`.

8. Prefix command `svy` now supports new option `coeflegend` to display the coefficients' legend rather than the coefficient table. The legend shows how you would type a coefficient in an expression, in a test command, or in a constraint definition. See [R] **estimation options**.

9. Prefix command `svy` now supports new option `nocnsreport` to suppress reporting constraints; see [R] **estimation options**.

1.3.9 What's new in statistics (multiple imputation)

1. All of it. Multiple imputation is about the analysis of data for which some values are missing. See [MI] **intro**.

2. New command `misstable` makes tables that help you understand the pattern of missing values in your data; see [R] **misstable** and [MI] **mi misstable**.

3. Estimation commands that may be used with `mi estimate` include the following:

command	entry	description
Linear regression models		
regress	[R] **regress**	Linear regression
cnsreg	[R] **cnsreg**	Constrained linear regression
mvreg	[R] **mvreg**	Multivariate regression
Binary-response regression models		
logistic	[R] **logistic**	Logistic regression, reporting odds ratios
logit	[R] **logit**	Logistic regression, reporting coefficients
probit	[R] **probit**	Probit regression
cloglog	[R] **cloglog**	Complementary log-log regression
binreg	[R] **binreg**	GLM for the binomial family
Count-response regression models		
poisson	[R] **poisson**	Poisson regression
nbreg	[R] **nbreg**	Negative binomial regression
gnbreg	[R] **nbreg**	Generalized negative binomial regression
Ordinal-response regression models		
ologit	[R] **ologit**	Ordered logistic regression
oprobit	[R] **oprobit**	Ordered probit regression
Categorical-response regression models		
mlogit	[R] **mlogit**	Multinomial (polytomous) logistic regression
mprobit	[R] **mprobit**	Multinomial probit regression
clogit	[R] **clogit**	Conditional (fixed-effects) logistic regression
Quantile regression models		
qreg	[R] **qreg**	Quantile regression
iqreg	[R] **qreg**	Interquantile range regression
sqreg	[R] **qreg**	Simultaneous-quantile regression
bsqreg	[R] **qreg**	Quantile regression with bootstrap standard errors
Survival regression models		
stcox	[ST] **stcox**	Cox proportional hazards model
streg	[ST] **streg**	Parametric survival models
stcrreg	[ST] **stcrreg**	Competing-risks regression
Other regression models		
glm	[R] **glm**	Generalized linear models
areg	[R] **areg**	Linear regression with a large dummy-variable set
rreg	[R] **rreg**	Robust regression
truncreg	[R] **truncreg**	Truncated regression
Descriptive statistics		
mean	[R] **mean**	Estimate means
proportion	[R] **proportion**	Estimate proportions
ratio	[R] **ratio**	Estimate ratios
Survey regression models		
svy:	[SVY] **svy**	Estimation commands for survey data (excluding commands that are not listed above)

1.3.10   What's new in graphics

1. A release highlight, text in graphs now supports multiple fonts. You can display symbols, Greek letter, subscripts, superscripts, as well as text in multiple font faces including bold and italic. See [G] *text*. Everything is automatic, but you can set up the fonts to be used; see [G] **graph set**, [G] *ps_options*, and [G] *eps_options*.

2. Stata's Graph Editor can now record a series of edits and apply them to other graphs; see *Graph Recorder* in [G] **graph editor**. You can also apply recorded edits from the command line. See [G] **graph play** and see option play(*recordingname*) in [G] *std_options* and [G] **graph use**.

3. The dialog box for graph twoway now allows plots to be reordered when multiple plots have been defined.

1.3.11   What's new in programming

1. The big news in programming concerns parsing varlists containing factor variables, dealing with factor variables, and processing matrices whose row or column names contain factor variables.

   a. syntax will allow varlists to contain factor variables if new specifier fv is among the specifiers in the description of the varlist, for instance,

      ```
      syntax varlist(fv) [if] [in] [, Detail]
      ```

      Similarly, syntax will allow a varlist option to include factor variables if fv is included among its specifiers:

      ```
      syntax varlist(fv) [if] [in] [, Detail] EQ(varlist fv)
      ```

      See [P] **syntax**.

   b. You can use resulting macro 'varlist' as the varlist for any Stata command that allows factor varlists.

   c. Factor varlists come in two flavors, general and specific. An example of a general factor varlist is mpg i.foreign. The corresponding specific factor varlist might be

      ```
      mpg i(0 1)b0.foreign
      ```

      A specific factor varlist is specific with respect to a given problem, which is to say, a given dataset and subsample. The specific varlist identifies the values taken on by factor variables and the base.

      Users usually specify general factor varlists, although they can specify specific ones. In the process of your program, a factor varlist, if it is general, will become specific. This is usually automatic.

      Existing commands _rmcoll and _rmdcoll now accept a general or specific factor varlist and return a specific varlist in r(varlist). See [P] **_rmcoll**.

      Existing command ml accepts a general or specific factor varlist and returns a specific varlist, in this case in the row and column names of the vectors and matrices it produces; see [R] **ml**. The same applies to Mata's new moptimize() function, which is equivalent to ml; see [M-5] **moptimize( )**.

      Similarly, all Stata estimation commands that allow factor varlists return the specific varlist in the row and column names of e(b) and e(V).

      Factor varlist mpg i(0 1)b0.foreign is specific. The same varlist could be written mpg i0b.foreign i1.foreign, so that is specific, too. The first is specific and unexpanded.

The second is specific and expanded. New command `fvexpand` takes a general or specific (expanded or unexpanded) factor varlist, `if` or `in`, and returns a fully expanded, specific varlist. See [P] **fvexpand**.

New command `fvunab` takes a general or specific factor varlist and returns it in the same form, but with variable names unabbreviated. See [P] **unab**.

d. Matrix row and column names are now generalized to include factor variables. The row or column names contain the elements from a fully expanded, specific factor varlist. Because a fully expanded, specific factor varlist is a factor varlist, the contents of the row or column names can be used with other Stata commands as a varlist. Unrelatedly, the equation portion of the row or column name now has a maximum length of 127 rather than the previous 32.

e. The treatment of variables that are omitted because of collinearity has changed. Previously, such variables were dropped from `e(b)` and `e(V)` except by `regress`, which included the variables but set the corresponding element of `e(b)` to zero and similarly set the corresponding row and column of `e(V)` to zero. Now all Stata estimators that allow factor variables work like `regress`.

Also, if you want to know why the variable was dropped, you can look at the corresponding element of the row or column name. The syntax of an expanded, specific varlist allows operators o and b. Operator o indicates omitted either because the user specified omitted or because of collinearity; b indicates omitted because of being a base category. For instance, `o.mpg` would indicate that `mpg` was omitted, whereas `i0b.foreign` would indicate that `foreign = 0` was omitted because it was the base category. Either way, the corresponding element of `e(b)` will be zero, as will the corresponding rows and columns of `e(V)`.

This new treatment of omitted variables—previously called dropped variables—can cause old user-written programs to break. This is especially true of old postestimation commands not designed to work with `regress`. If you set `version` to 10 or earlier before estimation, however, then estimation results will be stored in the old way and the old postestimation commands will work. The solution is

```
. version 10
. estimation_command  ...
. old_postestimation_command  ...
. version 11
```

When running under `version` 10 or earlier, you may not use factor variables with the estimation command.

f. Because omitted variables are now part of estimation results, constraints play a larger role in the implementation of estimators. Omitted variables have coefficients constrained to be zero. `ml` now handles such constraints automatically and posts in `e(k_autoCns)` the number of such constraints, which can be due to the variable being used as the base, being empty, or being omitted. `makecns` similarly saves in `r(k_autoCns)` the number of such constraints, and in `r(clist)`, the constraints used. The matrix of constraints is now posted with `ereturn post` and saved, as usual, in `e(Cns)`. `ereturn matrix` no longer posts constraints. Old behavior is preserved under version control. See [R] **ml**, [P] **makecns**, and [P] **ereturn**.

g. There are additional commands to assist in using and manipulating factor varlists that are documented only online; type `help undocumented` in Stata.

2. Factor variables also allow interactions. Up to eight-way interactions are allowed.

a. Consider the interaction a#b. If each took on two levels, the unexpanded, specific varlist would be `i(1 2)b1.a#i(1 2)b1.b`. The expanded, specific varlist would be `1b.a#1b.b 1b.a#2.b 2.a#1b.b 2.a#2.b`.

b. Consider the interaction c.x#c.x, where x is continuous. The unexpanded and expanded, specific varlists are the same as the general varlist: c.x#c.x.

c. Consider the interaction a#c.x. The unexpanded, specific varlist is i(1 2).a#c.x, and the expanded, specific varlist is 1.a#c.x 2.a#c.x.

d. All these varlists are handled in the same way that factor variables are handled, as outlined in item 1 above.

3. New command fvrevar creates equivalent, temporary variables for any factor variables, interactions, or times-series–operated variables so that older commands can be easily converted to working with factor variables. We hasten to add that, in general, Stata does not follow the fvrevar approach. Think of this fvrevar as a generalization of tsrevar. See [R] **fvrevar**.

4. Factor variables lead to a number of additions to what is saved in e() and sometimes r():

a. Estimation commands that post e(V) now post the corresponding rank of the matrix in scalar e(rank).

b. Estimation commands that allow constraints now post the constraints matrix in matrix e(Cns).

c. In many estimation commands allowing constraints, and in the programming command makecns, scalar e(k_autoCns) is now posted containing the sum of the number of base, empty, and omitted constraints.

d. Programming command makecns now save the constraints used in macro r(clist).

e. Estimation commands that allow factor variables now post in macro e(asbalanced) the name of each factor variable participating in e(b) that was fvset design asbalanced and post in macro e(asobserved) the name of each factor variable participating in e(b) that was fvset design asobserved.

f. Estimation commands now post in macros how new command margins is to treat their prediction statistics when the statistics require special treatment. These macros are e(marginsok), e(marginsnotok), and e(marginsprop).

e(marginsok) specifies the name of predictors that are to be allowed and that appear to violate margins' usual rules, such as dependent variables being involved in the calculation.

e(marginsnotok) are statistics that margins fails to identify as violating assumptions but that do and should not be allowed.

e(marginsprop) provides special signals as to how statistics for the estimator must be handled. Currently allowed are combinations of addcons, noeb, and nochainrule. addcons means that the estimated equations have no constant even if the user did not specify noconstant at estimation time. noeb means that the estimator does not store the covariate names in the column names of e(b). nochainrule means that the chain rule may not be used to calculate derivatives.

g. Matrix e(V_modelbased), the model-based VCE, is now posted by most estimation commands that allow robust variance estimation by bootstrap and jackknife.

h. Existing command sktest now returns in matrix r(N) the matrix of observation counts and in matrix r(Utest) the matrix of test results.

5. Existing command estimates describe using now saves in scalar r(nestresults) the number of sets of estimation results saved in the .ster file.

6. Existing command correlate saves in matrix r(C) the correlation or covariance matrix.

7. Existing command ml has been rewritten. It is now implemented in terms of new Mata function and optimization engine moptimize(). The new ml handles automatic or implied constraints,

posts some additional information to e(), and allows evaluators written in Mata as well as ado. See [R] **maximize** for an overview and see [R] **ml** and [M-5] **moptimize( )**.

8. Existing command estimates save now has option append, which allows storing more than one set of estimation results in the same file; see [R] **estimates save**.

9. Existing commands ereturn post and ereturn repost now work with more commands, including logit, mlogit, ologit, oprobit, probit, qreg, _qreg, regress, stcox, and tobit. Also, ereturn post and ereturn repost now allow weights to be specified and save them in e(wtype) and e(wexp). See [P] **ereturn**.

10. Existing command markout has new option sysmissok, which excludes observations with variables equal to system missing (.) but not to extended missing (.a, .b, ..., .z); see [P] **mark**. This has to do with new emphasis on imputation of missing values; see [MI] **intro**.

11. New commands varabbrev and unabbrev make it easy to temporarily reset whether Stata allows variable-name abbreviations; see [P] **varabbrev**.

12. New programming function smallestdouble() returns the smallest double-precision number greater than zero; see [D] **functions**.

13. creturn has new returned values:

    a. c(noisily) returns 0 when output is being suppressed and 1 otherwise. Thus programmers can avoid executing code whose only purpose is to display output.

    b. c(smallestdouble) returns the smallest double-precision value that is greater than 0.

    c. c(tmpdir) returns the temporary directory being used by Stata.

    d. c(eqlen) returns the maximum length that Stata allows for equation names.

14. Existing extended macro function :dir has new option respectcase, which causes :dir to respect uppercase and lowercase when performing filename matches. This option is relevant only for Windows.

15. Stata has new string functions strtoname(), soundex(), and soundex_nara(); see [D] **functions**.

16. Stata has 17 new numerical functions: sinh(), cosh(), asinh(), and acosh(); hypergeometric() and hypergeometricp(); nbinomial(), nbinomialp(), and nbinomialtail(); invnbinomial() and invnbinomialtail(); poisson(), poissonp(), and poissontail(); invpoisson() and invpoissontail(); and binomialp(); see [D] **functions**.

17. Stata has nine new random-variate functions for beta, binomial, chi-squared, gamma, hypergeometric, negative binomial, normal, Poisson, and Student's t: rbeta(), rbinomial(), rchi2(), rgamma(), rhypergeometric(), rnbinomial(), rnormal(), rpoisson(), and rt(), respectively. Also, old function uniform() is renamed runiform(). All random-variate functions start with r. See [D] **functions**.

18. Existing function clear has new syntax clear matrix, which clears (drops) all Stata matrices, as distinguished from clear mata, which drops all Mata matrices and functions. See [D] **clear**.

19. These days, commands intended for use by end-users are often being used as subroutines by other end-user commands. Some of these commands preserve the data simply so that, should something go wrong or the user press *Break*, the original data can be restored. Sometimes, when such commands are used as subroutines, the caller has already preserved the data. Therefore, all programmers are requested to include option nopreserve on commands that preserve the data for no other reason than error recovery, and thus speed execution when commands are used as subroutines. See [P] **nopreserve option**.

1.3.12 What's new in Mata

1. Mata now allows full object-oriented programming! A class is a set of variables, related functions, or both tied together under one name. One class can be derived from another via inheritance. Variables can be public, private, protected, or static. Functions can be public, private, protected, static, or virtual. Members, whether variables or functions, can be final. Classes, member functions, and access to member variables and calls to member functions are fully compiled—not interpreted—meaning there is no speed penalty for casting your program in terms of a class. See [M-2] **class**.

2. The new `moptimize()` suite of functions comprises Stata's new optimization engine used by `ml` and thereby, either directly or indirectly, by nearly all official Stata estimation commands. `moptimize()` provides full support for Stata's new factor variables. See [M-5] **moptimize( )**, [R] **ml**, and [R] **maximize**.

   `moptimize` is important. The full story is that Stata's `ml` is implemented in terms of Mata's `moptimize()`, which in turn is implemented in terms of Mata's `optimize()`. `optimize()` finds parameters $\mathbf{p} = (p_1, p_2, \ldots, p_n)$ that maximize or minimize $f(p)$. `moptimize()` finds coefficients $\mathbf{b} = (\mathbf{b}_1, \mathbf{b}_2, \ldots, \mathbf{b}_n)$, where $p_1 = \mathbf{X}_1\mathbf{b}_1$, $p_2 = \mathbf{X}_2\mathbf{b}_2$, ..., $p_n = \mathbf{X}_n\mathbf{b}_n$.

3. New function suite `deriv()` produces numerically calculated first and second derivatives of vector functions; see [M-5] **deriv( )**.

4. Improvements have been made to `optimize()`:

   a. `optimize()` with constraints is now faster for evaluator types d0 and v0 and for all gradient-based techniques. Also, it is faster for evaluator types d1 and v1 when used with constraints and with the nr (Newton–Raphson) technique.

   b. Gauss–Newton optimization, also known as quadratic optimization, is now available as technique gn. Evaluator functions must be of type 'q'.

   c. `optimize()` can now switch between techniques bhhh, nr, bfgs, and dfp (between Berndt–Hall–Hall–Hausman, Newton–Raphson, Broyden–Fletcher–Goldfarb–Shanno, and Davidon–Fletcher–Powell).

   d. `optimize()`, when output of the convergence values is requested in the trace log, now displays the identity and value of the convergence criterion that is closest to being met.

   e. `optimize()` has 15 new initialization functions:

`optimize_init_cluster()`	`optimize_init_trace_dots()`
`optimize_init_colstripe()`	`optimize_init_trace_gradient()`
`optimize_init_conv_ignorenrtol()`	`optimize_init_trace_Hessian()`
`optimize_init_conv_warning()`	`optimize_init_trace_params()`
`optimize_init_evaluations()`	`optimize_init_trace_step()`
`optimize_init_gnweightmatrix()`	`optimize_init_trace_tol()`
`optimize_init_iterid()`	`optimize_init_trace_value()`
`optimize_init_negH()`	

   Also, new function `optimize_result_evaluations()` reports the number of times the evaluator is called.

5. Existing functions `st_data()` and `st_view()` now allow the variables to be specified as a string scalar with space-separated names, as well as a string row vector with elements being names. In addition, when a string scalar is used, you now specify either or both time-series–operated variables (e.g., `l.gnp`) and factor variables (e.g., `i.rep78`).

6. Thirty-four LAPACK (Linear Algebra PACKage) functions are now available in as-is form and more are coming. LAPACK is the premier software for solving systems of simultaneous equations,

eigenvalue problems, and singular value decompositions. Many of Mata's matrix functions are and have been implemented using LAPACK. We are now in the process of making all the double-precision LAPACK real and complex functions available in raw form for those who want to program their own advanced numerical techniques. See [M-5] **lapack( )** and [R] **copyright lapack**.

7. New function suite `eigensystemselect()` computes the eigenvectors for selected eigenvalues; see [M-5] **eigensystemselect( )**.

8. New function suite `geigensystem()` computes generalized eigenvectors and eigenvalues; see [M-5] **geigensystem( )**.

9. New function suites `hessenbergd()` and `ghessenbergd()` compute the (generalized) Hessenberg decompositions; see [M-5] **hessenbergd( )** and [M-5] **ghessenbergd( )**.

10. New function suites `schurd()` and `gschurd()` compute the (generalized) Schur decompositions; see [M-5] **schurd( )** and [M-5] **gschurd( )**.

11. New function `_negate()` quickly negates a matrix in place; see [M-5] **_negate( )**.

12. New functions `Dmatrix()`, `Kmatrix()`, and `Lmatrix()` compute the duplication matrix, commutation matrix, and elimination matrix used in computing derivatives of functions of symmetric matrices; see [M-5] **Dmatrix( )**, [M-5] **Kmatrix( )**, and [M-5] **Lmatrix( )**.

13. New function `sublowertriangle()` extracts the lower triangle of a matrix, where lower triangle means below a specified diagonal; see [M-5] **sublowertriangle( )**.

14. New function `hasmissing()` returns whether a matrix contains any missing values; see [M-5] **missing( )**.

15. New function `strtoname()` performs the same actions as Stata's `strtoname()` function: it converts a general string to a string meeting the Stata naming conventions. See [M-5] **strtoname( )**.

16. New function `abbrev()` performs the same actions as Stata's `abbrev()` function: it returns abbreviated variable names. See [M-5] **abbrev( )**.

17. New function `_st_tsrevar()` is a handle-the-error-yourself variation of existing function `st_tsrevar()`; see [M-5] **st_tsrevar( )**.

18. Existing functions `ghk()` and `ghkfast()`, which evaluate multivariate normal integrals, have improved syntax; see [M-5] **ghk( )** and [M-5] **ghkfast( )**.

19. Existing functions `vec()` and `vech()` are now faster for both real and complex matrices; see [M-5] **vec( )**.

20. Mata has 13 new distribution-related functions: `hypergeometric()` and `hypergeometricp()`; `nbinomial()`, `nbinomialp()`, and `nbinomialtail()`; `invnbinomial()` and `invnbinomialtail()`; `poisson()`, `poissonp()`, and `poissontail()`; `invpoisson()` and `invpoissontail()`; and `binomialp()`; see [M-5] **normal( )**.

21. Mata has nine new random-variate functions for beta, binomial, chi-squared, gamma, hypergeometric, negative binomial, normal, Poisson, and Student's *t*: `rbeta()`, `rbinomial()`, `rchi2()`, `rgamma()`, `rhypergeometric()`, `rnbinomial()`, `rnormal()`, `rpoisson()`, and `rt()`, respectively.

Also, `rdiscrete()` is provided for drawing from a general discrete distribution.

Old functions `uniform()` and `uniformseed()` are replaced with `runiform()` and `rseed()`. All random-variate functions start with **r**. See [M-5] **runiform( )**.

22. Existing functions `sinh()`, `cosh()`, `asinh()`, and `acosh()` now have improved accuracy; see [M-5] **sin( )**.

23. New function `soundex()` returns the soundex code for a name and consists of a letter followed by three numbers. New function `soundex_nara()` returns the U.S. Census soundex for a name and also consists of a letter followed by three numbers, but is produced by a different algorithm. See [M-5] **soundex( )**.

24. Existing function $J(r, c, val)$ now allows *val* to be specified as a matrix and creates an $r*\text{rows}(val) \times c*\text{cols}(val)$ result. The third argument, *val*, was previously required to be 1×1. Behavior in the 1×1 case is unchanged. See [M-5] **J( )**.

25. Existing functions `sort()`, `_sort()`, and `order()` sorted the rows of a matrix based on up to 500 of its columns. This limit has been removed. See [M-5] **sort( )**.

26. New function `asarray()` provides associative arrays; see [M-5] **asarray( )**.

27. New function `hash1()` provides Jenkins' one-at-a-time hash function; see [M-5] **hash1( )**.

28. Mata object-code libraries (.mlib's) may now contain up to 2,048 functions and may contain up to 1,024 by default. Use `mlib create`'s new `size()` option to change the default. The previous fixed maximum was 500. See [M-3] **mata mlib**.

29. Mata on 64-bit computers now supports matrices larger than 2 gigabytes when the computer has sufficient memory.

30. One hundred and nine existing functions now take advantage of multiple cores when using Stata/MP.
    They are

acos()	factorial()	minutes()
arg()	Fden()	mm()
asin()	floatround()	mmC()
atan2()	floor()	mod()
atan()	Ftail()	mofd()
betaden()	gammaden()	month()
binomial()	gammap()	msofhours()
binomialtail()	gammaptail()	msofminutes()
binormal()	halfyear()	msofseconds()
ceil()	hh()	nbetaden()
chi2()	hhC()	nchi2()
chi2tail()	hofd()	nFden()
Cofc()	hours()	nFtail()
cofC()	ibeta()	nibeta()
Cofd()	ibetatail()	normal()
cofd()	invbinomial()	normalden()
comb()	invbinomialtail()	npnchi2()
cos()	invchi2()	qofd()
day()	invchi2tail()	quarter()
dgammapda()	invF()	round()
dgammapdada()	invFtail()	seconds()
dgammapdadx()	invgammap()	sin()
dgammapdx()	invgammaptail()	sqrt()
dgammapdxdx()	invibeta()	ss()
digamma()	invibetatail()	tan()
dofC()	invnchi2()	tden()
dofc()	invnFtail()	trigamma()
dofh()	invnibeta()	trunc()
dofm()	invnormal()	ttail()
dofq()	invttail()	week()
dofw()	ln()	wofd()
dofy()	lnfactorial()	year()
dow()	lngamma()	yh()
doy()	lnnormal()	ym()
exp()	lnnormalden()	yq()
F()	mdy()	yw()

1.3.13   What's more

We have not listed all the changes, but we have listed the important ones.

Stata is continually being updated, and those updates are available for free over the Internet. All
you have to do is type

    . update query

and follow the instructions.

To learn what has been added since this manual was printed, select **Help > What's New?** or type

    . help whatsnew

We hope that you enjoy Stata 11.

1.4 References

Chambers, J. M., W. S. Cleveland, B. Kleiner, and P. A. Tukey. 1983. *Graphical Methods for Data Analysis*. Belmont, CA: Wadsworth.

Everitt, B. S. 2006. *The Cambridge Dictionary of Statistics*. 3rd ed. Cambridge: Cambridge University Press.

Freedman, L. S. 1982. Tables of the number of patients required in clinical trials using the logrank test. *Statistics in Medicine* 1: 121–129.

Heyde, C. C., and E. Seneta, ed. 2001. *Statisticians of the Centuries*. New York: Springer.

Johnson, N. L., and S. Kotz, ed. 1997. *Leading Personalities in Statistical Sciences: From the Seventeenth Century to the Present*. New York: Wiley.

Lachin, J. M., and M. A. Foulkes. 1986. Evaluation of sample size and power for analyses of survival with allowance for nonuniform patient entry, losses to follow-up, noncompliance, and stratification. *Biometrics* 42: 507–519.

Rubinstein, L. V., M. H. Gail, and T. J. Santner. 1981. Planning the duration of a comparative clinical trial with loss to follow-up and a period of continued observation. *Journal of Chronic Diseases* 34: 469–479.

Schoenfeld, D. A. 1981. The asymptotic properties of nonparametric tests for comparing survival distributions. *Biometrika* 68: 316–319.

Stock, J. H., and M. W. Watson. 2008. Heteroskedasticity-robust standard errors for fixed effects panel data regression. *Econometrica* 76: 155–174.

Tarone, R. E. 1985. On heterogeneity tests based on efficient scores. *Biometrika* 72: 91–95.

Upton, G., and I. Cook. 2006. *A Dictionary of Statistics*. 2nd ed. Oxford: Oxford University Press.

2 A brief description of Stata

Stata is a statistical package for managing, analyzing, and graphing data.

Stata is available for a variety of platforms. Stata may be used either as a point-and-click application or as a command-driven package.

Stata's GUI provides an easy interface for those new to Stata and for experienced Stata users who wish to execute a command that they seldom use.

The command language provides a fast way to communicate with Stata and to communicate more complex ideas.

Here is an extract of a Stata session using the GUI:

(Throughout the Stata manuals, we will refer to various datasets. These datasets are all available from http://www.stata-press.com/data/r11/. For easy access to them within Stata, type `webuse` *dataset_name*, or select **File > Example Datasets...** and click on *Stata 11 manual datasets*.)

```
. webuse lbw
(Hosmer & Lemeshow data)
```

We select **Data > Describe data > Summary statistics** and choose to summarize variables `low`, `age`, and `smoke`, whose names we obtained from the Variables window. We click on **OK**.

```
. summarize low age smoke
```

Variable	Obs	Mean	Std. Dev.	Min	Max
low	189	.3121693	.4646093	0	1
age	189	23.2381	5.298678	14	45
smoke	189	.3915344	.4893898	0	1

Stata shows us the command that we could have typed in command mode—summarize low age smoke—before displaying the results of our request.

Next we fit a logistic regression model of low on age and smoke. We select **Statistics > Binary outcomes > Logistic regression (reporting odds ratios)**, fill in the fields, and click on **OK**.

```
. logistic low age smoke
```

Logistic regression				Number of obs	=	189
				LR chi2(2)	=	7.40
				Prob > chi2	=	0.0248
Log likelihood = -113.63815				Pseudo R2	=	0.0315

low	Odds Ratio	Std. Err.	z	P>|z|	[95% Conf. Interval]	
age	.9514394	.0304194	-1.56	0.119	.8936482	1.012968
smoke	1.997405	.642777	2.15	0.032	1.063027	3.753081

Here is an extract of a Stata session using the command language:

```
. use http://www.stata-press.com/data/r11/auto
(1978 Automobile Data)
. summarize mpg weight
```

Variable	Obs	Mean	Std. Dev.	Min	Max
mpg	74	21.2973	5.785503	12	41
weight	74	3019.459	777.1936	1760	4840

The user typed summarize mpg weight and Stata responded with a table of summary statistics. Other commands would produce different results:

```
. generate gp100m = 100/mpg
. label var gp100m "Gallons per 100 miles"
. format gp100m %5.2f
. correlate gp100m weight
(obs=74)
```

	gp100m	weight
gp100m	1.0000	
weight	0.8544	1.0000

```
. regress gp100m weight gear_ratio
```

Source	SS	df	MS
Model	87.4543721	2	43.7271861
Residual	32.1218886	71	.452420967
Total	119.576261	73	1.63803097

Number of obs = 74
F(2, 71) = 96.65
Prob > F = 0.0000
R-squared = 0.7314
Adj R-squared = 0.7238
Root MSE = .67262

gp100m	Coef.	Std. Err.	t	P>|t|	[95% Conf. Interval]
weight	.0014769	.0001556	9.49	0.000	.0011665 .0017872
gear_ratio	.1566091	.2651131	0.59	0.557	-.3720115 .6852297
_cons	.0878243	1.198434	0.07	0.942	-2.301786 2.477435

```
. scatter gp100m weight, by(foreign)
```

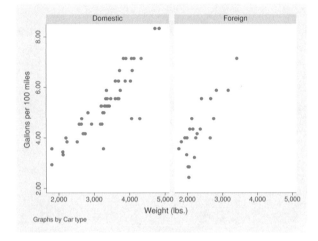

The user-interface model is type a little, get a little, etc., so that the user is always in control.

Stata's model for a dataset is that of a table—the rows are the observations and the columns are the variables:

```
. list mpg weight gp100m in 1/10
```

	mpg	weight	gp100m
1.	22	2,930	4.55
2.	17	3,350	5.88
3.	22	2,640	4.55
4.	20	3,250	5.00
5.	15	4,080	6.67
6.	18	3,670	5.56
7.	26	2,230	3.85
8.	20	3,280	5.00
9.	16	3,880	6.25
10.	19	3,400	5.26

Observations are numbered; variables are named.

Stata is fast. That speed is due partly to careful programming, and partly because Stata keeps the data in memory. Stata's file model is that of a word processor: a dataset may exist on disk, but the dataset in memory is a copy. Datasets are loaded into memory, where they are worked on, analyzed, changed, and then perhaps stored back on disk.

Working on a copy of the data in memory makes Stata safe for interactive use. The only way to harm the permanent copy of your data on disk is if you explicitly save over it.

Having the data in memory means that the dataset size is limited by the amount of computer memory. Stata stores the data in memory in a compressed format—you will be surprised how much data can fit. Nevertheless, if you work with large datasets, you may run into memory constraints. There are two solutions to this problem:

1. By default, Stata/MP and Stata/SE allocate 50 MB to Stata's data areas, and you can change it; see [U] **6 Setting the size of memory**.

   By default, Stata/IC allocates 10 MB to Stata's data areas, and you can change it; see [U] **6 Setting the size of memory**.

   Small Stata allows up to 99 variables and 1200 observations. Its memory allocation cannot be changed.

2. You will want to learn how to compress your data as much as possible; see [D] **compress**.

3 Resources for learning and using Stata

Contents

3.1 Overview

The *Getting Started* manual, *User's Guide*, and *Reference* manuals are the primary tools for learning about Stata; however, there are many other sources of information. A few are listed below.

- Stata itself. Stata has a subject table of contents online with links to the help system and dialog boxes that make it easy to find and to execute a Stata command. See [U] **4 Stata's help and search facilities**.

- The Stata web site. Visit http://www.stata.com. Much of the site is dedicated to user support; see [U] **3.2 The Stata web site (www.stata.com)**.

- The Stata Press web site. Visit http://www.stata-press.com. This site contains the datasets used throughout the Stata manuals; see [U] **3.3 The Stata Press web site (www.stata-press.com)**.

- The Stata listserver. An active group of Stata users communicate over an Internet listserver, which you can join for free; see [U] **3.4 The Stata listserver**.

- The Stata software distribution site and other user-provided software distribution sites. Stata itself can download and install updates and additions. We provide official updates to Stata—type `update query` or select **Help > Official Updates**. We also provide user-written additions to Stata and links to other user-provided sites—type `net` or select **Help > SJ and User-written Programs**; see [U] **3.6 Updating and adding features from the web**.

- The *Stata Journal* and the *Stata Technical Bulletin*. The *Stata Journal* contains reviewed papers, regular columns, book reviews, and other material of interest to researchers applying statistics in a variety of disciplines. The *Stata Technical Bulletin*, the predecessor to the *Stata Journal*, contains articles and user-written commands. See [U] **3.5 The Stata Journal**.

- NetCourses. We offer training via the Internet. Details are in [U] **3.7.1 NetCourses**.

- Public training courses. We offer in-depth training courses at third-party sites around the country. Details are in [U] **3.7.2 Public training courses**.

- On-site training courses. We can come to your institution to provide customized training. Details are in [U] **3.7.3 On-site training courses**.

- Books and support materials. Supplementary Stata materials are available; see [U] **3.8 Books and other support materials**.

- Technical support. We provide technical support by email, telephone, and fax; see [U] **3.9 Technical support**.

3.2   The Stata web site (www.stata.com)

Point your browser to http://www.stata.com and click on **Support**. More than half our web site is dedicated to providing support to users.

- The web site provides FAQs (frequently asked questions) on Windows, Mac, Unix, statistics, programming, Internet capabilities, graphics, and data management. These FAQs run the gamut from "I cannot save/open files" to "What does 'completely determined' mean in my logistic regression output?" Most users will find something of interest.

- Visiting the web site is one way that you can subscribe to the Stata listserver; see [U] **3.4 The Stata listserver**.

- The web site provides detailed information about NetCourses, along with the current schedule; see [U] **3.7.1 NetCourses**.

- The web site provides information about Stata courses and meetings, both in the United States and elsewhere.

- The web site provides an online bookstore for Stata-related books and other supplementary materials; see [U] **3.8 Books and other support materials**.

- The web site provides links to information about statistics: other statistical software providers, book publishers, statistical journals, statistical organizations, and statistical listservers.

- The web site provides links to Stata resources for learning Stata at http://www.stata.com/links/resources.html. Be sure to look at these materials, as many outstanding resources about Stata are listed here.

In short, the web site provides up-to-date information on all support materials and, where possible, provides the materials themselves. Visit http://www.stata.com if you can.

3.3   The Stata Press web site (www.stata-press.com)

Point your browser to http://www.stata-press.com. This site is devoted to the publications and activities of Stata Press.

- Datasets that are used in the Stata *Reference* manuals and other books published by Stata Press may be downloaded. Visit http://www.stata-press.com/data/. These datasets can be used in Stata by simply typing use http://www.stata-press.com/data/r11/auto. You could also type webuse auto; see [D] **webuse**.

- An online catalog of all our books and multimedia products is at http://www.stata-press.com/catalog.html. We have tried to include enough information, such as table of contents and preface material, so that you may tell whether the book is appropriate for you.

- Information about forthcoming publications is posted at http://www.stata-press.com/forthcoming.html.

3.4 The Stata listserver

The Stata listserver (Statalist) is an independently operated, real-time list of Stata users on the Internet. Anyone may join. Instructions for doing so can be found at http://www.stata.com by clicking on Support and then Statalist or by emailing service@stata.com.

Many knowledgeable users are active on the list, as are the StataCorp technical staff. We recommend that new users subscribe, observe the exchanges, and, if it turns out not to be useful, unsubscribe.

3.5 The Stata Journal

The *Stata Journal* (SJ) is a printed and electronic journal, published quarterly, containing articles about statistics, data analysis, teaching methods, and effective use of Stata's language. The *Journal* publishes reviewed papers together with shorter notes and comments, regular columns, tips, book reviews, and other material of interest to researchers applying statistics in a variety of disciplines. The *Journal* is a publication for all Stata users, both novice and experienced, with different levels of expertise in statistics, research design, data management, graphics, reporting of results, and of Stata, in particular.

Tables of contents for past issues and abstracts of the articles are available at http://www.stata-journal.com/archives.html. PDF copies of articles published at least three years ago are available for free from the *Stata Journal* web site.

We recommend that all users subscribe to the SJ. Visit http://www.stata-journal.com to learn more about the *Stata Journal* and to order your subscription.

To obtain any programs associated with articles in the SJ, type

```
. net from http://www.stata-journal.com/software
```

or

- Select **Help > SJ and User-written Programs**
- Click on **Stata Journal**

The Stata Technical Bulletin

For 10 years, the *Stata Technical Bulletin* (STB) served as the means of distributing new commands and Stata upgrades, both user-written and "official". After 10 years of continual publication, the STB evolved into the *Stata Journal*. The Internet provided an alternative delivery mechanism for user-written programs, so the emphasis shifted from user-written programs to more expository articles. Although the STB is no longer published, many of the programs and articles that appeared in it are still valuable today. PDF copies of all issues of the STB are available for free at http://www.stata.com/bookstore/stbj.html. To obtain the programs that were published in the STB, type

```
. net from http://www.stata.com
. net cd stb
```

3.6   Updating and adding features from the web

Stata itself is web aware.

First, try this:

```
. use http://www.stata.com/manual/oddeven, clear
```

That will load an uninteresting dataset into your computer from our web site. If you have a home page, you can use this feature to share datasets with coworkers. Save a dataset on your home page, and researchers worldwide can use it. See [R] **net**.

3.6.1   Official updates

Although we follow no formal schedule for the release of updates, we typically provide updates to Stata approximately every 3 weeks. Installing the updates is easy. Type

```
. update query
```

or select **Help > Official Updates**. Do not be concerned; nothing will be installed unless and until you say so. Once you have installed the update, you can type

```
. help whatsnew
```

or select **Help > What's New?** to find out what has changed. We distribute official updates to fix bugs and to add new features.

3.6.2   Unofficial updates

There are also "unofficial" updates—additions to Stata written by Stata users, which includes members of the StataCorp technical staff. Stata is programmable, and even if you never write a Stata program, you may find these additions useful, some of them spectacularly so. Start by typing

```
. net from http://www.stata.com
```

or select **Help > SJ and User-written Programs**.

Be sure to visit the SSC Archive. The `ssc` command makes it easy for you to install and uninstall packages from SSC. Type

```
. ssc whatsnew
```

to find out what's new at the site. If you find something that interests you, type

```
. ssc describe pkgname
```

for more information. If you have already installed a package you can check for optionally and install updates by typing

```
. adoupdate pkgname
```

To check for and optionally install updates to all the packages you have previously installed, type

```
. adoupdate all
```

Periodically, you can type

```
. news
```

or select **Help > News** to display a short message from our web site telling you what is newly available.

See [U] **28 Using the Internet to keep up to date**.

3.7 Training

3.7.1 NetCourses

We offer courses on Stata at the introductory and advanced levels. Courses on software are typically expensive and time consuming. They are expensive because, in addition to the direct costs of the course, participants must travel to the course site. Courses over the Internet save everyone time and money.

We offer courses over the Internet and call them Stata NetCourses^{TM}.

- **What is a NetCourse?**
  A NetCourse is a course offered through the Stata web site that varies in length from 7 to 8 weeks. Everyone with an email address and a web browser can participate.

- **How does it work?**
  Every Friday a lecture is posted on a password-protected web site. After reading the lecture over the weekend or perhaps on Monday, participants then post questions and comments on a message board. Course leaders typically respond to the questions and comments on the same day they are posted. Other participants are encouraged to amplify or otherwise respond to the questions or comments as well. The next lecture is then posted on Friday, and the process repeats.

- **How much of my time does it take?**
  It depends on the course, but the introductory courses are designed to take roughly 3 hours per week.

- **There are three of us here—can just one of us enroll and then redistribute the NetCourse materials ourselves?**
  We ask that you not. NetCourses are priced to cover the substantial time input of the course leaders. Moreover, enrollment is typically limited to prevent the discussion from becoming unmanageable. The value of a NetCourse, just like a real course, is the interaction of the participants, both with each other and with the course leaders.

- **I've never taken a course by Internet before. I can see that it might work, but then again, it might not. How do I know I will benefit?**
  All Stata NetCourses come with a 30-day satisfaction guarantee. The 30 days begins after the conclusion of the final lecture.

You can learn more about the current NetCourse offerings by visiting http://www.stata.com/netcourse.

NetCourseNow

A NetCourseNow offers the same material as NetCourses but it allows you to choose the time and pace of the course, and you have a personal NetCourse instructor.

- **What is a NetCourseNow?**
  A NetCourseNow offers the same material as a NetCourse, but allows you to move at your own pace and to specify a starting date. With a NetCourseNow, you also have the added benefit of a personal NetCourse instructor whom you can email directly with questions about lectures and exercises. You must have an email address and a web browser to participate.

- **How does it work?**
  All course lectures and exercises are posted at once, and you are free to study at your own pace. You will be provided with the email address of your personal NetCourse instructor to contact when you have questions.

- **How much of my time does it take?**
  A NetCourseNow allows you to set your own pace. How long the course takes and how much time you spend per week is up to you.

3.7.2 Public training courses

Public training courses are intensive, in-depth courses taught by StataCorp at third-party sites around the country.

- **How is a public training course taught?**
  These are interactive, hands-on sessions. Participants work along with the instructor so that they can see firsthand how to use Stata. Questions are encouraged.

- **Do I need my own computer?**
  Because the sessions are in computer labs running the latest version of Stata, there is no need to bring your own computer. Of course, you may bring your own computer if you have a registered copy of Stata you can use.

- **Do I get any notes?**
  You get a complete set of notes for each class, which includes not only the materials from the lessons but also all the output from the example commands.

See http://www.stata.com/training/public.html for all course offerings.

3.7.3 On-site training courses

On-site training courses are courses that are tailored to the needs of an institution. StataCorp personnel can come to your site to teach what you need, whether it be to teach new users or to show how to use a specialized tool in Stata.

- **How is an on-site training course taught?**
  These are interactive, hands-on sessions, just like our public-training courses. You will need a computer for each participant.

- **What topics are available?**
  We offer training in anything and everything related to Stata. You work with us to put together a curriculum that matches your needs.

- **How does licensing work?**
  We will supply you with the licenses you need for the training session, whether the training is in a lab or for individuals working on laptops. We will ship the licensing and installation instructions so that you can have everything up and running before the session starts.

See http://www.stata.com/training/onsite.html for all the details.

3.8 Books and other support materials

3.8.1 For readers

There are books published about Stata, both by us and by others. Visit the Stata bookstore at http://www.stata.com/bookstore. For the books that we carry, we include the table of contents and comments written by a member of our technical staff, explaining why we think this book might interest you.

3.8.2   For authors

If you have written a book related to Stata and would like us to consider carrying it in our bookstore, email bookstore@stata.com.

If you are writing a book, join our free Author Support Program. Stata professionals are available to review your Stata code to ensure that it is efficient and reflects modern usage, production specialists are available to help format Stata output, and editors and statisticians are available to ensure the accuracy of Stata-related content. Visit http://www.stata.com/authorsupport.

If you are thinking about writing a Stata-related book, consider publishing it with Stata Press. Email submissions@statapress.com.

3.9   Technical support

We are committed to providing superior technical support for Stata software. To assist you as efficiently as possible, please follow the procedures listed below.

3.9.1   Register your software

You must register your software to be eligible for technical support, updates, special offers, and other benefits. By registering, you will receive the *Stata News*, and you may access our support staff for free with any question that you encounter. You may register your software either electronically or by mail.

Electronic registration: After installing Stata and successfully entering your License and Authorization Key, your default web browser will open to the online registration form at the Stata web site. You may also manually point your web browser to http://www.stata.com/register/ if you wish to register your copy of Stata at a later time.

Mail-in registration: Fill in the registration card that came with Stata and mail it to StataCorp.

3.9.2   Before contacting technical support

Before you spend the time gathering the information our technical support department needs, make sure that the answer does not already exist in the help files. You can use the `help` and `search` commands to find all the entries in Stata that address a given subject. Be sure to try selecting **Help > Contents**. Check the manual for a particular command. There are often examples that address questions and concerns. Another good source of information is our web site. You should keep a bookmark to our frequently asked questions page (http://www.stata.com/support/faqs/) and check it occasionally for new information.

If you do need to contact technical support, visit http://www.stata.com/support/tech-support/ for more information.

3.9.3   Technical support by email

This is the preferred method of asking a technical support question. It has the following advantages:

- You will receive a prompt response from us saying that we have received your question and that it has been forwarded to *Technical Services* to answer.
- We can route your question to a specialist for your particular question.

- Questions submitted via email may be answered after normal business hours, or even on weekends or holidays. Although we cannot promise that this will happen, it may, and your email inquiry is bound to receive a faster response than leaving a message on Stata's voicemail.

- If you are receiving an error message or an unexpected result, it is easy to include a log file that demonstrates the problem.

Please see visit http://www.stata.com/support/tech-support/ for information about contacting technical support.

3.9.4 Technical support by phone or fax

Our installation support telephone number is 979-696-4600. Please have your serial number handy. It is also best if you are at your computer when you call. Telephone support is reserved for installation questions. If your question does not involve installation, the question should be submitted via email or fax.

Send fax requests to 979-696-4601. If possible, collect the relevant information in a log file and include the file in your fax.

Please see visit http://www.stata.com/support/tech-support/ for information about contacting technical support.

3.9.5 Comments and suggestions for our technical staff

By all means, send in your comments and suggestions. Your input is what determines the changes that occur in Stata between releases, so if we do not hear from you, we may not include your most desired new feature! Email is preferred, as this provides us with a permanent copy of your request. When requesting new features, please include any references that you would like us to review should we develop those new features. Email your suggestions to service@stata.com.

4 Stata's help and search facilities

4.1   Introduction

To access Stata's help, you will either

1. select **Help** from the menus, or

2. use the `help`, `search`, `findit`, and `hsearch` commands.

Regardless of the method you use, results will be shown in the Viewer or Results windows. Blue text indicates a hypertext link, so you can click to go to related entries.

4.2   Getting started

The first time you use help, try one of the following:

1. Select **Help > Advice** form the menu bar, or

2. Type `help advice`.

(Continued on next page)

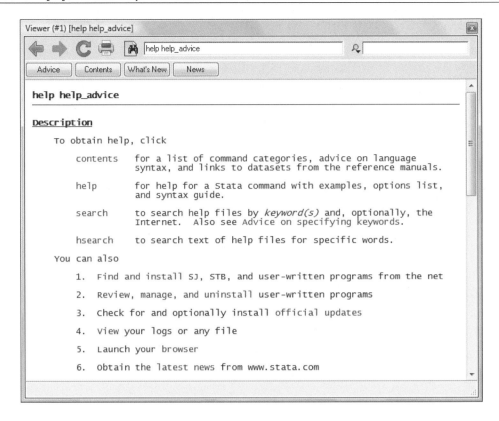

Advice presents you with four alternatives:

1. contents: Click on that and you will be taken to a system organized by topic: Basics, Data management, Statistics, Graphics, and Programming and matrices.

2. help: Click on that and you can type the name of a Stata command and go directly to its online help.

3. search: Click on that and you can perform a keyword search.

4. hsearch: Click on that and you can do a search of the contents of the help files much like search engines on the Internet search the contents of the web.

The above are the four main features of Stata's help system, and you can access each in various ways:

1. Topical help:

> Select **Help > Advice**, click on contents, or
>
> Select **Help > Contents**, or
>
> Type help contents

2. Help on a command or topic:

> Select **Help > Advice**, click on help, or
>
> Select **Help > Stata Command...**, or
>
> Type help *commandname*

3. Keyword search:

> Select **Help > Advice**, click on search, or
>
> Select **Help > Search...**, or
>
> Type search *keyword(s)*

4. Text search:

> Select **Help > Advice**, click on hsearch, or
>
> Type hsearch *whatever*

4.3   help: Stata's help system

When you

1. Select **Help > Stata command...**
   Type a command name in the Command edit field
   Click on OK, or

2. Type help followed by a command name

you access Stata's online help files. These files provide shortened versions of what is in the printed manuals. Let's access the online help for Stata's ttest command. Do one of the following:

1. Select **Help > Stata command...**
   Type ttest in the Command edit field
   Click on OK, or

2. Type help ttest

Regardless of which you do, the result will be

(*Continued on next page*)

The trick is in already knowing that Stata's command for testing equality of means is `ttest` and not, say `meanstest`. There are two solutions to that problem, topical help and searching. Topical help you access by selecting **Help > Contents** or by typing `help contents`.

4.4   Accessing PDF manuals from help entries

Every help file in Stata links to the equivalent manual entry. If you are reading `help ttest`, simply click on [R] `ttest` in the **Title** section of the help file to go directly to the [R] **ttest** manual entry.

We provide recommended settings for your PDF viewer to optimize it for Stata's documentation at http://www.stata.com/support/faqs/res/documentation.html.

4.5   Searching

If you do not know the name of the Stata command you are looking for, you can search for it by keyword,

1. Select **Help > Search...**
   Type keywords in the edit field
   Click on OK

2. Type `search` followed by the keywords

or you can search the text of Stata's help files,

3. Type `hsearch` followed by text

`search` and `hsearch` each have their own advantages.

`search` is available by both menu and command; `hsearch` is available by command only (and from **Help > Advice**).

`search` matches the keywords you specify to a database and returns matches found in Stata commands, FAQs at www.stata.com, and articles that have appeared in the *Stata Journal*. Optionally, it can also find user-written additions to Stata available over the web. To do that, from the Search dialog box select *Search all* or, on the `search` command, specify the `all` option.

`hsearch` searches the text of the Stata help files on your computer. That does not include FAQs at www.stata.com and articles that have appeared in the *Stata Journal*, but it does include any help files you have written and the help files associated with any user-written additions you may have installed.

`search` does a better job when what you want is based on terms commonly used or when what you are looking for might not already be installed on your computer.

`hsearch` does a better job when the search terms are odder or when what you want might already be installed.

It is sometimes a good idea to use both.

4.6 More on search

However you access `search`—command or menu—it does the same thing. You tell `search` what you want information about, and it searches for relevant entries. If you want `search` to look for the topic across all sources, including the online help, the FAQs at the Stata web site, the *Stata Journal*, and all Stata-related Internet sources including user-written additions, specify "Search all" from the Search dialog or, on the `search` command, specify the `all` option. (Command `findit` is a synonym for `search, all`, so many users type `findit ...` rather than `search ... , all`.)

`search` can be used broadly or narrowly. For instance, if you want to perform the Kolmogorov–Smirnov test for equality of distributions, you could type

```
. search Kolmogorov-Smirnov test of equality of distributions
[R]     ksmirnov . . . . . . Kolmogorov-Smirnov equality of distributions test
        (help ksmirnov)
```

In fact, we did not have to be nearly so complete—typing `search Kolmogorov-Smirnov` would have been adequate. Had we specified our request more broadly—looking up `equality of distributions`—we would have obtained a longer list that included `ksmirnov`.

Here are guidelines for using `search`.

- Capitalization does not matter. Look up Kolmogorov-Smirnov or kolmogorov-smirnov.

- Punctuation does not matter. Look up kolmogorov smirnov.

- Order of words does not matter. Look up smirnov kolmogorov.

- You may abbreviate, but how much depends. Break at syllables. Look up kol smir. search tends to tolerate a lot of abbreviation; it is better to abbreviate than to misspell.

- The prepositions for, into, of, on, to, and with are ignored. Use them—look up equality of distributions—or omit them—look up equality distributions—it makes no difference.

- search tolerates plurals, especially when they can be formed by adding an s. Even so, it is better to look up the singular. Look up normal distribution, not normal distributions.

- Specify the search criterion in English, not in computer jargon.

- Use American spellings. Look up `color`, not `colour`.

- Use nouns. Do not use -ing words or other verbs. Look up `median tests`, not `testing medians`.

- Use few words. Every word specified further restricts the search. Look up `distribution`, and you get one list; look up `normal distribution`, and the list is a sublist of that.

- Sometimes words have more than one context. The following words can be used to restrict the context:

  a. `data`, meaning in the context of data management. Order could refer to the order of data or to order statistics. Look up `order data` to restrict order to its data-management sense.

  b. `statistics` (abbreviation `stat`), meaning in the context of statistics. Look up `order statistics` to restrict order to the statistical sense.

  c. `graph` or `graphs`, meaning in the context of statistical graphics. Look up `median graphs` to restrict the list to commands for graphing medians.

  d. `utility` (abbreviation `util`), meaning in the context of utility commands. The search command itself is not data management, not statistics, and not graphics; it is a utility.

  e. `programs` or `programming` (abbreviation `prog`), to mean in the context of programming. Look up `programming scalar` to obtain a sublist of scalars in programming.

search has other features, as well; see [U] **4.9 search: All the details**.

4.7   More on help

Both `help` and `search` are understanding of some mistakes. For instance, you may abbreviate a command name. If you type either `help regres` or `help regress`, you will bring up the help file for `regress`.

When `help` cannot find the command you are looking for, try `search`. In this case, typing `search regres` would find the command, but that would be because 'regres' is an abbreviation of the word regression, which probably appears in the keyword database.

Stata can run into some problems with abbreviations. For instance, Stata has a command with the inelegant name `ksmirnov`. You forget and think the command is called `ksmir`:

```
. help ksmir
help for ksmir not found
try help contents or search ksmir
```

This is a case where `help` gives bad advice because typing `search ksmir` will do you no good. You should type `search` followed by what you are really looking for: `search kolmogorov smirnov`.

4.8   help contents: Table of contents for Stata's help system

Typing `help contents` or selecting **Help > Contents** provides another way of locating entries in the documentation and online help. Whichever you use, you will be presented with a long table of contents, organized topically.

```
. help contents
```

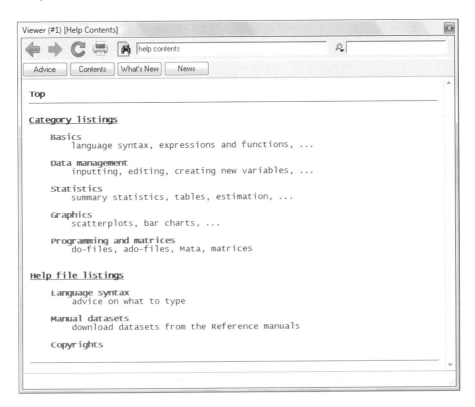

4.9   search: All the details

The search command actually provides a few features that are not available from the **Help** menu. The full syntax of the search command is

search *word* [*word* ...] [, [local | net | all] <u>au</u>thor <u>entry</u> <u>ex</u>act faq

<u>h</u>istorical or <u>man</u>ual sj]

where <u>underlining</u> indicates the minimum allowable abbreviation and [brackets] indicate optional.

local, the default (unless changed by set searchdefault), specifies that the search be performed using only Stata's keyword database.

net specifies that the search be performed across the materials available via Stata's net command. Using search word [*word* ...], net is equivalent to typing net search word [*word* ...] (without options); see [R] **net**.

all specifies that the search be performed across both the local keyword database and the net materials.

author specifies that the search be performed on the basis of author's name rather than keywords.

entry specifies that the search be performed on the basis of entry IDs rather than keywords.

exact prevents matching on abbreviations.

faq limits the search to entries found in the FAQs at http://www.stata.com.

historical adds to the search entries that are of historical interest only. By default, such entries are not listed. Past entries are classified as historical if they discuss a feature that later became an official part of Stata. Updates to historical entries will always be found, even if historical is not specified.

or specifies that an entry be listed if any of the words typed after search are associated with the entry. The default is to list the entry only if all the words specified are associated with the entry.

manual limits the search to entries in the *User's Guide* and all the *Reference* manuals.

sj limits the search to entries in the *Stata Journal* and the *Stata Technical Bulletin*.

4.9.1 How search works

search has a database—a file—containing the titles, etc., of every entry in the *User's Guide*, *Reference* manuals, articles in the *Stata Journal* and in the *Stata Technical Bulletin*, and FAQs at http://www.stata.com. In this file is a list of words associated with each entry, called keywords.

When you type search *xyz*, search reads this file and compares the list of keywords with *xyz*. If it finds *xyz* in the list or a keyword that allows an abbreviation of *xyz*, it displays the entry.

When you type search *xyz abc*, search does the same thing but displays an entry only if it contains both keywords. The order does not matter, so you can search linear regression or search regression linear.

How many entries search finds depends on how the search database was constructed. We have included a plethora of keywords under the theory that, for a given request, it is better to list too much rather than risk listing nothing at all. Still, you are in the position of guessing the keywords. Do you look up normality test, normality tests, or tests of normality? Normality test would be best, but all would work. In general, use the singular, and strike the unnecessary words. We provide guidelines for specifying keywords in [U] **4.6 More on search** above.

4.9.2 Author searches

search ordinarily compares the words following search with the keywords for the entry. If you specify the author option, however, it compares the words with the author's name. In the search database, we have filled in author names for *Stata Journal* and STB articles and for FAQs.

For instance, in [R] **kdensity**, you will discover that Isaías H. Salgado-Ugarte wrote the first version of Stata's kdensity command and published it in the STB. Assume that you have read his original and find the discussion useful. You might now wonder what else he has written in the STB. To find out, type

```
. search Salgado-Ugarte, author
  (output omitted )
```

Names like Salgado-Ugarte are confusing to some people. search does not require you specify the entire name; what you type is compared with each "word" of the name, and, if any part matches, the entry is listed. The hyphen is a special character, and you can omit it. Thus you can obtain the same list by looking up Salgado, Ugarte, or Salgado Ugarte without the hyphen.

Actually, to find all entries written by Salgado-Ugarte, you need to type

```
. search Salgado-Ugarte, author historical
  (output omitted )
```

Prior inserts in the STB that provide a feature that later was superseded by a built-in feature of Stata are marked as historical in the search database and, by default, are not listed. The `historical` option ensures that all entries are listed.

4.9.3 Entry ID searches

If you specify the `entry` option, `search` compares what you have typed with the entry ID. The entry ID is not the title—it is the reference listed to the left of the title that tells you where to look. For instance, in

```
[R]     regress . . . . . . . . . . . . . . . . . . . . . . Linear regression
        (help regress)
```

"[R] regress" is the entry ID. In

```
GS      . . . . . . . . . . . . . . . . . . . . . . . Getting Started manual
```

"GS" is the entry ID. In

```
SJ-6-4   st0113  . Testing for cross-sectional dependence in panel-data models
         (help xtcsd if installed) . . . . . . R. E. De Hoyos and V. Sarafidis
         Q4/06   SJ 6(4): 482--496
         tests for the presence of cross-sectional dependence in
         panels with many cross-sectional units and few time-series
         observations
```

"SJ-6-4 st0113" is the entry ID.

`search` with the `entry` option searches these entry IDs.

Thus, you could generate a table of contents for the *Reference* manuals by typing

```
. search [R], entry
  (output omitted )
```

You could generate a table of contents for the 16th issue of the STB by typing

```
. search STB-16, entry historical
  (output omitted )
```

The `historical` option here is possibly important. STB-16 was published in November 1993, and perhaps some of its inserts have been marked as historical.

You could obtain a list of all inserts associated with *dm36* by typing

```
. search dm36, entry historical
  (output omitted )
```

Again, we include the `historical` option if any of the relevant inserts have been marked historical.

4.9.4 FAQ searches

To search across the FAQs, specify the `faq` option:

```
. search logistic regression, faq
  (output omitted )
```

4.9.5   Return codes

In addition to indexing the entries in the *User's Guide* and all the *Stata Reference* manuals, `search` also can be used to look up return codes.

To see information about return code 131, type

```
. search rc 131

[R]     error messages  . . . . . . . . . . . . . . . . . . . . .  Return code 131
        not possible with test;
        You requested a test of a hypothesis that is nonlinear in the
        variables.  test tests only linear hypotheses.  Use testnl.
```

To get a list of all Stata return codes, type

```
. search rc
(output omitted )
```

4.10   net search: Searching net resources

When you select **Help > Search**, there are two types of searches to choose. The first, which has been discussed in the previous sections, is to **Search documentation and FAQs**. The second is to **Search net resources**. This feature of Stata searches resources over the Internet.

When you choose **Search net resources** in the search dialog box and enter *keywords* in the field, Stata searches all user-written programs on the Internet, including user-written additions published in the *Stata Journal* and the STB. The results are displayed in the Viewer, and you can click to go to any of the matches found.

Equivalently, you can type `net search` *keywords* on the Stata command line to display the results in the Results window. For the full syntax for using the `net search` command, see [R] **net search**.

4.11   hsearch: An alternative to search

`hsearch` is available from command mode, and by clicking on `hsearch` from **Help > Advice**. Just like you can type `search` *anything*, you can type `hsearch` *anything*. Whereas `search` bases its results on a file of keywords for official Stata commands, official FAQs, and the *Stata Journal*, `hsearch` searches the text of the help files on your computer. `hsearch` searches all the help files, whether official or not, i.e., whether the help files are part of Stata as supplied by StataCorp or from user-written additions you have installed or from help files you wrote yourself.

`hsearch` shows what is installed on your computer.

`search` shows what is official and includes FAQs and *Stata Journal* contributions.

5 Flavors of Stata

5.1 Platforms

Stata is available for a variety of computers, including

Stata for Windows, 32-bit x86
Stata for Windows, 64-bit x86-64
Stata for Windows, 64-bit Itanium

Stata for Mac, 32-bit Intel
Stata for Mac, 64-bit Intel
Stata for Mac, PowerPC

Stata for AIX, 64-bit
Stata for Linux, 32-bit x86
Stata for Linux, 64-bit x86-64
Stata for Linux, 64-bit Itanium
Stata for Solaris, 64-bit Sparc
Stata for Solaris, 64-bit x86-64

Which version of Stata you run does not matter—Stata is Stata. You instruct Stata in the same way and Stata produces the same results, right down to the random-number generator. Even files can be shared. A dataset created on one computer can be used on any other computer, and the same goes for graphs, programs, or any file Stata uses or produces. Moving files across platforms is simply a matter of copying them; no translation is required.

Some computers, however, are faster than others. Some computers have more memory than others. Computers with more memory, and faster computers, are better.

The list above includes both 32- and 64-bit computers. 64-bit Stata runs faster than 32-bit Stata and 64-bit Stata will allow processing data in excess of 2 gigabytes, assuming you have enough memory. 32-bit Stata will run on 64-bit hardware.

When you purchase Stata, you may install it on any of the above platforms. Stata licenses are not locked to a single operating system.

5.2   Stata/MP, Stata/SE, Stata/IC, and Small Stata

Stata is available in four flavors, although perhaps sizes would be a better word. The flavors are, from largest to smallest, Stata/MP, Stata/SE, Stata/IC, and Small Stata. Small Stata is not available under Unix.

Stata/MP is the multiprocessor version of Stata. It runs on multiple CPUs or on multiple cores, from two to 64. Stata/MP uses however many CPUs or cores you tell it to use (even one). Stata/MP is the fastest version of Stata. Even so, all the details of parallelization are handled internally and you use Stata/MP just like you use any other flavor of Stata.

Stata/SE is like Stata/MP, but for single CPUs. Stata/SE will run on multiple CPUs or multiple-core computers, but it will use only one CPU or core. SE stands for special edition.

Both Stata/MP and Stata/SE have the same limits and the same capabilities and are intended for those who work with large datasets. You may have up to 32,767 variables with either. Statistical models may have up to 11,000 variables.

Stata/IC is standard Stata. IC stands for intercooled, a name used before the introduction of Stata/SE and Stata/MP to indicate that it was at the time the top version of Stata. Up to 2,047 variables are allowed. Statistical models may have up to 800 variables.

Stata/MP, Stata/SE, and Stata/IC all allow up to 2,147,583,647 observations, assuming you have enough memory.

Small Stata is intended for students and limited to 99 variables and 1,200 observations.

5.2.1   Determining which version you own

Check your License and Authorization Key. Included with every copy of Stata is a paper License and Authorization Key that contains codes that you will input during installation. This determines which flavor of Stata you have and for which platform.

Contact us or your distributor if you want to upgrade from one flavor to another. Usually, all you need is an upgraded paper License and Authorization Key with the appropriate codes. All flavors of Stata are on the same DVD.

If you purchased one flavor of Stata and want to use a lesser version, you may. You might want to do this if you had a large computer at work and a smaller one at home. Please remember, however, that you have only one license (or however many licenses you purchased). You may, both legally and ethically, install Stata on both computers and then use one or the other, but you should not use them both simultaneously.

5.2.2   Determining which version is installed

If Stata is already installed, you can find out which Stata you are using by entering Stata as you normally do and typing about:

```
. about
Stata/SE 11.0 for Windows (32-bit)
Born date
Copyright (C) 1985-2009
Total physical memory:       506600 KB
Available physical memory:    83040 KB
11-user Stata network perpetual license:
        Serial number:  4011041234
          Licensed to:  Alan R. Riley
                        StataCorp
```

5.3   Size limits of Stata/MP, SE, IC, and Small Stata

Here are some of the different size limits for Stata/MP, Stata/SE, Stata/IC, and Small Stata. Type `help limits` for a longer list.

Maximum size limits for Stata/MP, Stata/SE, Stata/IC, and Small Stata

	Stata/MP and SE	Stata/IC	Small Stata
Number of observations	limited only by memory	limited only by memory	fixed at approx. 1,000
Number of variables	32,767	2,047	fixed at 99
Width of a dataset	393,192	24,564	800
Maximum # of right-hand-side variables	10,998	798	99
Number of characters in a macro	1,081,511	165,200	8,681
Number of characters in a command	1,081,527	165,216	8,697

Stata/MP and Stata/SE allow more variables, larger models, longer macros, and a longer command line than Stata/IC. The longer command line and macro length are required because of the greater number of variables allowed. Larger models means that Stata/MP and Stata/SE can fit statistical models with more independent variables.

Small Stata is limited. It is intended for student use and often used in undergraduate labs.

5.4   Speed comparison of Stata/MP, SE, IC, and Small Stata

We have written a white paper comparing the performance of Stata/MP with Stata/SE; see http://www.stata.com/statamp/report.pdf. The white paper includes command-by-command performance measurements.

In summary, on a 2-CPU or dual-core computer, Stata/MP will run commands in 71% of the time required by Stata/SE. There is variation; some commands run in half the time and others are not sped up at all. Statistical estimation commands run in 59% of the time. Numbers quoted are medians. Average performance gains are higher because commands that take longer to execute are generally sped up more.

Stata/MP running on four CPUs runs in 50% (all commands) and 36% (estimation commands) of the time required by Stata/SE. Both numbers are median measures.

Stata/MP supports up to 64 CPUs.

Stata/IC is slower than Stata/SE, but those differences emerge only when processing datasets that are pushing the limits of Stata/IC. Stata/SE has a larger memory footprint and uses that extra memory for larger look-aside tables to more efficiently process large datasets. The real benefits of the larger tables become apparent only after exceeding the limits of Stata/IC. Stata/SE was designed for processing large datasets.

Small Stata is, by comparison to all the above, slow, but given its limits, no one notices. Small Stata was designed to have a minimal memory footprint, and to achieve that, different logic is sometimes used. For instance, in Stata's `test` command, it must compute the matrix calculation $\mathbf{RZR}'$ (where $\mathbf{Z} = (\mathbf{X}'\mathbf{X})^{-1}$). Stata/MP, Stata/SE, and Stata/IC make the calculation in a straightforward way, which is to form $\mathbf{T} = \mathbf{RZ}$ and then calculate $\mathbf{TR}'$. This requires temporarily storing the matrix $\mathbf{T}$. Small Stata, on the other hand, goes into more complicated code to form the result directly—code that requires temporary storage of only one scalar. This code, in effect, recalculates intermediate results over and over again, and so it is slower. Also, because Small Stata is designed to work with small datasets, it uses different memory-management routines. These memory-management routines use 2-byte rather than 4-byte offsets and therefore require only half the memory to track locations.

The differences are all technical and internal. From the user's point of view, Stata/MP, Stata/SE, Stata/IC, and Small Stata work the same way.

5.5   Feature comparison of Stata/MP, SE, and IC

The features of all flavors of Stata on all platforms are the same. The differences are in speed and in limits as discussed above. To learn more, type `help stata/mp`, `help stata/se`, `help stata/ic`, or `help small stata`.

6 Setting the size of memory

Contents

6.1 Memory-size considerations

Stata works with a copy of the data that it loads into memory.

By default, Stata/MP and Stata/SE allocate 50 megabytes and Stata/IC allocates 10 megabytes to Stata's data areas, and you can change it.

By default, Small Stata allocates about 950 K to Stata's data areas, and you cannot change it.

You can even change the allocation to be larger than the physical amount of memory on your computer because Windows, Mac, and Unix systems provide virtual memory.

Virtual memory is slow but adequate in rare cases when you have a dataset that is too large to load into real memory. If you use large datasets often, we recommend that you add more memory to your computer.

One way to change the allocation is when you start Stata. Instructions for doing this are provided in

Windows	[GSW]	**C.4 Specifying the amount of memory allocated**
Mac	[GSM]	**C.2 Specifying the amount of memory allocated**
Unix	[GSU]	**C.2 Specifying the amount of memory allocated**

Also, if you use Stata/MP, Stata/SE, or Stata/IC for Windows, Unix, or Mac, you can change the total amount of memory allocated while Stata is running. That is the topic of this chapter.

It does not matter which method you use. Being able to change the total on the fly is convenient, but even if you cannot do this, it just means that you specify it ahead of time. If later you need more, simply exit Stata and reinvoke it with the larger total.

6.2 Setting memory size on the fly: Stata/MP and Stata/SE

There are three limits in Stata/MP and Stata/SE that affect memory allocation and usage. The three limits are

1. `maxvar`, the maximum number of variables allowed in a dataset. This limit is initially set to 5,000; you can increase it up to 32,767.

2. `matsize`, the largest dimension of a matrix in Stata (in Mata, matrices are limited in size only by memory): this limit is initially set to 800, and you can increase it up to 11,000. This usually relates to the maximum number of independent variables allowed in the models that you fit, and thus, the dimension of the estimated variance–covariance matrix. However, in some panel-data models, covariance or correlation matrices must be fit, and their dimensions depend on either the number of panels (groups) in your data or the number of observations in your dataset. This limit does not apply to Mata matrices; see the *Mata Reference Manual.*

3. `memory`, the amount of memory Stata requests from the operating system to store your data. This limit is initially set to 50 megabytes in Stata/MP and Stata/SE. You may set it to as large a number as your operating system will allow.

You set the limits using the

$$\text{set maxvar} \ \# \qquad \left[, \ \underline{\text{permanently}}\right]$$

$$\text{set matsize} \ \# \qquad \left[, \ \underline{\text{permanently}}\right]$$

$$\text{set memory} \ \#\left[\text{b}|\text{k}|\text{m}|\text{g}\right] \ \left[, \ \underline{\text{permanently}}\right]$$

commands. For instance, you might type

```
. set maxvar   5000
. set matsize  900
. set memory   60m
```

The order in which you set the limits does not matter. If you specify the `permanently` option when you set a limit, in addition to making the change right now, Stata will remember the new limit and use it in the future when you invoke Stata:

```
. set maxvar   5000, permanently
. set matsize  900, permanently
. set memory   60m, permanently
```

You can reset the current or permanent limits whenever and as often as you wish.

6.2.1 Advice on setting maxvar

set maxvar # $\left[, \ \underline{\text{permanently}}\right]$

where $2{,}048 \leq \# \leq 32{,}767$

Why is there a limit on `maxvar`? Why not just set `maxvar` to 32,767 and be done with it? Because simply allowing room for variables, even if they do not exist, causes Stata to consume memory and, if you will be using only datasets with a lot fewer variables, you will be wasting memory.

The formula for the amount of memory consumed by `set maxvar` is approximately

$$\text{megs} = .3147 * (\text{maxvar}/1000) + .002$$

For instance, if you set `maxvar` to 20,000, the memory would be approximately

$$\text{megs} = .3147 * 20 + .002 = 6.296 \text{ megs}$$

and if you left it at the default, the memory use would be roughly

$$\text{megs} = .3147 * 5 + .002 = 1.575 \text{ megs}$$

Thus how big you set `maxvar` does not dramatically affect memory usage. Still, at `maxvar`=32,000, memory use is 10.072 MB.

Recommendation: think about datasets with the most variables that you typically use. `set maxvar` to a few hundred or even 1,000 above that. (The memory cost of an extra 1,000 variables is only .315 megs.)

Remember, you can always reset `maxvar` temporarily by typing `set maxvar`.

❑ Technical note

The formula above is only approximate, and the formula given is the formula appropriate for 32-bit computers. When you `set maxvar`, Stata/MP and Stata/SE will give you a memory report showing the exact amount of memory used:

```
. set maxvar 10000
```

Current memory allocation

settable	current value	description	memory usage (1M = 1024k)
set maxvar	10000	max. variables allowed	3.149M
set memory	50M	max. data space	50.000M
set matsize	400	max. RHS vars in models	1.254M
			14.403M

❑

6.2.2   Advice on setting matsize

set matsize # $\left[\text{, } \underline{\text{permanently}} \right]$

where $10 \leq \# \leq 11{,}000$

Although `matsize` can theoretically be set up to 11,000, on all but 64-bit computers, you will be unable to do that, and, even if you succeeded, Stata/SE would probably run out of memory subsequently. The value of `matsize` has a dramatic effect on memory usage, the formula being

$$\text{megs} = (8 * \text{matsize}^2 + 88 * \text{matsize})/(1024^2)$$

This formula is valid across all computers, 32-bit and 64-bit. For instance, the above formula states

matsize	memory use
400	1.254M
800	4.950M
1,600	19.666M
3,200	78.394M
6,400	313.037M
11,000	924.080M

The formula, in fact, is an understatement of the amount of memory certain Stata commands use and is an understatement of what you will certainly use yourself if you use matrices directly. The formula gives the amount of memory required for one matrix and 11 vectors. If two matrices are required, the numbers above are nearly doubled. When you `set matsize`, if you specify too large a value, Stata will refuse, but remember that just because Stata does not complain, you still may run into problems later. What might happen is that Stata could be running a command and then complain, "op. sys. refuses to provide memory"; r(909).

For `matsize` = 11,000, nearly 1 gigabyte of memory is required, and doubling that would require nearly 2 gigabytes of memory. On most 32-bit computers, 2 gigabytes is the maximum amount of memory the operating system will allocate to one task, so nearly nothing would be left for all the rest of Stata.

Why, then, is `matsize` allowed to be set so large? Because on 64-bit computers, such large amounts cause no difficulty.

For "reasonable" values of matsize (say, up to 3,200), memory consumption is not too great. Choose a reasonable value given the kinds of models you fit, and remember that you can always reset the value.

6.2.3 Advice on setting memory

set memory #[b|k|m|g] [, permanently]

where # ≥ 500k and (b, k, m, and g may be typed in uppercase.)

The advice for setting memory is the same as for Stata/IC: set enough so that your datasets fit easily, and do not set so much that you exceed physical memory present on your computer, except in emergencies.

You may set memory in bytes (b), kilobytes (k), megabytes (m), or gigabytes (g), but the number specified must be an integer, so if you want to set 1.5g, you set 1500m. Actually, 1.5g is 1536m because the formulas for a kilobyte, megabyte, and gigabyte are

```
1024 bytes     = 1 kilobyte
1024 kilobytes = 1 megabyte
1024 megabytes = 1 gigabyte
```

This detail does not matter, but this is the rule that Stata uses when presenting numbers, so do not be surprised when 2000k is not displayed as 2M, or 2M is displayed as 2048k.

If you have a large 32-bit computer, the maximum amount of memory you can set may surprise you. Many people think that 32-bit computers can allow up to 4 gigabytes of memory and that, in a sense, is true. Some 32-bit computers will even allow you to install 4 gigabytes of physical memory. Nevertheless, most modern operating systems will allocate a maximum of one-half the theoretical maximum to individual tasks; i.e., most operating systems will allow Stata only 2 gigabytes of memory (even if they have 4 gigabytes of memory)!

The same one-half rule applies to 64-bit computers, but half the theoretical limit is still 536,870,912 gigabytes, so no one much cares.

This one-half limit is imposed by the operating system, not by Stata, and the operating system developers have good technical reasons for imposing the rule.

6.3   Setting memory size on the fly: Stata/IC

You can reallocate memory on the fly. Assume you have changed nothing about how Stata starts, so you get the default 10 megabytes of memory allocated to Stata's data areas. You are working with a large dataset and now wish to increase it to 32 megabytes. You can type

```
. set memory 32m
(32768k)
```

and, if your operating system can provide the memory to Stata, Stata will work with the new total. Later in the session, if you want to release that memory and work with only 2 megabytes, you could type

```
. set memory 2m
(2048k)
```

There is only one restriction on the set memory command: whenever you change the total, there cannot be any data already in memory. If you have a dataset in memory, save it, clear memory, reset the total, and then use it again. We are getting ahead of ourselves, but you might type

```
. save mydata, replace
file mydata.dta saved

. clear

. set memory 32m
(32768k)

. use mydata
```

When you request the new allocation, your operating system might refuse to provide it:

```
. set memory 512m
op. sys. refuses to provide memory
r(909);
```

If that happens, you are going to have to take the matter up with your operating system. In the above example, Stata asked for 512 megabytes and the operating system said no.

For most 32-bit computers, the absolute maximum amount of memory that can theoretically be allocated will be approximately $2^{(32-1)}$ bytes (2 gigabytes), regardless of the operating system. In practice, the amount of memory available to any one application on a system is affected by many factors and may be somewhat less than the theoretical maximum.

Sixty-four bit computers can theoretically have up to $2^{(64-1)}$ bytes (more than 2 billion gigabytes). In practice, 64-bit computers will have as much memory as is affordable. We are aware of sites using Stata with datasets consuming more than 10 gigabytes of memory.

6.4   The memory command

memory helps you figure out whether you have sufficient memory to do something.

(Continued on next page)

```
. use regsmpl
(NLS Women 14-26 in 1968)

. memory
```

	bytes	
Details of set memory usage		
overhead (pointers)	114,136	10.88%
data	913,088	87.08%
data + overhead	1,027,224	97.96%
free	21,344	2.04%
Total allocated	1,048,568	100.00%
Other memory usage		
system overhead	677,289	
set matsize usage	16,320	
programs, saved results, etc.	505	
Total	694,114	
Grand total	1,742,682	

Having 21,344 bytes free is not much. You might increase the amount of memory allocated to Stata's data areas by specifying set memory 2m.

```
. save regsmpl
file regsmpl.dta saved

. clear

. set memory 2m
(2048k)

. use regsmpl
(NLS Women 14-26 in 1968)

. memory
```

	bytes	
Details of set memory usage		
overhead (pointers)	114,136	5.44%
data	913,088	43.54%
data + overhead	1,027,224	48.98%
free	1,069,920	51.02%
Total allocated	2,097,144	100.00%
Other memory usage		
system overhead	677,289	
set matsize usage	16,320	
programs, saved results, etc.	667	
Total	694,276	
Grand total	2,791,420	

More than 1 MB free: that is better. See [D] **memory** for more information.

6.5   Virtual memory and speed considerations

When you use more memory than is physically available on your computer, Stata slows down. If you are only using a little more memory than on your computer, performance is probably not too bad. On the other hand, when you are using a lot more memory than is on your computer, performance will be noticeably affected. In these cases, we recommend that you

```
. set virtual on
```

Virtual memory systems exploit locality of reference, which means that keeping objects closer together allows virtual memory systems to run faster. `set virtual` controls whether Stata should perform extra work to arrange its memory to keep objects close together. By default, `virtual` is set `off`. `set virtual` can be used with Stata/MP, Stata/SE, and Stata/IC on all supported operating systems.

In general, you want to leave `set virtual` set to the default of `off` so that Stata will run faster.

When you `set virtual on`, you are asking Stata to arrange its memory so that objects are kept closer together. This requires Stata to do a substantial amount of work. We recommend setting `virtual on` only when the amount of memory in use drastically exceeds what is physically available. In these cases, setting `virtual on` will help, but performance will still be slow. If you are using virtual memory often, you should consider adding memory to your computer.

6.6   An issue when returning memory to Unix

There is a surprising issue of returning memory that Unix users need to understand. Let's say that you set memory to 128 megabytes, went along for a while, and then, being a good citizen, returned most of it:

```
. set memory 2m
(2048k)
```

Theoretically, 126 megabytes was returned to the operating system for use by other processes. If you use Mac or Windows, that is exactly what happens and, with some Unix systems, that is what happens, too.

Other Unix systems, however, are strange about returned memory in a misguided effort to be efficient: they do not really take the memory back. Instead, they leave it allocated to you in case you ask for it back later. Still other Unix systems sort of take the memory back: they put it in a queue for your use, but, if you do not ask for it back in 5 or 10 minutes, then they return it to the real system pool!

The unfortunate situation is that we, at Stata, cannot force the operating system to take the memory back. Stata returns the memory to Unix, and then Unix does whatever it wants with it.

So, let's review: you make your Stata smaller in an effort to be a good citizen. You return the memory so that other users can use it, or perhaps so you can use it with some other software.

If you use Windows, the memory really is returned and all works exactly as you anticipated.

If you use Unix, it might go back immediately, it might go back in 5 or 10 minutes, or it might never go back. In the last case, the only way to really return the memory is to exit Stata. All Unix systems agree on that: when a process ends, the memory really does go back into the pool.

To find out how your Unix works, you need to experiment. We would publish a table and just tell you, but we have found that within manufacturer the way their Unix works will vary by subrelease! The experiment is tedious but not difficult:

1. Bring up a Stata and make it really big; use a lot of memory, so much that you are virtually hogging the computer.

2. Go to another window or session and bring up another Stata. Verify that you cannot make it big—that you get the "system limit exceeded" message.

3. Go back to the first Stata, leaving the second running, and make it smaller.

4. Go to the second Stata and try again to make it big. If you succeed, then your Unix returns memory instantly.

5. If you still get the "system limit exceeded" message, wait 5 minutes and try again. If it now works, your system delays accepting returned memory for about 5 minutes.

6. If you still get the "system limit exceeded" message, wait another 5 minutes and try again. If it now works, your system delays accepting returned memory for about 10 minutes.

7. Go to the first Stata and exit from it.

8. Go to the second Stata and try to make it big again. If it now works, your system never really accepts returned memory. If it still does not work, start all over again. Some other process took memory and corrupted your experiment.

If you are one of the unfortunates who have a Unix that never accepts returned memory, you will just have to remember that you must exit and reenter Stata to really give memory back.

7 –more– conditions

Contents

7.1 Description

When you see —more— at the bottom of the screen,

Press ...	and Stata...
letter *l* or *Enter*	displays the next line
letter *q*	acts as if you pressed *Break*
Spacebar or any other key	displays the next screen

Also, you can press the *clear –more– condition* button, the button labeled **Go** with a circle around it.

—more— is Stata's way of telling you that it has something more to show you, but showing you that something more will cause the information on the screen to scroll off.

7.2 set more off

If you type set more off, —more— conditions will never arise and Stata's output will scroll by at full speed.

If you type set more on, —more— conditions will be restored at the appropriate places.

Programmers: Do-file writers sometimes include set more off in their do-files because they do not care to interactively watch the output. They want Stata to proceed at full speed because they plan on making a log of the output that they will review later. Do-filers need not bother to set more on at the conclusion of their do-file. Stata automatically restores the previous set more when the do-file (or program) concludes.

7.3 The more programming command

Ado-file programmers need take no special action to have —more— conditions arise when the screen is full. Stata handles that automatically.

If, however, you wish to force a —more— condition early, you can include the more command in your program. The syntax of more is

    more

more takes no arguments.

For more information, see [P] **more**.

8 Error messages and return codes

8.1   Making mistakes

When an error occurs, Stata produces an error message and a *return code*. For instance,

```
. list myvar
no variables defined
r(111);
```

We ask Stata to list the variable named myvar. Because we have no data in memory, Stata responds with the message "no variables defined" and a line that reads "r(111)".

The "no variables defined" is called the error message.

The 111 is called the return code. You can click on blue return codes to get a detailed explanation of the error.

8.1.1   Mistakes are forgiven

After "no variables defined" and r(111), all is forgiven; it is as if the error never occurred.

Typically, the message will be enough to guide you to a solution, but if it is not, the numeric return codes are documented in [P] **error**.

8.1.2   Mistakes stop user-written programs and do-files

Whenever an error occurs in a user-written program or do-file, the program or do-file immediately stops execution and the error message and return code are displayed.

For instance, consider the following do-file:

```
─────────────────────────────────────── begin myfile.do ───────
use http://www.stata-press.com/data/r11/auto
decribe
list
─────────────────────────────────────── end myfile.do ───────
```

Note the second line—you meant to type describe but typed decribe. Here is what happens when you execute this do-file by typing do myfile:

```
. do myfile

. use http://www.stata-press.com/data/r11/auto
(1978 Automobile Data)
```

71

```
. decribe
unrecognized command:  decribe
r(199);

end of do-file
r(199);

. _
```

The first error message and return code were caused by the illegal `decribe`. This then caused the do-file itself to be aborted; the valid `list` command was never executed.

8.1.3   Advanced programming to tolerate errors

Errors are not only of the typographical kind; some are substantive. A command that is valid in one dataset might not be valid in another. Moreover, in advanced programming, errors are sometimes anticipated: use one dataset if it is there, but use another if you must.

Programmers can access the return code to determine whether an error occurred, which they can then ignore, or, by examining the return code, code their programs to take the appropriate action. This is discussed in [P] **capture**.

You can also prevent do-files from stopping when errors occur by using the `do` command's `nostop` option.

```
. do myfile, nostop
```

8.2   The return message for obtaining command timings

In addition to error messages and return codes, there is something called a return message, which you normally do not see. Normally, if you typed `summarize tempjan`, you would see

```
. use http://www.stata-press.com/data/r11/citytemp
(City Temperature Data)

. summarize tempjan
    Variable |      Obs       Mean    Std. Dev.      Min        Max
-------------+--------------------------------------------------------
     tempjan |      954   35.74895   14.18813        2.2       72.6
```

If you were to type

```
. set rmsg on
r; t=0.00 10:21:22
```

sometime during your session, Stata would display return messages:

```
. summarize tempjan
    Variable |      Obs       Mean    Std. Dev.      Min        Max
-------------+--------------------------------------------------------
     tempjan |      954   35.74895   14.18813        2.2       72.6
r; t=0.01 10:21:26
```

The line that reads `r; t=0.01 10:21:26` is called the return message.

The `r;` indicates that Stata successfully completed the command.

The `t=0.01` shows the amount of time, in seconds, it took Stata to perform the command (timed from the point you pressed *Enter* to the time Stata typed the message). This command took a hundredth of a second. Stata also shows the time of day with a 24-hour clock. This command completed at 10:21 a.m.

Stata can run commands stored in files (called do-files) and can log output. Some users find the detailed return message helpful with do-files. They construct a long program and let it run overnight, logging the output. They come back the next morning, look at the output, and discover a mistake in some portion of the job. They can look at the return messages to determine how long it will take to rerun that portion of the program.

You may `set rmsg on` whenever you wish.

When you want Stata to stop displaying the detailed return message, type `set rmsg off`.

9 The Break key

Contents

9.1   Making Stata stop what it is doing

When you want to make Stata stop what it is doing and return to the Stata dot prompt, you click on
Break:

Stata for Windows:	click on the **Break** button (it is the button with the big red X), or press *Ctrl+Pause/Break*
Stata for Mac:	click on the **Break** button or press *Command+*. (period)
Stata for Unix(GUI):	click on the **Break** button or press *Ctrl+k*
Stata for Unix(console):	press *Ctrl+c* or press *q*

Elsewhere in this manual, we describe this action as simply clicking on *Break*. Break tells Stata to
cancel what it is doing and return control to you as soon as possible.

If you click on *Break* in response to the input prompt or while you are typing a line, Stata ignores
it, because you are already in control.

If you click on *Break* while Stata is doing something—creating a new variable, sorting a dataset,
making a graph, etc.—Stata stops what it is doing, undoes it, and issues an input prompt. The state
of the system is the same as if you had never issued the command.

▷ Example 1

You are fitting a logit model, type the command, and, as Stata is working on the problem, realize
that you omitted an important variable:

```
. logit foreign mpg weight
Iteration 0:   log likelihood =  -45.03321
Iteration 1:   log likelihood = -29.898968
—Break—
r(1);

.
```

When you clicked on *Break*, Stata responded by typing —Break— and then typing r(1);. Clicking
on *Break* always results in a return code of 1—that is why return codes are called return codes and
not error codes. The 1 does not indicate an error, but it does indicate that the command did not
complete its task.

◁

9.2   Side effects of clicking on Break

In general, there are no side effects of clicking on Break. We said above that Stata undoes what it is doing so that the state of the system is the same as if you had never issued the command. There are two exceptions to that statement.

If you are reading data from disk by using `insheet`, `infile`, or `infix`, whatever data have already been read will be left behind in memory, the theory being that perhaps you stopped the process so you could verify that you were reading the right data correctly before sitting through the whole process. If not, you can always `drop _all`.

```
. infile v1-v9 using workdata
(eof not at end of obs)
(4 observations read)
—Break—
r(1);
```

The other exception is `sort`. You have a large dataset in memory, decide to sort it, and then change your mind.

```
. sort price
—Break—
r(1);
```

If the dataset was previously sorted by, say, the variable `prodid`, it is no longer. When you click on *Break* in the middle of a `sort`, Stata marks the data as unsorted.

9.3   Programming considerations

There are basically no programming considerations for handling Break because Stata handles it all automatically. If you write a program or do-file, execute it, and then click on *Break*, Stata stops execution just as it would with an internal command.

Advanced programmers may be concerned about cleaning up after themselves; perhaps they have generated a temporary variable they intended to drop later or a temporary file they intended to erase later. If a Stata user clicks on *Break*, how can you ensure that these temporary variables and files will be erased?

If you obtain names for such temporary items from Stata's `tempname`, `tempvar`, and `tempfile` commands, Stata will automatically erase the temporary items; see [U] **18.7 Temporary objects**.

There are instances, however, when a program must commit to executing a group of commands without interruption, or the user's data would be left in an intermediate or undefined state. In these instances, Stata provides a

```
nobreak {
        ...
}
```

construct; see [P] **break**.

10   Keyboard use

Contents

10.1   Description

The keyboard should operate much the way you would expect, with a few additions:

- There are some unexpected keys you can press to obtain previous commands you have typed. Also, you can click once on a command in the Review window to reload it, or click on it twice to reload and execute; this feature is discussed in the *Getting Started* manuals.

- There are a host of command-editing features for Stata for Unix(console) users because their user interface does not offer such features.

- Regardless of operating system or user interface, if there are *F*-keys on your keyboard, they have special meaning and you can change the definitions of the keys.

10.2   F-keys

Windows users: *F10* is reserved internally by Windows; you cannot program this key.

By default, Stata defines the *F*-keys to mean

F-key	Definition
F1	help
F2	#review;
F3	describe;
F7	save
F8	use

The semicolons at the end of some entries indicate an implied *Enter*.

help shows a Stata help file—you use it by typing help followed by the name of a Stata command; see [U] **4 Stata's help and search facilities**. You can type help or you can press *F1*, type the Stata command, and press *Enter*.

#review is the command to show the last few commands you issued. It is described in [U] **10.5 Editing previous lines in Stata**. Rather than typing #review and pressing *Enter*, you can simply press *F2*. You do not press *Enter* following *F2* because the definition of F2 ends in a semicolon—Stata presses the *Enter* key for you.

describe is the Stata command to report the contents of data loaded into memory. It is explained in [D] **describe**. Normally, you type describe and press *Enter*. You can also press *F3*.

77

save is the command to save the data in memory into a file, and use is the command to load data; see [D] **use** and [D] **save**. The syntax of each is the same: save or use followed by a filename. You can type the commands or you can press *F7* or *F8* followed by the filename.

You can change the definitions of the *F*-keys. For instance, the command to list data is list; you can read about it in [D] **list**. The syntax is list to list all the data, or list followed by the names of some variables to list just those variables (there are other possibilities).

If you wanted *F3* to mean list, you could type

```
. global F3 "list "
```

In the above, F3 refers to the letter *F* followed by *3*, not the *F3* key. Note the capitalization and spacing of the command.

You type global in lowercase, type F3, and then type "list ". The space at the end of list is important. In the future, rather than typing list mpg weight, you want to be able to press the *F3* key and then type only mpg weight. You put a space in the definition of F3 so that you would not have to type a space in front of the first variable name after pressing *F3*.

Now say you wanted *F5* to mean list all the data—list followed by *Enter*. You could define

```
. global F5 "list;"
```

Now you would have two ways of listing all the data: press *F3*, and then press *Enter*, or press *F5*. The semicolon at the end of the definition of *F5* will press *Enter* for you.

If you really want to change the definitions of *F3* and *F5*, you will probably want to change the definition every time you invoke Stata. One way would be to type the two global commands every time you invoke Stata. Another way would be to type the two commands into an ASCII text file called profile.do. Stata executes the commands in profile.do every time it is launched if profile.do is placed in the appropriate directory:

Windows:	put profile.do in the "start-in" directory; see [GSW] **C.3 Executing commands every time Stata is started**
Mac:	put profile.do in your home directory; see [GSM] **C.1 Executing commands every time Stata is started**
Unix:	put profile.do someplace along your shell's path; see [GSU] **C.1 Executing commands every time Stata is started**

You can use the *F*-keys any way you desire: they contain a string of characters, and pressing the *F*-key is equivalent to typing those characters.

❏ Technical note

[*Stata for Unix(console) users.*] Sometimes Unix assigns a special meaning to the *F*-keys, and if it does, those meanings supersede our meanings. Stata provides a second way to get to the *F*-keys. Press *Ctrl+F*, release the keys, and then press a number from 0 through 9. Stata interprets *Ctrl+F* plus 1 as equivalent to the *F1* key, *Ctrl+F* plus 2 as *F2*, and so on. *Ctrl+F* plus 0 means *F10*. These keys will work only if they are properly mapped in your termcap or terminfo entry.

❏

❑ Technical note

On some international keyboards, the left single quote is used as an accent character. In this case, we recommend mapping this character to one of your function keys. In fact, you might find it convenient to map both the left single quote (') and right single quote (') characters so that they are next to each other.

Within Stata, open the Do-file Editor. Type the following two lines in the Do-file Editor:

```
global F4 '
global F5 '
```

Save the file as `profile.do` into your Stata directory. If you already have a `profile.do` file, append the two lines to your existing `profile.do` file.

Exit Stata and restart it. You should see the startup message

```
running C:\Program Files\Stata11\profile.do ...
```

or some variant of it depending on where your Stata is installed. Press *F4* and *F5* to verify that they work.

If you did not see the startup message, you did not save the `profile.do` in your home folder.

You can, of course, map to any other function keys, but *F1*, *F2*, *F3*, *F7*, and *F8* are already used.

❑

10.3   Editing keys in Stata

Users have available to them the standard editing keys for their operating system. So, Stata should just edit what you type in the natural way—the Stata Command window is a standard edit window.

Also, you can fetch commands from the Review window into the Command window. Click on a command in the Review window, and it is loaded into the Command window, where you can edit it. Alternatively, if you double-click on a line in the Review window, it is loaded and executed.

Another way to get lines from the Review window into the Command window is with the *PgUp* and *PgDn* keys. Press *PgUp* and Stata loads the last command you typed into the Command window. Press it again and Stata loads the line before that, and so on. *PgDn* goes in the opposite direction.

Another editing key that interests users is *Esc*. This key clears the Command window.

In summary,

Press	Result
PgUp	Steps back through commands and moves command from Review window to Command window
PgDn	Steps forward through commands and moves command from Review window to Command window
Esc	Clears Command window

(Continued on next page)

10.4   Editing keys in Stata for Unix(console)

Certain keys allow you to edit the line that you are typing. Because Stata supports a variety of computers and keyboards, the location and the names of the editing keys are not the same for all Stata users.

Every keyboard has the standard alphabet keys (*QWERTY* and so on), and every keyboard has a *Ctrl* key. Some keyboards have extra keys located to the right, above, or left, with names like *PgUp* and *PgDn*.

Throughout this manual we will refer to Stata's editing keys using names that appear on nobody's keyboard. For instance, PrevLine is one of the Stata editing keys—it retrieves a previous line. Hunt all you want, but you will not find it on your keyboard. So, where is PrevLine? We have tried to put it where you would naturally expect it. On keyboards with a key labeled *PgUp*, *PgUp* is the PrevLine key, but on everybody's keyboard, no matter which version of Unix, brand of keyboard, or anything else, *Ctrl+R* also means PrevLine.

When we say press PrevLine, now you know what we mean: press *PgUp* or *Ctrl+R*. The editing keys are the following:

Name for editing key	Editing key	Function
Kill	*Esc* on PCs and *Ctrl+U*	Deletes the line and lets you start over.
Dbs	*Backspace* on PCs and *Backspace*, *Rubout*, or *Delete* on other computers	Backs up and deletes one character.
Lft	←, *4* on the numeric keypad for PCs, and *Ctrl+H*	Moves the cursor left one character without deleting any characters.
Rgt	→, *6* on the numeric keypad for PCs, and *Ctrl+L*	Moves the cursor forward one character.
Up	↑, *8* on the numeric keypad for PCs, and *Ctrl+O*	Moves the cursor up one physical line on a line that takes more than one physical line. Also see PrevLine.
Dn	↓, *2* on the numeric keypad for PCs, and *Ctrl+N*	Moves the cursor down one physical line on a line that takes more than one physical line. Also see NextLine.
PrevLine	*PgUp* and *Ctrl+R*	Retrieves a previously typed line. You may press PrevLine multiple times to step back through previous commands.
NextLine	*PgDn* and *Ctrl+B*	The inverse of PrevLine.
Seek	*Ctrl+Home* on PCs and *Ctrl+W*	Goes to the line number specified. Before pressing Seek, type the line number. For instance, typing *3* and then pressing Seek is the same as pressing PrevLine three times.
Ins	*Ins* and *Ctrl+E*	Toggles insert mode. In insert mode, characters typed are inserted at the position of the cursor.
Del	*Del* and *Ctrl+D*	Deletes the character at the position of the cursor.
Home	*Home* and *Ctrl+K*	Moves the cursor to the start of the line.
End	*End* and *Ctrl+P*	Moves the cursor to the end of the line.
Hack	*Ctrl+End* on PCs, and *Ctrl+X*	Hacks off the line at the cursor.
Tab	⊣ on PCs, *Tab*, and *Ctrl+I*	Moves the cursor forward eight spaces.
Btab	⊢ on PCs, and *Ctrl+G*	The inverse of Tab.

▷ Example 1

It is difficult to demonstrate the use of editing keys on paper. You should try each of them. Nevertheless, here is an example:

. summarize price wa̲ht

You typed summarize price waht and then pressed the *Lft* key (← key or *Ctrl+H*) three times to maneuver the cursor back to the a of waht. If you were to press *Enter* right now, Stata would see the command summarize price waht, so where the cursor is does not matter when you press *Enter*. If you wanted to execute the command summarize price, you could back up one more character and then press the Hack key. We will assume, however, that you meant to type weight.

If you were now to press the letter *e* on the keyboard, an e would appear on the screen to replace the a, and the cursor would move under the character h. We now have we̲ht. You press *Ins*, putting Stata into insert mode, and press *i* and *g*. The line now says summarize price weig̲ht, which is correct, so you press *Enter*. We did not have to press *Ins* before every character we wanted to insert. The *Ins* key is a toggle: If we press it again, Stata turns off insert mode, and what we type replaces what was there. When we press *Enter*, Stata forgets all about insert mode, so we do not have to remember from one command to the next whether we are in insert mode.

◁

❏ Technical note

Stata performs its editing magic from the information about your terminal recorded in /etc/termcap(5) or, under System V, /usr/lib/terminfo(4). If some feature does not appear to work, the entry for your terminal in the termcap file or terminfo directory is probably incorrect. Contact your system administrator.

❏

10.5   Editing previous lines in Stata

In addition to what is said below, remember that the Review window also shows the contents of the review buffer.

You may edit previously typed lines, or at least any of the last 25 or so lines. Stata records every line you type in a wraparound buffer. A wraparound buffer is a buffer of finite length in which the most recent thing you type replaces the oldest thing stored in the buffer. Stata's buffer is 8,697 characters long for Small Stata, 165,200 characters long for Stata/IC, and can range from 67,800 to 1,081,527 for Stata/MP and Stata/SE.

One way to retrieve lines is with the PrevLine and NextLine keys. Remember, PrevLine and NextLine are the names we attach to these keys—there are no such keys on your keyboard. You have to look back at the previous section to find out which keys correspond to PrevLine and NextLine on your computer. To save you the effort this time, PrevLine probably corresponds to *PgUp* and NextLine probably corresponds to *PgDn*.

Suppose you wanted to reissue the third line back. You could press PrevLine three times and then press *Enter*. If you made a mistake and pressed PrevLine four times, you could press NextLine to go forward in the buffer. You do not have to count lines because, each time you press PrevLine or NextLine, the current line is displayed on your monitor. Simply press the key until you find the line you want.

Another method for reviewing previous lines, `#review`, is convenient when you want to see the lines in context.

▷ Example 2

Typing `#review` by itself causes Stata to list the last five commands you typed. (You need not type `#review`—pressing *F2* has the same effect.) For instance,

```
. #review
5 list make mpg weight if abs(res)>6
4 list make mpg weight if abs(res)>5
3 tabulate foreign if abs(res)>5
2 regress mpg weight weight2
1 test weight2=0
. _
```

We can see from the listing that the last command typed by the user was `test weight2=0`. Or, you may just look at the Review window to see the history of commands you typed.

◁

▷ Example 3

Perhaps the command you are looking for is not among the last five commands you typed. You can tell Stata to go back any number of lines. For instance, typing `#review 15` tells Stata to show you the last 15 lines you typed:

```
. #review 15
15 replace resmpg=mpg-pred
14 summarize resmpg, detail
13 drop predmpg
12 describe
11 sort foreign
10 by foreign: summarize mpg weight
9 * lines that start with a * are comments.
8 * they go into the review buffer too.
7 summarize resmpg, detail
6 list make mpg weight
5 list make mpg weight if abs(res)>6
4 list make mpg weight if abs(res)>5
3 tabulate foreign if abs(res)>5
2 regress mpg weight weight2
1 test weight2=0
. _
```

If you wanted to resubmit the 10th previous line, you could type 10 and press Seek, or you could press PrevLine 10 times. No matter which of the above methods you prefer for retrieving lines, you may edit previous lines by using the editing keys.

◁

10.6   Tab expansion of variable names

Another way to quickly enter a variable name is to take advantage of Stata's variable name completion feature. Simply type the first few letters of the variable name in the Command window and press the *Tab* key. Stata will automatically type the rest of the variable name for you. If more than one variable name matches the letters you have typed, Stata will complete as much as it can and beep at you to let you know that you have typed a nonunique variable abbreviation.

Elements of Stata

11 Language syntax

Contents

11.1 Overview

With few exceptions, the basic Stata language syntax is

$$\left[\texttt{by } \textit{varlist}:\right] \ \textit{command} \ \left[\textit{varlist}\right] \ \left[\texttt{=}\textit{exp}\right] \ \left[\texttt{if } \textit{exp}\right] \ \left[\texttt{in } \textit{range}\right] \ \left[\textit{weight}\right] \ \left[, \ \textit{options}\right]$$

where square brackets distinguish optional qualifiers and options from required ones. In this diagram, *varlist* denotes a list of variable names, *command* denotes a Stata command, *exp* denotes an algebraic expression, *range* denotes an observation range, *weight* denotes a weighting expression, and *options* denotes a list of options.

11.1.1   varlist

Most commands that take a subsequent *varlist* do not require that you explicitly type one. If no *varlist* appears, these commands assume a *varlist* of _all, the Stata shorthand for indicating all the variables in the dataset. In commands that alter or destroy data, Stata requires that the *varlist* be specified explicitly. See [U] **11.4 varlists** for a complete description.

▷ Example 1

The summarize command lists the mean, standard deviation, and range of the specified variables. In [R] **summarize**, we see that the syntax diagram for summarize is

$$\underline{\text{su}}\text{mmarize} \ \left[\textit{varlist} \right] \ \left[\textit{if} \right] \ \left[\textit{in} \right] \ \left[\textit{weight} \right] \ \left[, \ \textit{options} \right]$$

Farther down on the manual page is a table summarizing options, but let's focus on the syntax diagram itself first. Because everything except the word summarize is enclosed in square brackets, the simplest form of the command is "summarize". Typing summarize without arguments is equivalent to typing summarize _all; all the variables in the dataset are summarized. Underlining denotes the shortest allowed abbreviation, so we could have typed just su; see [U] **11.2 Abbreviation rules**.

The table that defines *options* looks like this:

options	description
Main	
detail	display additional statistics
meanonly	suppress the display; calculate only the mean; programmer's option
format	use variable's display format
separator(#)	draw separator line after every # variables; default is separator(5)

Thus we learn we could also type, for instance, summarize, detail or summarize, detail format.

As another example, the drop command eliminates variables or observations from a dataset. When dropping variables, its syntax is

drop *varlist*

drop has no option table because it has no options.

In fact, nothing is optional. Typing drop by itself would result in the error message "varlist or in range required". To drop all the variables in the dataset, we must type drop _all.

Even before looking at the syntax diagram, we could have predicted that *varlist* would be required—drop is destructive, so Stata requires us to spell out our intent. The syntax diagram informs us that *varlist* is required because *varlist* is not enclosed in square brackets. Because drop is not underlined, it cannot be abbreviated.

◁

11.1.2 by varlist:

The by *varlist*: prefix causes Stata to repeat a command for each subset of the data for which the values of the variables in *varlist* are equal. When prefixed with by *varlist*:, the result of the command will be the same as if you had formed separate datasets for each group of observations, saved them, and then gave the command on each dataset separately. The data must already be sorted by *varlist*, although by has a sort option; see [U] **11.5 by varlist: construct** for more information.

▷ Example 2

Typing summarize marriage_rate divorce_rate produces a table of the mean, standard deviation, and range of marriage_rate and divorce_rate, using all the observations in the data:

```
. use http://www.stata-press.com/data/r11/census12
(1980 Census data by state)

. summarize marriage_rate divorce_rate
```

Variable	Obs	Mean	Std. Dev.	Min	Max
marriage_r~e	50	.0133221	.0188122	.0074654	.1428282
divorce_rate	50	.0056641	.0022473	.0029436	.0172918

Typing by region: summarize marriage_rate divorce_rate produces one table for each region of the country:

```
. sort region

. by region: summarize marriage_rate divorce_rate
```

-> region = N Cntrl

Variable	Obs	Mean	Std. Dev.	Min	Max
marriage_r~e	12	.0099121	.0011326	.0087363	.0127394
divorce_rate	12	.0046974	.0011315	.0032817	.0072868

-> region = NE

Variable	Obs	Mean	Std. Dev.	Min	Max
marriage_r~e	9	.0087811	.001191	.0075757	.0107055
divorce_rate	9	.004207	.0010264	.0029436	.0057071

-> region = South

Variable	Obs	Mean	Std. Dev.	Min	Max
marriage_r~e	16	.0114654	.0025721	.0074654	.0172704
divorce_rate	16	.005633	.0013355	.0038917	.0080078

-> region = West

Variable	Obs	Mean	Std. Dev.	Min	Max
marriage_r~e	13	.0218987	.0363775	.0087365	.1428282
divorce_rate	13	.0076037	.0031486	.0046004	.0172918

The dataset must be sorted on the by variables:

```
. use http://www.stata-press.com/data/r11/census12
(1980 Census data by state)
. by region: summarize marriage_rate divorce_rate
not sorted
r(5);
. sort region
. by region: summarize marriage_rate divorce_rate
(output appears)
```

We could also have asked that by sort the data:

```
. by region, sort: summarize marriage_rate divorce_rate
(output appears)
```

by *varlist*: can be used with most Stata commands; we can tell which ones by looking at their syntax diagrams. For instance, we could obtain the correlations by `region`, between `marriage_rate` and `divorce_rate`, by typing by `region: correlate marriage_rate divorce_rate`.

◁

❏ Technical note

The *varlist* in by *varlist*: may contain up to 32,767 variables with Stata/MP and Stata/SE or 2,047 variables with Stata/IC; these are the maximum allowed in the dataset. For instance, if we had data on automobiles and wished to obtain means according to market category (`market`) broken down by manufacturer (`origin`), we could type by `market origin: summarize`. That *varlist* contains two variables: `market` and `origin`. If the data were not already sorted on `market` and `origin`, we would first type `sort market origin`.

❏

❏ Technical note

The *varlist* in by *varlist*: may contain string variables, numeric variables, or both. In the example above, `region` is a string variable, in particular, a `str7`. The example would have worked, however, if `region` were a numeric variable with values 1, 2, 3, and 4, or even 12.2, 16.78, 32.417, and 152.13.

❏

11.1.3 if exp

The `if` *exp* qualifier restricts the scope of a command to those observations for which the value of the expression is *true* (which is equivalent to the expression being nonzero; see [U] **13 Functions and expressions**).

▷ Example 3

Typing `summarize marriage_rate divorce_rate if region=="West"` produces a table for the western region of the country:

```
. summarize marriage_rate divorce_rate if region == "West"
    Variable |      Obs        Mean    Std. Dev.        Min        Max
-------------+--------------------------------------------------------
  marriage_r~e |       13    .0218987    .0363775    .0087365    .1428282
  divorce_rate |       13    .0076037    .0031486    .0046004    .0172918
```

The double equal sign in `region=="West"` is not an error. Stata uses a *double* equal sign to denote equality testing and one equal sign to denote assignment; see [U] **13 Functions and expressions**.

A command may have at most one `if` qualifier. If you want the summary for the West restricted to observations with values of `marriage_rate` in excess of 0.015, do *not* type `summarize marriage_rate divorce_rate if region=="West" if marriage_rate>.015`. Instead type

```
. summarize marriage_rate divorce_rate if region == "West" & marriage_rate >.015
    Variable |      Obs        Mean    Std. Dev.        Min        Max
-------------+--------------------------------------------------------
  marriage_r~e |        1    .1428282           .    .1428282    .1428282
  divorce_rate |        1    .0172918           .    .0172918    .0172918
```

You may not use the word *and* in place of the symbol "&" to join conditions. To select observations that meet one condition *or* another, use the "|" symbol. For instance, `summarize marriage_rate divorce_rate if region=="West" | marriage_rate>.015` summarizes all observations for which region is West *or* `marriage_rate` is greater than 0.015.

◁

> Example 4

`if` may be combined with `by`. Typing `by region: summarize marriage_rate divorce_rate if marriage_rate>.015` produces a set of tables, one for each region, reflecting summary statistics on `marriage_rate` and `divorce_rate` among observations for which `marriage_rate` exceeds 0.015:

```
. by region: summarize marriage_rate divorce_rate if marriage_rate >.015
-----------------------------------------------------------------------
-> region = N Cntrl
    Variable |      Obs        Mean    Std. Dev.        Min        Max
-------------+--------------------------------------------------------
  marriage_r~e |        0
  divorce_rate |        0
-----------------------------------------------------------------------
-> region = NE
    Variable |      Obs        Mean    Std. Dev.        Min        Max
-------------+--------------------------------------------------------
  marriage_r~e |        0
  divorce_rate |        0
-----------------------------------------------------------------------
-> region = South
    Variable |      Obs        Mean    Std. Dev.        Min        Max
-------------+--------------------------------------------------------
  marriage_r~e |        2    .0163219    .0013414    .0153734    .0172704
  divorce_rate |        2    .0061813    .0025831    .0043548    .0080078
-----------------------------------------------------------------------
-> region = West
    Variable |      Obs        Mean    Std. Dev.        Min        Max
-------------+--------------------------------------------------------
  marriage_r~e |        1    .1428282           .    .1428282    .1428282
  divorce_rate |        1    .0172918           .    .0172918    .0172918
```

The results indicate that there are no states in the Northeast and North Central regions for which `marriage_rate` exceeds 0.015, whereas there are two such states in the South and one state in the West.

◁

11.1.4 in range

The in *range* qualifier restricts the scope of the command to a specific observation range. A range specification takes the form $\#_1 \left[/\#_2 \right]$, where $\#_1$ and $\#_2$ are positive or negative integers. Negative integers are understood to mean "from the end of the data", with -1 referring to the last observation. The implied first observation must be less than or equal to the implied last observation.

The first and last observations in the dataset may be denoted by f and l (lowercase letter), respectively. F is allowed as a synonym for f, and L is allowed as a synonym for l. A range specifies absolute observation numbers within a dataset. As a result, the in qualifier may not be used when the command is preceded by the by *varlist*: prefix; see [U] **11.5 by varlist: construct**.

▷ Example 5

Typing `summarize marriage_rate divorce_rate in 5/25` produces a table based on the values of `marriage_rate` and `divorce_rate` in observations 5–25:

```
. summarize marriage_rate divorce_rate in 5/25
```

Variable	Obs	Mean	Std. Dev.	Min	Max
marriage_r~e	21	.0096001	.0013263	.0075757	.0125884
divorce_rate	21	.004726	.0012025	.0029436	.0072868

This is, admittedly, a rather odd thing to want to do. It would not be odd, however, if we substituted list for summarize. If we wanted to see the states with the 10 lowest values of `marriage_rate`, we could type `sort marriage_rate` followed by `list marriage_rate in 1/10`.

Typing `summarize marriage_rate divorce_rate in f/l` is equivalent to typing `summarize marriage_rate divorce_rate`—all observations are summarized.

◁

▷ Example 6

Typing `summarize marriage_rate divorce_rate in 5/25 if region=="South"` produces a table based on the values of the two variables in observations 5–25 for which the value of region is South:

```
. summarize marriage_rate divorce_rate in 5/25 if region=="South"
```

Variable	Obs	Mean	Std. Dev.	Min	Max
marriage_r~e	4	.0108886	.0015061	.0089201	.0125884
divorce_rate	4	.0054448	.0011166	.0041485	.0068685

The ordering of the in and if qualifiers is not significant. The command could also have been specified as `summarize marriage_rate divorce_rate if region=="South" in 5/25`.

◁

⊳ Example 7

Negative in ranges can be useful with sort. For instance, we have data on automobiles and wish to list the five with the highest mileage ratings:

```
. use http://www.stata-press.com/data/r11/auto
(1978 Automobile Data)
. sort mpg
. list make mpg in -5/l
```

	make	mpg
70.	Toyota Corolla	31
71.	Plym. Champ	34
72.	Subaru	35
73.	Datsun 210	35
74.	VW Diesel	41

◁

11.1.5 =exp

=exp specifies the value to be assigned to a variable and is most often used with generate and replace. See [U] **13 Functions and expressions** for details on expressions and [D] **generate** for details on the generate and replace commands.

⊳ Example 8

Expression	Meaning
generate newvar=oldvar+2	creates a new variable named newvar equal to oldvar+2
replace oldvar=oldvar+2	changes the contents of the existing variable oldvar
egen newvar=rank(oldvar)	creates newvar containing the ranks of oldvar (see [D] **egen**)

◁

11.1.6 weight

weight indicates the weight to be attached to each observation. The syntax of *weight* is

$$[weightword=exp]$$

where you actually type the square brackets and where *weightword* is one of

weightword	Meaning
weight	default treatment of weights
fweight *or* frequency	frequency weights
pweight	sampling weights
aweight *or* cellsize	analytic weights
iweight	importance weights

The underlining indicates the minimum acceptable abbreviation. Thus weight may be abbreviated w or we, etc.

▷ Example 9

Before explaining what the different types of weights mean, let's obtain the population-weighted mean of a variable called `median_age` from data containing observations on all 50 states of the United States. The dataset also contains a variable named `pop`, which is the total population of each state.

```
. use http://www.stata-press.com/data/r11/census12
(1980 Census data by state)
. summarize median_age [weight=pop]
(analytic weights assumed)
```

Variable	Obs	Weight	Mean	Std. Dev.	Min	Max
median_age	50	225907472	30.11047	1.66933	24.2	34.7

In addition to telling us that our dataset contains 50 observations, Stata informs us that the sum of the weight is 225,907,472, which was the number of people living in the United States as of the 1980 census. The weighted mean is 30.11. We were also informed that Stata assumed that we wanted "analytic" weights.   ◁

`weight` is each command's idea of what the "natural" weights are and is one of `fweight`, `pweight`, `aweight`, or `iweight`. When you specify the vague `weight`, the command informs you which kind it assumes. Not every command supports every kind of weight. A note below the syntax diagram for a command will tell you which weights the command supports.

Stata understands four kinds of weights:

1. `fweight`s, or frequency weights, indicate duplicated observations. `fweight`s are always integers. If the `fweight` associated with an observation is 5, that means there are really 5 such observations, each identical.

2. `pweight`s, or sampling weights, denote the inverse of the probability that this observation is included in the sample because of the sampling design. A `pweight` of 100, for instance, indicates that this observation is representative of 100 subjects in the underlying population. The scale of these weights does not matter in terms of estimated parameters and standard errors, except when estimating totals and computing finite-population corrections with the `svy` commands; see [SVY] **survey**.

3. `aweight`s, or analytic weights, are inversely proportional to the variance of an observation; i.e., the variance of the jth observation is assumed to be σ^2/w_j, where w_j are the weights. Typically, the observations represent averages, and the weights are the number of elements that gave rise to the average. For most Stata commands, the recorded scale of `aweight`s is irrelevant; Stata internally rescales them to sum to N, the number of observations in your data, when it uses them.

4. `iweight`s, or importance weights, indicate the relative "importance" of the observation. They have no formal statistical definition; this is a catch-all category. Any command that supports `iweight`s will define how they are treated. They are usually intended for use by programmers who want to produce a certain computation.

See [U] **20.18 Weighted estimation** for a thorough discussion of weights and their meaning.

❑ Technical note

When you do not specify a weight, the result is equivalent to specifying [fweight=1].   ❑

11.1.7   options

Many commands take command-specific options. These are described along with each command in the *Reference* manuals. Options are indicated by typing a comma at the end of the command, followed by the options you want to use.

▷ Example 10

Typing `summarize marriage_rate` produces a table of the mean, standard deviation, minimum, and maximum of the variable `marriage_rate`:

```
. summarize marriage_rate

    Variable |     Obs      Mean   Std. Dev.      Min       Max
-------------+--------------------------------------------------
  marriage_r~e |    50   .0133221   .0188122   .0074654   .1428282
```

The syntax diagram for `summarize` is

$$\underline{\text{su}}\text{mmarize}\ \big[\textit{varlist}\big]\ \big[\textit{if}\big]\ \big[\textit{in}\big]\ \big[\textit{weight}\big]\ \big[\text{, } \textit{options}\big]$$

followed by the option table

options	description
Main	
<u>d</u>etail	display additional statistics
<u>mean</u>only	suppress the display; calculate only the mean; programmer's option
<u>f</u>ormat	use variable's display format
<u>sep</u>arator(#)	draw separator line after every # variables; default is separator(5)

Thus the options allowed by `summarize` are `detail` or `meanonly`, `format`, and `separator()`. The shortest allowed abbreviations for these options are `d` for `detail`, `mean` for `meanonly`, `f` for `format`, and `sep()` for `separator()`; see [U] **11.2 Abbreviation rules**.

Typing `summarize marriage_rate, detail` produces a table that also includes selected percentiles, the four largest and four smallest values, the skewness, and the kurtosis.

```
. summarize marriage_rate, detail

                        marriage_rate
-------------------------------------------------------------
      Percentiles      Smallest
 1%    .0074654        .0074654
 5%    .0078956        .0075757
10%    .0080043        .0078956       Obs                50
25%    .0089399        .0079079       Sum of Wgt.        50

50%    .0105669                       Mean          .0133221
                        Largest       Std. Dev.     .0188122
75%    .0122899        .0146266
90%    .0137832        .0153734       Variance      .0003539
95%    .0153734        .0172704       Skewness      6.718494
99%    .1428282        .1428282       Kurtosis      46.77306
```

◁

❑ Technical note

Once you have typed the *varlist* for the command, you can place options anywhere in the command. You can type `summarize marriage_rate divorce_rate if region=="West", detail`, or you can type `summarize marriage_rate divorce_rate, detail, if region=="West"`. You use a second comma to indicate a return to the command line as opposed to the option list. Leaving out the comma after the word `detail` would cause an error because Stata would attempt to interpret the phrase `if region=="West"` as an option rather than as part of the command.

You may not type an option in the middle of a *varlist*. Typing `summarize marriage_rate, detail, divorce_rate` will result in an error.

Options need not be specified contiguously. You may type `summarize marriage_rate divorce_rate, detail, if region=="South", noformat`. Both `detail` and `noformat` are options.

❑

❑ Technical note

Most options are toggles—they indicate that something either is or is not to be done. Sometimes it is difficult to remember which is the default. The following rule applies to all options: if *option* is an option, then no*option* is an option as well, and vice versa. Thus if we could not remember whether `detail` or `nodetail` were the default for `summarize` but we knew that we did not want the detail, we could type `summarize, nodetail`. Typing the `nodetail` option is unnecessary, but Stata will not complain.

Some options take *arguments*. The Stata `kdensity` command has an `n(#)` option that indicates the number of points at which the density estimate is to be evaluated. When an option takes an argument, the argument is enclosed in parentheses.

Some options take more than one argument. In such cases, arguments should be separated from one another by commas. For instance, you might see in a syntax diagram

saving(*filename*[, replace])

Here `replace` is the (optional) second argument. *Lists*, such as lists of variables (varlists) and lists of numbers (numlists), are considered to be one argument. If a syntax diagram reported

powers(*numlist*)

the list of numbers would be one argument, so the elements would not be separated by commas. You would type, for instance, `powers(1 2 3 4)`. In fact, Stata will tolerate commas here, so you could type `powers(1,2,3,4)`.

Some options take string arguments. `regress` has an `eform()` option that works this way—for instance, `eform("Exp Beta")`. To play it safe, you should type the quotes surrounding the string, although it is not required. If you do not type the quotes, any sequence of two or more consecutive blanks will be interpreted as one blank. Thus `eform(Exp  beta)` would be interpreted the same as `eform(Exp beta)`.

❑

11.1.8   numlist

A *numlist* is a list of numbers. Stata allows certain shorthands to indicate ranges:

numlist	meaning
2	just one number
1 2 3	three numbers
3 2 1	three numbers in reversed order
.5 1 1.5	three different numbers
1 3 -2.17 5.12	four numbers in jumbled order
1/3	three numbers: 1, 2, 3
3/1	the same three numbers in reverse order
5/8	four numbers: 5, 6, 7, 8
-8/-5	four numbers: -8, -7, -6, -5
-5/-8	four numbers: -5, -6, -7, -8
-1/2	four numbers: -1, 0, 1, 2
1 2 to 4	four numbers: 1, 2, 3, 4
4 3 to 1	four numbers: 4, 3, 2, 1
10 15 to 30	five numbers: 10, 15, 20, 25, 30
1 2:4	same as 1 2 to 4
4 3:1	same as 4 3 to 1
10 15:30	same as 10 15 to 30
1(1)3	three numbers: 1, 2, 3
1(2)9	five numbers: 1, 3, 5, 7, 9
1(2)10	the same five numbers, 1, 3, 5, 7, 9
9(-2)1	five numbers: 9, 7, 5, 3, and 1
-1(.5)2.5	the numbers -1, $-.5$, 0, .5, 1, 1.5, 2, 2.5
1[1]3	same as 1(1)3
1[2]9	same as 1(2)9
1[2]10	same as 1(2)10
9[-2]1	same as 9(-2)1
-1[.5]2.5	same as -1(.5)2.5
1 2 3/5 8(2)12	eight numbers: 1, 2, 3, 4, 5, 8, 10, 12
1,2,3/5,8(2)12	the same eight numbers
1 2 3/5 8 10 to 12	the same eight numbers
1,2,3/5,8,10 to 12	the same eight numbers
1 2 3/5 8 10:12	the same eight numbers

poisson's constraints() option has syntax constraints(*numlist*). Thus you could type constraints(2 4 to 8), constraints(2(2)8), etc.

11.1.9   datelist

A *datelist* is a list of dates or times and is often used with graph options when the variable being graphed has a date format. For a description of how dates and times are stored and manipulated in Stata, see [U] **24 Working with dates and times**. Calendar dates, also known as %td dates, are recorded in Stata as the number of days since 01jan1960, so 0 means 01jan1960, 1 means 02jan1960, and 16,541 means 15apr2005. Similarly, -1 means 31dec1959, -2 means 30dec1959, and $-16,541$ means 18sep1914. In such a case, a datelist is either a list of dates, as in

15apr1973 17apr1973 20apr1973 23apr1973

or it is a first and last date with an increment between, as in

17apr1973(3)23apr1973

or it is a combination:

15apr1973 17apr1973(3)23apr1973

Dates specified with spaces, slashes, or commas must be bound in parentheses, as in

> (15 apr 1973) (april 17, 1973) (3) (april 23, 1973)

Evenly spaced calendar dates are not especially useful, but with other time units, even spacing can be useful, such as

> 1999q1(1)2005q1

when %tq dates are being used. 1999q1(1)2005q1 means every quarter between 1991q1 and 2005q1. 1999q1(4)2005q1 would mean every first quarter.

To interpret a datelist, Stata first looks at the format of the related variable and then uses the corresponding date-to-numeric translation function. For instance, if the variable has a %td format, the td() function is used to translate the date; if the variable has a %tq format, the tq() function is used; and so on.

11.1.10 Prefix commands

Stata has a handful of commands that are used to prefix other Stata commands. by varlist:, discussed in section [U] **11.1.2 by varlist:**, is in fact an example of a prefix command. In that section, we demonstrated by using

> by region: summarize marriage_rate divorce_rate

and later,

> by region, sort: summarize marriage_rate divorce_rate

and although we did not, we could also have demonstrated

> by region, sort: summarize marriage_rate divorce_rate, detail

Each of the above runs the summarize command separately on the data for each region.

by itself follows standard Stata syntax:

$$\text{by } varlist[, \ options]: \ \ldots$$

In by region, sort: summarize marriage_rate divorce_rate, detail, region is by's varlist and sort is by's option, just as marriage_rate and divorce_rate are summarize's varlist and detail is summarize's option.

by is not the only prefix command, and the full list of such commands is

Prefix command	description
by	run command on subsets of data
statsby	same as by, but collect statistics from each run
rolling	run command on moving subsets and collect statistics
bootstrap	run command on bootstrap samples
jackknife	run command on jackknife subsets of data
permute	run command on random permutations
simulate	run command on manufactured data
svy	run command and adjust results for survey sampling
mi estimate	run command on multiply imputed data and adjust results for multiple imputation (MI)
nestreg	run command with accumulated blocks of regressors, and report nested model comparison tests
stepwise	run command with stepwise variable inclusion/exclusion
xi	run command after expanding factor variables and interactions; for most commands, using factor variables is preferred to using xi (see [U] **11.4.3 Factor variables**)
fracpoly	run command with fractional polynomials of one regressor
mfp	run command with multiple fractional polynomial regressors
capture	run command and capture its return code
noisily	run command and show the output
quietly	run command and suppress the output
version	run command under specified version

The last group—capture, noisily, quietly, and version—have to do with programming Stata and, for historical reasons, capture, noisily, and quietly allow you to omit the colon, so one programmer might code

      quietly regress ...

and another

      quietly: regress ...

All the other prefix commands require the colon. In addition to the corresponding reference manual entries, you may want to consult Baum (2009) for a richer discussion of prefix commands.

11.2   Abbreviation rules

Stata allows abbreviations. In this manual, we usually avoid abbreviating commands, variable names, and options to ensure readability:

      . summarize myvar, detail

Experienced Stata users, on the other hand, tend to abbreviate the same command as

      . sum myv, d

As a general rule, command, option, and variable names may be abbreviated to the shortest string of characters that uniquely identifies them.

This rule is violated if the command or option does something that cannot easily be undone; the command must then be spelled out in its entirety.

Also, a few common commands and options are allowed to have even shorter abbreviations than the general rule would allow.

The general rule is applied, without exception, to variable names.

11.2.1   Command abbreviation

The shortest allowed abbreviation for a command or option can be determined by looking at the command's syntax diagram. This minimal abbreviation is shown by underlining:

regress

rename

replace

rotate

run

If there is no underlining, no abbreviation is allowed. For example, replace may not be abbreviated, the underlying reason being that replace changes the data.

regress can be abbreviated reg, regr, regre, or regres, or it can be spelled out in its entirety.

Sometimes short abbreviations are also allowed. Commands that begin with the letter *d* include decode, describe, destring, dir, discard, display, do, and drop, which suggests that the shortest allowable abbreviation for describe is desc. However, because describe is such a commonly used command, you may abbreviate it with the single letter d. You may also abbreviate the list command with the single letter l.

The other exception to the general abbreviation rule is that commands that alter or destroy data must be spelled out completely. Two commands that begin with the letter *d*, discard and drop, are destructive in the sense that, once you give one of these commands, there is no way to undo the result. Therefore, both must be spelled out.

The final exceptions to the general rule are commands implemented as ado-files. Such commands may not be abbreviated. Ado-file commands are external, and their names correspond to the names of disk files.

11.2.2   Option abbreviation

Option abbreviation follows the same logic as command abbreviation: you determine the minimum acceptable abbreviation by examining the command's syntax diagram. The syntax diagram for summarize reads, in part,

summarize ... , detail format

The detail option may be abbreviated d, de, det, ..., detail. Similarly, option format may be abbreviated f, fo, ..., format.

The clear and replace options occur with many commands. The clear option indicates that even though completing this command will result in the loss of all data in memory, and even though the data in memory have changed since the data were last saved on disk, you want to continue. clear must be spelled out, as in use newdata, clear.

The `replace` option indicates that it is okay to save over an existing dataset. If you type `save mydata` and the file `mydata.dta` already exists, you will receive the message "file mydata.dta already exists", and Stata will refuse to overwrite it. To allow Stata to overwrite the dataset, you would type `save mydata, replace`. `replace` may not be abbreviated.

❑ Technical note

    `replace` is a stronger modifier than `clear` and is one you should think about before using. With a mistaken `clear`, you can lose hours of work, but with a mistaken `replace`, you can lose days of work.

❑

11.2.3 Variable-name abbreviation

- Variable names may be abbreviated to the shortest string of characters that uniquely identifies them given the data currently loaded in memory.

  If your dataset contained four variables, `state`, `mrgrate`, `dvcrate`, and `dthrate`, you could refer to the variable `dvcrate` as `dvcrat`, `dvcra`, `dvcr`, `dvc`, or `dv`. You might type `list dv` to list the data on `dvcrate`. You could not refer to the variable `dvcrate` as `d`, however, because that abbreviation does not distinguish `dvcrate` from `dthrate`. If you were to type `list d`, Stata would respond with the message "ambiguous abbreviation". (If you wanted to refer to *all* variables that started with the letter *d*, you could type `list d*`; see [U] **11.4 varlists**.)

- The character ~ may be used to mean that "zero or more characters go here". For instance, `r~8` might refer to the variable `rep78`, or `rep1978`, or `repair1978`, or just `r8`. (The ~ character is similar to the * character in [U] **11.4 varlists**, except that it adds the restriction "and only one variable matches this specification".)

  Above, we said that you could abbreviate variables. You could type `dvcr` to refer to `dvcrate`, but, if there were more than one variable that started with the letters `dvcr`, you would receive an error. Typing `dvcr` is the same as typing `dvcr~`.

11.3 Naming conventions

A name is a sequence of one to 32 letters (A–Z and a–z), digits (0–9), and underscores (_).

Programmers: Local macro names can have no more than 31 characters in the name; see [U] **18.3.1 Local macros**.

Stata reserves the following names:

_all	double	long	_rc
_b	float	_n	_skip
byte	if	_N	str#
_coef	in	_pi	using
_cons	int	_pred	with

You may not use these reserved names for your variables.

The first character of a name must be a letter or an underscore. We recommend, however, that you not begin your variable names with an underscore. All of Stata's built-in variables begin with an underscore, and we reserve the right to incorporate new _variables freely.

Stata respects case; that is, `myvar`, `Myvar`, and `MYVAR` are three distinct names.

All objects in Stata—not just variables—follow this naming convention.

11.4   varlists

A *varlist* is a list of variable names. The variable names in a *varlist* refer either exclusively to new (not yet created) variables or exclusively to existing variables. A *newvarlist* always refers exclusively to new (not yet created) variables.

11.4.1   Lists of existing variables

In lists of existing variable names, variable names may be repeated.

▷ Example 11

If you type list state mrgrate dvcrate state, the variable state will be listed twice, once in the leftmost column and again in the rightmost column of the list.

◁

Existing variable names may be abbreviated as described in [U] **11.2 Abbreviation rules**. You may also use "*" to indicate that "zero or more characters go here". For instance, if you suffix * to a partial variable name (for example, sta*), you are referring to all variable names that start with that letter combination. If you prefix * to a letter combination (for example, *rate), you are referring to all variables that end in that letter combination. If you put * in the middle (for example, m*rate), you are referring to all variables that begin and end with the specified letters. You may put more than one * in an abbreviation.

▷ Example 12

If the variables poplt5, pop5to17, and pop18p are in our dataset, we may type pop* as a shorthand way to refer to all three variables. For instance, list state pop* lists the variables state, poplt5, pop5to17, and pop18p.

If we had a dataset with variables inc1990, inc1991, ..., inc1999 along with variables incfarm1990, ..., incfarm1999; pop1990, ..., pop1999; and ms1990, ..., ms1999, then *1995 would be a shorthand way of referring to inc1995, incfarm1995, pop1995, and ms1995. We could type, for instance, list *1995.

In that same dataset, typing list i*95 would be a shorthand way of listing inc1995 and incfarm1995.

Typing list i*f*95 would be a shorthand way of listing to incfarm1995.

◁

~ is an alternative to *, and really, it means the same thing. The difference is that ~ indicates that if more than one variable matches the specified pattern, Stata will complain rather than substituting all the variables that match the specification.

▷ Example 13

In the previous example, we could have typed list i~f~95 to list incfarm1995. If, however, our dataset also included variable infant1995, then list i*f*95 would list both variables and list i~f~95 would complain that i~f~95 is an ambiguous abbreviation.

◁

You may use ? to specify that one character goes here. Remember, * means zero or more characters go here, so ?* can be used to mean one or more characters goes here, ??* can be used to mean two or more characters go here, and so on.

> ## Example 14

In a dataset containing variables rep1, rep2, ..., rep78, rep? would refer to rep1, rep2, ..., rep9, and rep?? would refer to rep10, rep11, ..., rep78.

◁

You may place a dash (-) between two variable names to specify all the variables stored between the two listed variables, inclusive. You can determine storage order by using describe; it lists variables in the order in which they are stored.

> ## Example 15

If the dataset contains the variables state, mrgrate, dvcrate, and dthrate, in that order, typing list state-dvcrate is equivalent to typing list state mrgrate dvcrate. In both cases, three variables are listed.

◁

11.4.2   Lists of new variables

In lists of *new variables*, no variable names may be repeated or abbreviated.

You may specify a dash (-) between two variable names that have the same letter prefix and that end in numbers. This form of the dash notation indicates a range of variable names in ascending numerical order.

For example, typing input v1-v4 is equivalent to typing input v1 v2 v3 v4. Typing infile state v1-v3 ssn using rawdata is equivalent to typing infile state v1 v2 v3 ssn using rawdata.

You may specify the storage type before the variable name to force a storage type other than the default. The numeric storage types are byte, int, long, float (the default), and double. The string storage types are str#, where # is replaced with an integer between 1 and 244, inclusive, representing the maximum length of the string. See [U] **12 Data**.

For instance, the list var1 str8 var2 var3 specifies that var1 and var3 be given the default storage type and that var2 be stored as a str8—a string whose maximum length is eight characters.

The list var1 int var2 var3 specifies that var2 be stored as an int. You may use parentheses to bind a list of variable names. The list var1 int(var2 var3) specifies that both var2 and var3 be stored as ints. Similarly, the list var1 str20(var2 var3) specifies that both var2 and var3 be stored as str20s. The different storage types are listed in [U] **12.2.2 Numeric storage types** and [U] **12.4.4 String storage types**.

> ## Example 16

Typing infile str2 state str10 region v1-v5 using mydata reads the state and region strings from the file mydata.raw and stores them as str2 and str10, respectively, along with the variables v1 through v5, which are stored as the default storage type float (unless we have specified a different default with the set type command).

Typing `infile str10(state region) v1-v5 using mydata` would achieve almost the same result, except that the `state` and `region` values recorded in the data would both be assigned to `str10` variables. (We could then use the `compress` command to shorten the strings. See [D] **compress**; it is well worth reading.)

◁

❏ Technical note

You may append a colon and a *value label name* to numeric variables. (See [U] **12.6 Dataset, variable, and value labels** for a description of value labels.) For instance, `var1 var2:myfmt` specifies that the variable `var2` be associated with the value label stored under the name `myfmt`. This has the same effect as typing the list `var1 var2` and then subsequently giving the command `label values var2 myfmt`.

The advantage of specifying the value label association with the colon notation is that value labels can then be assigned by the current command; see [D] **input** and [D] **infile (free format)**.

❏

▷ Example 17

Typing `infile int(state:stfmt region:regfmt) v1-v5 using mydata, automatic` reads the state and region data from the file `mydata.raw` and stores them as `int`s, along with the variables `v1` through `v5`, which are stored as the default storage type.

In our previous example, both state and region were strings, so how can strings be stored in a numeric variable? See [U] **12.6 Dataset, variable, and value labels** for the complete answer. The colon notation specifies the name of the value label, and the `automatic` option tells Stata to assign unique numeric codes to all character strings. The numeric code for state, which Stata will make up on the fly, will be stored in the `state` variable. The mapping from numeric codes to words will be stored in the value label named `stfmt`. Similarly, regions will be assigned numeric codes, which are stored in `region`, and the mapping will be stored in `regfmt`.

If we were to `list` the data, the `state` and `region` variables would look like strings. `state`, for instance, would appear to contain things like `AL`, `CA`, and `WA`, but actually it would contain only numbers like 1, 2, 3, and 4.

◁

11.4.3   Factor variables

Factor variables are extensions of varlists of existing variables. When a command allows factor variables, in addition to typing variable names from your data, you can type factor variables, which might look like

> i.*varname*

> i.*varname*#i.*varname*

> i.*varname*#i.*varname*#i.*varname*

> i.*varname*##i.*varname*

> i.*varname*##i.*varname*##i.*varname*

Factor variables create indicator variables from categorical variables and are allowed with most estimation and postestimation commands, along with a few other commands.

Consider a variable named group that takes on the values 1, 2, and 3. Stata command list allows factor variables, so we can see how factor variables are expanded by typing

```
. list group i.group in 1/5
```

	group	1b. group	2. group	3. group
1.	1	0	0	0
2.	1	0	0	0
3.	2	0	1	0
4.	2	0	1	0
5.	3	0	0	1

There are no variables named 1b.group, 2.group, and 3.group in our data; there is only the variable named group. When we type i.group, however, Stata acts as if the variables 1b.group, 2.group, and 3.group exist. 1b.group, 2.group, and 3.group are called virtual variables.

Start at the right of the listing. 3.group is the virtual variable that equals 1 when group = 3, and 0 otherwise. 2.group is the virtual variable that equals 1 when group = 2, and 0 otherwise. 1b.group is different. The b is a marker indicating base value. 1b.group is a virtual variable equal to 0. If the i.group collection was included in a linear regression, virtual variable 1b.group would drop out from the estimation because it does not vary, and thus the coefficients on 2.group and 3.group would measure the change from group = 1. Hence the term base value.

The categorical variable to which factor-variable operators are applied must contain nonnegative integers with values in the range 0 to 32,740, inclusive.

❏ Technical note

We said above that 3.group equals 1 when group = 3 and equals 0 otherwise. We should have added that 3.group equals missing when group contains missing. To be precise, 3.group equals 1 when group = 3, equals system missing (.) when group ≥ ., and equals 0 otherwise.

❏

❏ Technical note

We said above that when we typed i.group, Stata acts as if the variables 1b.group, 2.group, and 3.group exist, and that might suggest that the act of typing i.group somehow created the virtual variables. That is not true; the virtual variables always exist.

In fact, i.group is an abbreviation for 1b.group, 2.group, and 3.group. In any command that allows factor variables, you can specify virtual variables. Thus the listing above could equally well have been produced by typing

```
. list group 1b.group 2.group 3.group in 1/5
```

#.*varname* is defined as equal to 1 when *varname* = #, equal to system missing (.) when *varname* ≥ ., and equal to 0 otherwise. Thus 4.group is defined even when group takes on only the values 1, 2, and 3. 4.group would be equal to 0 in all observations. Referring to 4.group would not produce an error such as "virtual variable not found".

❏

11.4.3.1   Factor-variable operators

i.group is called a factor variable, although more correctly, we should say that group is a categorical variable to which factor-variable operators have been applied. There are four factor-variable operators:

operator	description
i.	unary operator to specify indicators
c.	unary operator to treat as continuous
#	binary operator to specify interactions
##	binary operator to specify full-factorial interactions

When you type i.group, it forms the indicators for the unique values of group. We will usually say this more briefly as i.group forms indicators for the levels of group, and sometimes we will abbreviate the statement even more and say i.group forms indicators for group.

The c. operator means continuous. We will get to that below.

and ##, pronounced cross and factorial cross, are operators for use with pairs of variables.

i.group#i.sex means to form indicators for each combination of the levels of group and sex.

group#sex means the same thing, which is to say that use of # implies the i. prefix.

group#c.age (or i.group#c.age) means the interaction of the levels of group with the continuous variable age. This amounts to forming i.group and then multiplying each level by age. We already know that i.group expands to the virtual variables 1b.group, 2.group, and 3.group, so group#c.age results in the collection of variables equal to 1b.group*age, 2.group*age, and 3.group*age. 1b.group*age will just be zero because 1b.group is zero. 2.group*age will be age when group = 2, and 0 otherwise. 3.group*age will be age when group = 3, and 0 otherwise. In a linear regression of y on age and group#c.age, 1b.group*age will be omitted, 2.group*age will measure the change in the age coefficient for group = 2 relative to the base group, and 3.group*age will measure the change for group = 3 relative to the base.

Here are some more examples of use of the operators:

factor specification	result
i.group	indicators for levels of group
i.group#i.sex	indicators for each combination of levels of group and sex, a two-way interaction
group#sex	same as i.group#i.sex
group#sex#arm	indicators for each combination of levels of group, sex, and arm, a three-way interaction
group##sex	same as i.group i.sex group#sex
group##sex##arm	same as i.group i.sex i.arm group#sex group#arm sex#arm group#sex#arm
sex#c.age	two variables—age for males and 0 elsewhere, and age for females and 0 elsewhere; if age is also in the model, one of the two virtual variables will be treated as a base
sex##c.age	same as i.sex age sex#c.age
c.age	same as age
c.age#c.age	age squared
c.age#c.age#c.age	age cubed

Several factor-variable terms are often specified in the same varlist, such as

```
. regress y  i.sex i.group sex#group age sex#c.age
```

or, equivalently,

```
. regress y  sex##group sex##c.age
```

11.4.3.2 Base levels

When we typed i.group, group = 1 became the base level. When we do not specify otherwise, the smallest level becomes the base level.

You can specify the base level of a factor variable by using the ib. operator. The syntax is

base operator[a]	description
ib#.	use # as base, # = value of variable
ib(##).	use the #th ordered value as base[b]
ib(first).	use smallest value as base (default)
ib(last).	use largest value as base
ib(freq).	use most frequent value as base
ibn.	no base level

[a]The i may be omitted. For instance, you can type ib2.group or b2.group.
[b]For example, ib(#2). means to use the second value as the base.

Thus, if you want to use group = 3 as the base, you can type ib3.group. You can type

```
. regress y  i.sex ib3.group sex#ib3.group age sex#c.age
```

or you can type

```
. regress y  i.sex ib3.group sex#group age sex#c.age
```

That is, you only have to set the base once. If you specify the base level more than once, it must be the same base level. You will get an error if you attempt to change base levels in midsentence.

If you type ib3.group, the virtual variables become 1.group, 2.group, and b3.group.

Were you to type ib(freq).group, the virtual variables might be b1.group, 2.group, and 3.group; 1.group, b2.group, and 3.group; or 1.group, 2.group, and b3.group, depending on the most frequent group in the data.

11.4.3.3 Setting base levels permanently

You can permanently set the base level by using the fvset command; see [R] **fvset**. For example,

```
. fvset base 3  group
```

sets the base for group to be 3. The setting is recorded in the data, and if the dataset is resaved, the base level will be remembered in future sessions.

If you want to set the base group back to the default, type

```
. fvset base default  group
```

If you want to set the base levels for a group of variables to be the largest value, you can type

```
. fvset base last  group sex arm
```

See [R] **fvset** for details.

Base levels can be temporarily overridden by using the ib. operator regardless of whether they are set explicitly.

11.4.3.4 Selecting levels

Typing i.group specifies virtual variables b1.group, 2.group, and 3.group. Regardless of whether you type i.group, you can access those virtual variables. You can, for instance, use them in expressions and if statements:

```
. list if 3.group
(output omitted )
. generate over_age = cond(3.group, age-21, 0)
```

Although throughout this section we have been typing #.group such as 3.group as if it is somehow distinctly different from i.group, the complete, formal syntax is i3.group. You are allowed to omit the i. The point is that i3.group is just a special case of i.group; i3.group specifies an indicator for the third level of group, and i.group specifies the indicators for all the levels of group. Anyway, the above commands could be typed as

```
. list if i3.group
(output omitted )
. generate over_age = cond(i3.group, age-21, 0)
```

Similarly, the virtual variables b1.group, 2.group, and 3.group more formally would be referred to as ib1.group, i2.group, and i3.group. You are allowed to omit the leading i whenever what appears after is a number or a b followed by a base specification.

You can select a range of levels—a range of virtual variables—by using the i(*numlist*).*varname*. This can be useful when specifying the model to be fit using estimation commands. You may not omit the i when specifying a numlist.

examples	description
i2.cat	single indicator for cat = 2
2.cat	same as i2.cat
i(2 3 4).cat	three indicators, cat = 2, cat = 3, and cat = 4; same as i2.cat i3.cat i4.cat
i(2/4).cat	same as i(2 3 4).cat
2.cat#1.sex	a single indicator that is 1 when cat = 2 and sex = 1 and is 0 otherwise
i2.cat#i1.sex	same as 2.cat#1.sex

11.4.3.5   Applying operators to a group of variables

Factor-variable operators may be applied to groups of variables by using parentheses. You may type, for instance,

    i.(group sex arm)

to mean i.group i.sex i.arm.

In the examples that follow, variables group, sex, arm, and cat are categorical, and variables age, wt, and bp are continuous:

examples	expansion
i.(group sex arm)	i.group i.sex i.arm
group#(sex arm cat)	group#sex group#arm group#cat
group##(sex arm cat)	i.group i.sex i.arm i.cat group#sex group#arm group#cat
group#(c.age c.wt c.bp)	group#c.age group#c.wt group#c.bp
group#c.(age wt bp)	same as group#(c.age c.wt c.bp)

Parentheses can shorten what you type and make it more readable. For instance,

    . regress y i.sex i.group sex#group age sex#c.age c.age#c.age sex#c.age#c.age

is easier to understand when written as

    . regress y sex##(group c.age c.age#c.age)

11.4.3.6 Using factor variables with time-series operators

Factor-variable operators may be combined with the L. and F. time-series operators, so you may specify lags and leads of factor variables in time-series applications. You could type iL.group or Li.group; the order of the operators does not matter. You could type L.group#L.arm or L.group#c.age.

Examples include

```
. regress y  b1.sex##(i(2/4).group cL.age cL.age#cL.age)
. regress y  2.arm#(sex#i(2/4)b3.group cL.age)
. regress y  2.arm##cat##(sex##i(2/4)b3.group cL.age#c.age) c.bp
>              c.bp#c.bp c.bp#c.bp#c.bp sex##c.bp#c.age
```

11.4.4 Time-series varlists

Time-series varlists are a variation on varlists of existing variables. When a command allows a time-series varlist, you may include time-series operators. For instance, L.gnp refers to the lagged value of variable gnp. The time-series operators are

operator	meaning
L.	lag x_{t-1}
L2.	2-period lag x_{t-2}
...	
F.	lead x_{t+1}
F2.	2-period lead x_{t+2}
...	
D.	difference $x_t - x_{t-1}$
D2.	difference of difference $x_t - x_{t-1} - (x_{t-1} - x_{t-2}) = x_t - 2x_{t-1} + x_{t-2}$
...	
S.	"seasonal" difference $x_t - x_{t-1}$
S2.	lag-2 (seasonal) difference $x_t - x_{t-2}$
...	

Time-series operators may be repeated and combined. L3.gnp refers to the third lag of variable gnp. So do LLL.gnp, LL2.gnp, and L2L.gnp. LF.gnp is the same as gnp. DS12.gnp refers to the one-period difference of the 12-period difference. LDS12.gnp refers to the same concept, lagged once.

D1. = S1., but D2. $\neq$ S2., D3. $\neq$ S3., and so on. D2. refers to the difference of the difference. S2. refers to the two-period difference. If you wanted the difference of the difference of the 12-period difference of gnp, you would write D2S12.gnp.

Operators may be typed in uppercase or lowercase. Most users would type d2s12.gnp instead of D2S12.gnp.

You may type operators however you wish; Stata internally converts operators to their canonical form. If you typed ld2ls12d.gnp, Stata would present the operated variable as L2D3S12.gnp.

In addition to using *operator#*, Stata understands *operator(numlist)* to mean a set of operated variables. For instance, typing L(1/3).gnp in a varlist is the same as typing L.gnp L2.gnp L3.gnp. The operators can also be applied to a list of variables by enclosing the variables in parentheses; e.g.,

```
. use http://www.stata-press.com/data/r11/gxmpl1
. list year L(1/3).(gnp cpi)
```

	year	L.gnp	L2.gnp	L3.gnp	L.cpi	L2.cpi	L3.cpi
1.	1989	.	.	.	.	.	.
2.	1990	5837.9	.	.	124	.	.
3.	1991	6026.3	5837.9	.	130.7	124	.
4.	1992	6367.4	6026.3	5837.9	136.2	130.7	124
5.	1993	6689.3	6367.4	6026.3	140.3	136.2	130.7
6.	1994	7098.4	6689.3	6367.4	144.5	140.3	136.2
7.	1995	7433.4	7098.4	6689.3	148.2	144.5	140.3
8.	1996	7851.9	7433.4	7098.4	152.4	148.2	144.5

The parentheses notation may be used with any operator. Typing D(1/3).gnp would return the first through third differences.

The parentheses notation may be used in operator lists with multiple operators, such as L(0/3)D2S12.gnp.

Operator lists may include up to one set of parentheses, which may enclose a *numlist*; see [U] **11.1.8 numlist**.

The time-series operators L. and F. may be combined with factor variables. If we want to lag the indicator variables for the levels of the factor variable region, we would type iL.region. We could also say that we are specifying the level indicator variables for the lag of the region variables. They are equivalent statements.

The numlists and parentheses notation from both factor varlists and time-series operators may be combined. For example, iL(1/3).region specifies the first three lags of the level indicators for region. If region has four levels, this is equivalent to typing i1L1.region i2L1.region i3L1.region i4L1.region i1L2.region i2L2.region i3L2.region i4L2.region i1L3.region i2L3.region i3L3.region i4L3.region. Pushing the notation further, i(1/2)L(1/3).(region education) specifies the first three lags of the level 1 and level 2 indicator variables for both the region and education variables.

❑ Technical note

The D. and S. time-series operators may not be combined with factor variables because such combinations could have two meanings. iD.a could be the level indicators for the difference of the variable a from its prior period, or it could be the level indicators differenced between the two periods. These are generally not the same values, nor even the same number of indicators. Moreover, they are rarely interesting.

❑

Before you can use time-series operators in varlists, you must set the time variable by using the tsset command:

```
. list l.gnp
time variable not set
r(111);
. tsset time
 (output omitted )
. list l.gnp
 (output omitted )
```

See [TS] **tsset**. The time variable must take on integer values. Also, the data must be sorted on the time variable. tsset handles this, but later you might encounter

```
. list l.mpg
not sorted
r(5);
```

Then type sort time or type tsset to reestablish the order.

The time-series operators respect the time variable. L2.gnp refers to gnp_{t-2}, regardless of missing observations in the dataset. In the following dataset, the observation for 1992 is missing:

```
. use http://www.stata-press.com/data/r11/gxmpl2
. list year gnp l2.gnp, separator(0)
```

	year	gnp	L2.gnp
1.	1989	5837.9	.
2.	1990	6026.3	.
3.	1991	6367.4	5837.9
4.	1993	7098.4	6367.4
5.	1994	7433.4	.
6.	1995	7851.9	7098.4

← note, filled in correctly

Operated variables may be used in expressions:

```
. generate gnplag2 = l2.gnp
(3 missing values generated)
```

Stata also understands cross-sectional time-series data. If you have cross sections of time series, you indicate this when you tsset the data:

```
. tsset country year
```

See [TS] **tsset**. In fact, you can type that, or you can type

```
. xtset country year
```

xtset is how you set panel data just as tsset is how you set time-series data and here the two commands do the same thing. Some panel datasets are not cross-sectional time series, however, in that the second variable is not time, so xtset also allows

```
. xtset country
```

See [XT] **xtset**.

11.5   by varlist: construct

by *varlist*: *command*

The by prefix causes *command* to be repeated for each unique set of values of the variables in the *varlist*. *varlist* may contain numeric, string, or a mixture of numeric and string variables. (*varlist* may not contain time-series operators.)

by is an optional prefix to perform a Stata command separately for each group of observations where the values of the variables in the *varlist* are the same.

During each iteration, the values of the system variables _n and _N are set in relation to the first observation in the by-group; see [U] **13.7 Explicit subscripting**. The in *range* qualifier cannot be used with by *varlist*: because ranges specify absolute rather than relative observation numbers.

❏ Technical note

The inability to combine in and by is not really a constraint because if provides all the functionality of in and a bit more. If you wanted to perform *command* for the first three observations in each of the by-groups, you could type

    . by *varlist*: *command* if _n<=3

❏

The results of *command* would be the same as if you had formed separate datasets for each group of observations, saved them, used each separately, and issued *command*.

➢ Example 18

We provide some examples using by in [U] **11.1.2 by varlist:** above. We demonstrate the effect of by on _n, _N, and explicit subscripting in [U] **13.7 Explicit subscripting**.

by requires that the data first be sorted. For instance, if we had data on the average January and July temperatures in degrees Fahrenheit for 420 cities located in the Northeast and West and wanted to obtain the averages, by region, across those cities, we might type

```
. use http://www.stata-press.com/data/r11/citytemp3
(City Temperature Data)
. by region: summarize tempjan tempjuly
not sorted
r(5);
```

Stata refused to honor our request because the data are not sorted by region. We must either sort the data by region first (see [D] **sort**) or specify by's sort option (which has the same effect):

(Continued on next page)

```
. by region, sort: summarize tempjan tempjuly
```

-> region = NE

Variable	Obs	Mean	Std. Dev.	Min	Max
tempjan	164	27.88537	3.543096	16.6	31.8
tempjuly	164	73.35	2.361203	66.5	76.8

-> region = N Cntrl

Variable	Obs	Mean	Std. Dev.	Min	Max
tempjan	284	21.69437	5.725392	2.2	32.6
tempjuly	284	73.46725	3.103187	64.5	81.4

-> region = South

Variable	Obs	Mean	Std. Dev.	Min	Max
tempjan	250	46.1456	10.38646	28.9	68
tempjuly	250	80.9896	2.97537	71	87.4

-> region = West

Variable	Obs	Mean	Std. Dev.	Min	Max
tempjan	256	46.22539	11.25412	13	72.6
tempjuly	256	72.10859	6.483131	58.1	93.6

◁

▷ Example 19

Using the same data as in the example above, we estimate regressions, by `region`, of average January temperature on average July temperature. Both temperatures are specified in degrees Fahrenheit.

```
. by region: regress tempjan tempjuly
```

-> region = NE

Source	SS	df	MS		
				Number of obs =	164
				F(1, 162) =	479.82
Model	1529.74026	1	1529.74026	Prob > F =	0.0000
Residual	516.484453	162	3.18817564	R-squared =	0.7476
				Adj R-squared =	0.7460
Total	2046.22471	163	12.5535258	Root MSE =	1.7855

tempjan	Coef.	Std. Err.	t	P>|t|	[95% Conf. Interval]	
tempjuly	1.297424	.0592303	21.90	0.000	1.180461	1.414387
_cons	-67.28066	4.346781	-15.48	0.000	-75.86431	-58.697

```
-> region = N Cntrl
      Source |       SS        df       MS              Number of obs =      284
-------------+------------------------------           F(  1,    282) =   115.89
       Model | 2701.97917       1  2701.97917          Prob > F      =   0.0000
    Residual | 6574.79175     282  23.3148644          R-squared     =   0.2913
-------------+------------------------------           Adj R-squared =   0.2887
       Total | 9276.77092     283  32.7801093          Root MSE      =   4.8285

     tempjan |     Coef.   Std. Err.      t    P>|t|     [95% Conf. Interval]
-------------+----------------------------------------------------------------
    tempjuly |  .9957259   .0924944    10.77   0.000     .8136589    1.177793
       _cons | -51.45888   6.801344    -7.57   0.000    -64.84673   -38.07103
```

```
-> region = South
      Source |       SS        df       MS              Number of obs =      250
-------------+------------------------------           F(  1,    248) =    95.17
       Model | 7449.51623       1  7449.51623          Prob > F      =   0.0000
    Residual | 19412.2231     248  78.2750933          R-squared     =   0.2773
-------------+------------------------------           Adj R-squared =   0.2744
       Total | 26861.7394     249  107.878471          Root MSE      =   8.8473

     tempjan |     Coef.   Std. Err.      t    P>|t|     [95% Conf. Interval]
-------------+----------------------------------------------------------------
    tempjuly |   1.83833   .1884392     9.76   0.000     1.467185    2.209475
       _cons |   -102.74   15.27187    -6.73   0.000    -132.8191   -72.66089
```

```
-> region = West
      Source |       SS        df       MS              Number of obs =      256
-------------+------------------------------           F(  1,    254) =     2.84
       Model | 357.161728       1  357.161728          Prob > F      =   0.0932
    Residual | 31939.9031     254   125.74765          R-squared     =   0.0111
-------------+------------------------------           Adj R-squared =   0.0072
       Total | 32297.0648     255  126.655156          Root MSE      =   11.214

     tempjan |     Coef.   Std. Err.      t    P>|t|     [95% Conf. Interval]
-------------+----------------------------------------------------------------
    tempjuly |  .1825482   .1083166     1.69   0.093    -.0307648    .3958613
       _cons |   33.0621    7.84194     4.22   0.000     17.61859     48.5056
```

The regressions show that a 1-degree increase in the average July temperature in the Northeast corresponds to a 1.3-degree increase in the average January temperature. In the West, however, it corresponds to a 0.18-degree increase, which is only marginally significant.

◁

❑ Technical note

by has a second syntax that is especially useful when you want to play it safe:

$$\text{by } varlist_1 \ (varlist_2): \ command$$

This says that Stata is to verify that the data are sorted by $varlist_1$ $varlist_2$ and then, assuming that is true, perform *command* by $varlist_1$. For instance,

```
. by subject (time): gen finalval = val[_N]
```

By typing this, we want to create new variable `finalval`, which contains, in each observation, the final observed value of `val` for each subject in the data. The final value will be the last value if, within subject, the data are sorted by time. The above command verifies that the data are sorted by `subject` and `time` and then, if they are, performs

```
. by subject: gen finalval = val[_N]
```

If the data are not sorted properly, an error message will instead be issued. Of course, we could have just typed

```
. by subject: gen finalval = val[_N]
```

after verifying for ourselves that the data were sorted properly, as long as we were careful to look.

by's second syntax can be used with by's `sort` option, so we can also type

```
. by subject (time), sort: gen finalval = val[_N]
```

which is equivalent to

```
. sort subject time
. by subject: gen finalval = val[_N]
```

❏

11.6   File-naming conventions

Some commands require that you specify a *filename*. Filenames are specified in the way natural for your operating system:

Windows	Unix	Mac
mydata	mydata	mydata
mydata.dta	mydata.dta	mydata.dta
c:mydata.dta	~friend/mydata.dta	~friend/mydata.dta
"my data"	"my data"	"my data"
"my data.dta"	"my data.dta"	"my data.dta"
myproj\mydata	myproj/mydata	myproj/mydata
"my project\my data"	"my project/my data"	"my project/my data"
C:\analysis\data\mydata	~/analysis/data/mydata	~/analysis/data/mydata
"C:\my project\my data"	"~/my project/my data"	"~/my project/my data"
..\data\mydata	../data/mydata	../data/mydata
"..\my project\my data"	"../my project/my data"	"../my project/my data"

In most cases, where *filename* is a file that you are loading, *filename* may also be a URL. For instance, we might specify use `http://www.stata-press.com/data/r11/nlswork`.

Usually (the exceptions being `copy`, `dir`, `ls`, `erase`, `rm`, and `type`), Stata automatically provides a file extension if you do not supply one. For instance, if you type use `mydata`, Stata assumes that you mean use `mydata.dta` because `.dta` is the file extension Stata normally uses for data files.

Stata provides 21 default file extensions that are used by various commands:

.ado	automatically loaded do-files
.dct	ASCII data dictionary
.do	do-file
.dta	Stata-format dataset
.dtasig	datasignature file
.gph	graph
.grec	Graph Editor recording (ASCII format)
.irf	impulse–response function datasets
.log	log file in text format
.mata	Mata source code
.mlib	Mata library
.mmat	Mata matrix
.mo	Mata object file
.out	file saved by outsheet
.raw	ASCII-format dataset
.smcl	log file in SMCL format
.sthlp	help files
.sum	checksum files to verify network transfers
.ster	saved estimates
.stptrace	parameter-trace file; see [MI] **mi ptrace**
.zip	zip file

You do not have to name your data files with the .dta extension—if you type an explicit file extension, it will override the default. For instance, if your dataset was stored as myfile.dat, you could type use myfile.dat. If your dataset was stored as simply myfile with no file extension, you could type the period at the end of the filename to indicate that you are explicitly specifying the null extension. You would type use myfile. to use this dataset.

All operating systems allow blanks in filenames, and so does Stata. However, if the filename includes a blank, you must enclose the filename in double quotes. Typing

    . save "my data"

would create the file my data.dta. Typing

    . save my data

would be an error.

❑ Technical note

Stata also uses 12 other file extensions. These files are of interest only to advanced programmers or are for Stata's internal use. They are

.class	class file for object-oriented programming; see [P] **class**
.dlg	dialog resource file
.idlg	dialog resource include file
.ihlp	help include file
.key	search's keyword database file
.maint	maintenance file (for Stata's internal use only)
.mnu	menu file (for Stata's internal use only)
.pkg	user-site package file
.plugin	compiled addition (DLL)
.scheme	control file for a graph scheme
.style	graph style file
.toc	user-site description file

❑

11.6.1   A special note for Mac users

Have you seen the notation `myfolder/myfile` before? This notation is called a path and describes the location of a file or folder (also called a directory).

You do not have to use this notation if you do not like it. You could instead restrict yourself to using files only in the current folder. If that turns out to be too restricting, Stata for Mac provides enough menus and buttons that you can probably get by. You may, however, find the notation convenient. If you do, here is the rest of the definition.

The character / is called a path delimiter and delimits folder names and filenames in a path. If the path starts with no path delimiter, the path is relative to the current folder.

For example, the path `myfolder/myfile` refers to the file `myfile` in the folder `myfolder`, which is contained in the current folder.

The characters .. refer to the folder containing the current folder. Thus `../myfile` refers to `myfile` in the folder containing the current folder, and `../nextdoor/myfile` refers to `myfile` in the folder `nextdoor` in the folder containing the current folder.

If a path starts with a path delimiter, the path is called an absolute path and describes a fixed location of a file or folder name, regardless of what the current folder is. The leading / in an absolute path refers to the root directory, which is the main hard drive from which the operating system is booted. For example, the path `/myfolder/myfile` refers to the file `myfile` in the folder `myfolder`, which is contained in the main hard drive.

The character ~ refers to the user's home directory. Thus the path `~/myfolder/myfile` refers to `myfile` in the folder `myfolder` in the user's home directory.

11.6.2   A special note for Unix users

Stata understands ~ to mean your home directory. Stata understands this, even if you do not use `csh(1)` as your shell.

11.7   References

Baum, C. F. 2009. *An Introduction to Stata Programming*. College Station, TX: Stata Press.

Kolev, G. I. 2006. Stata tip 31: Scalar or variable? The problem of ambiguous names. *Stata Journal* 6: 279–280.

Ryan, P. 2005. Stata tip 22: Variable name abbreviation. *Stata Journal* 5: 465–466.

12 Data

Contents

12.1 Data and datasets

Data form a rectangular table of numeric and string values in which each row is an observation on all the variables and each column contains the observations on one variable. Variables are designated by *variable names*. Observations are numbered sequentially from 1 to _N. The following example of data contains the first five odd and first five even positive integers, along with a string variable:

```
        odd   even    name
  1.      1      2    Bill
  2.      3      4    Mary
  3.      5      6     Pat
  4.      7      8   Roger
  5.      9     10    Sean
```

The observations are numbered 1 to 5, and the variables are named odd, even, and name. Observations are referred to by number, and variables by name.

A *dataset* is *data* plus labelings, formats, notes, and characteristics.

All aspects of *data* and *datasets* are defined here. Long (2009) offers a long-time Stata user's hard-won advice on how to manage data in Stata to promote accurate, replicable research.

12.2   Numbers

A *number* may contain a sign, an integer part, a decimal point, a fraction part, an e or E, and a signed integer exponent. Numbers may *not* contain commas; for example, the number 1,024 must be typed as 1024 (or 1024. or 1024.0). The following are examples of valid numbers:

```
5
-5
5.2
.5
5.2e+2
5.2e-2
```

❏ Technical note

Stata also allows numbers to be represented in a hexadecimal/binary format, defined as

$$\left[+|-\right]0.0\left[\langle zeros\rangle\right]\{\texttt{X|x}\}\texttt{-3ff}$$

or

$$\left[+|-\right]1.\langle hexdigit\rangle\left[\langle hexdigits\rangle\right]\{\texttt{X|x}\}\{+|-\}\langle hexdigit\rangle\left[\langle hexdigits\rangle\right]$$

The lead digit is always 0 or 1; it is 0 only when the number being expressed is zero. A maximum of 13 digits to the right of the hexadecimal point are allowed. The power ranges from $-3ff$ to $+3ff$. The number is expressed in hexadecimal (base 16) digits; the number $a\texttt{X}+b$ means $a \times 2^b$. For instance, $1.0\texttt{X}+3$ is 2^3 or 8. $1.8\texttt{X}+3$ is 12 because 1.8_{16} is $1 + 8/16 = 1.5$ in decimal and the number is thus $1.5 \times 2^3 = 1.5 \times 8 = 12$.

Stata can also display numbers using this format; see [U] **12.5.1 Numeric formats**. For example,

```
. di 1.81x+2
6.015625

. di %21x 6.015625
+1.8100000000000X+002
```

This hexadecimal format is of special interest to numerical analysts.

❏

12.2.1   Missing values

A number may also take on the special value *missing*, denoted by a period (.). You specify a missing value anywhere that you may specify a number. Missing values differ from ordinary numbers in one respect: any arithmetic operation on a missing value yields a missing value.

In fact, there are 27 missing values in Stata: '.', the one just discussed, as well as .a, .b, ..., and .z, which are known as extended missing values. The missing value '.' is known as the default or system missing value. In any case, some people use extended missing values to indicate why a certain value is unknown—the question was not asked, the person refused to answer, etc. Other people have no use for extended missing values and just use '.'.

Stata's default or system missing value will be returned when you perform an arithmetic operation on missing values or when the arithmetic operation is not defined, such as division by zero, or the logarithm of a nonpositive number.

```
. display 2/0
.

. list
```

	a
1.	.b
2.	.
3.	.a
4.	3
5.	6

```
. generate x = a + 1
(3 missing values generated)
. list
```

	a	x
1.	.b	.
2.	.	.
3.	.a	.
4.	3	4
5.	6	7

Numeric missing values are represented by "large positive values". The ordering is

$$\text{all numbers} < . < .a < .b < \cdots < .z$$

Thus the expression

$$\text{age} > 60$$

is true if variable age is greater than 60 or is missing. Similarly,

$$\text{gender} \, ! = 0$$

is true if gender is not zero or is missing.

The way to exclude missing values is to ask whether the value is less than '.', and the way to detect missing values is to ask whether the value is greater than or equal to '.'. For instance,

```
. list if age>60 & age<.

. generate agegt60 = 0 if age<=60
. replace agegt60 = 1 if age>60 & age<.

. generate agegt60 = (age>60) if age<.
```

(*Continued on next page*)

❏ Technical note

Before Stata 8, Stata only had one representation for missing values, the period (.).

To ensure that old programs and do-files continue to work properly, when version is set less than 8, all missing values are treated as being the same. Thus . == .a == .b == .z, and so '*exp==.*' and '*exp!=.*' work just as they previously did.

❏

▷ Example 1

We have data on the income of husbands and wives recorded in the variables hincome and wincome, respectively. Typing the list command, we see that your data contain

```
. use http://www.stata-press.com/data/r11/gxmpl3
. list
```

	hincome	wincome
1.	32000	0
2.	35000	34000
3.	47000	.b
4.	.z	50000
5.	.a	.

The values of wincome in the third and fifth observations are *missing*, as distinct from the value of wincome in the first observation, which is known to be zero.

If we use the generate command to create a new variable, income, that is equal to the sum of hincome and wincome, three missing values would be produced:

```
. generate income = hincome + wincome
(3 missing values generated)
. list
```

	hincome	wincome	income
1.	32000	0	32000
2.	35000	34000	69000
3.	47000	.b	.
4.	.z	50000	.
5.	.a	.	.

generate produced a warning message that 3 missing values were created, and when we list the data, we see that 47,000 plus *missing* yields *missing*.

◁

❏ Technical note

Stata stores numeric missing values as the largest 27 numbers allowed by the particular storage type; see [U] **12.2.2 Numeric storage types**. There are two important implications. First, if you sort on a variable that has missing values, the missing values will be placed last, and the sort order of any missing values will follow the rule regarding the properties of missing values stated above.

```
. sort wincome
. list wincome
```

	wincome
1.	0
2.	34000
3.	50000
4.	.
5.	.b

The second implication concerns relational operators and missing values. Do not forget that a missing value will be larger than any numeric value.

```
. list if wincome > 40000
```

	hincome	wincome	income
3.	.z	50000	.
4.	.a	.	.
5.	47000	.b	.

Observations 4 and 5 are listed because '.' and '.b' are both missing and thus are greater than 40,000. Relational operators are discussed in detail in [U] **13.2.3 Relational operators**.

❏

➢ Example 2

In producing statistical output, Stata ignores observations with missing values. Continuing with the example above, if we request summary statistics on hincome and wincome by using the summarize command, we obtain

```
. summarize hincome wincome
```

Variable	Obs	Mean	Std. Dev.	Min	Max
hincome	3	38000	7937.254	32000	47000
wincome	3	28000	25534.29	0	50000

Some commands discard the entire observation (known as *casewise deletion*) if one of the variables in the observation is missing. If we use the correlate command to obtain the correlation between hincome and wincome, for instance, we obtain

```
. correlate hincome wincome
(obs=2)
```

	hincome	wincome
hincome	1.0000	
wincome	1.0000	1.0000

The correlation coefficient is calculated over two observations.

◁

12.2.2 Numeric storage types

Numbers can be stored in one of five variable types: byte, int, long, float (the default), or double. bytes are, naturally, stored in 1 byte. ints are stored in 2 bytes, longs and floats in 4 bytes, and doubles in 8 bytes. The table below shows the minimum and maximum values for each storage type.

Storage type	Minimum	Maximum	Closest to 0 without being 0	Bytes
byte	-127	100	± 1	1
int	$-32,767$	$32,740$	± 1	2
long	$-2,147,483,647$	$2,147,483,620$	± 1	4
float	$-1.70141173319 \times 10^{38}$	$1.70141173319 \times 10^{38}$	$\pm 10^{-38}$	4
double	$-8.9884656743 \times 10^{307}$	$+8.9884656743 \times 10^{307}$	$\pm 10^{-323}$	8

Do not confuse the term *integer*, which is a characteristic of a number, with int, which is a storage type. For instance, the number 5 is an integer, no matter how it is stored; thus, if you read that an argument must be an integer, that does not mean that it must be stored as an int.

12.3 Dates and times

Stata has nine date, time, and date-and-time numeric encodings known collectively as %t variables or values. They are

%tC	calendar date and time, adjusted for leap seconds
%tc	calendar date and time, ignoring leap seconds
%td	calendar date
%tw	week
%tm	calendar month
%tq	financial quarter
%th	financial half-year
%ty	calendar year
%tg	generic—user defined

All except %ty and %tg are based on 0 = beginning of January 1960. %tc and %tC record the number of milliseconds since then. %td records the number of days. The others record the numbers of weeks, months, quarters, or half-years. %ty simply records the year and %tg records whatever you wish.

For a full discussion of working with dates and times, see [U] **24 Working with dates and times**.

12.4   Strings

A *string* is a sequence of printable characters and is typically enclosed in double quotes. The quotes are not considered a part of the string but delimit the beginning and end of the string. The following are examples of valid strings:

```
"Hello, world"
"String"
"string"
" string"
"string "
""
"x/y+3"
"1.2"
```

All the strings above are distinct; that is, "String" is different from "string", which is different from " string", which is different from "string ". Also, "1.2" is a string and not a number because it is enclosed in quotes.

All strings in Stata are of varying length, which means that Stata internally records the length of the string and never loses track. There is never a circumstance in which a string cannot be delimited by quotes, but there are rare instances where strings do not have to be delimited by quotes, such as during data input. In those cases, nondelimited strings are stripped of their leading and trailing blanks. Delimited strings are always accepted as is.

The special string "", often called *null string*, is considered by Stata to be a *missing*. No special meaning is given to the string containing one period, ".".

In addition to double quotes for enclosing strings, Stata also allows compound double quotes: '" and "'. You can type "*string*" or you can type '"*string*"', although users seldom type '"*string*"'. Compound double quotes are of special interest to programmers because they nest and provide a way for a quoted string to itself contain double quotes (either simple or compound). See [U] **18.3.5 Double quotes**.

12.4.1   Strings containing identifying data

String variables often contain identifying information, such as the patient's name or the name of the city or state. Such strings are typically listed but are not used directly in statistical analysis, although the data might be sorted on the string or datasets might be merged on the basis of one or more string variables.

12.4.2   Strings containing categorical data

Occasionally, strings contain information that is to be used directly in analysis, such as the patient's sex, which might be coded "male" or "female". Stata shows a decided preference for such information to be numerically encoded and stored in numeric variables. Stata's statistical routines treat string variables as if every observation records a numeric missing value.

Stata provides two commands for converting string variables into numeric codes and back again: encode and decode; see [U] **23.2 Categorical string variables** and [U] **11.4.3 Factor variables**. Also see [D] **destring** for information on mapping string variables to numeric and vice versa.

12.4.3   Strings containing numeric data

If a string variable contains the character representation of a number—for instance, `myvar` contains
"1", "1.2", and "-5.2"—you can convert it directly into a numeric variable by using the `real()`
function or the `destring` command, e.g., `generate newvar=real(myvar)`.

Similarly, if you want to convert a numeric variable to its string representation, you can use
the `string()` function or the `tostring` command, e.g., `generate as_str=string(numvar)`. See
[D] **functions**.

12.4.4   String storage types

Strings are stored in string variables with storage types `str1`, `str2`, ..., `str244`. The storage
type merely sets the maximum length of the string, not its actual length; thus, "example" has length
7 whether it is stored as a `str7`, a `str10`, or even a `str244`. On the other hand, an attempt to assign
the string "example" to a `str6` would result in "exampl".

The maximum length of a string in Stata is 244. String literals may exceed 244 characters, but
only the first 244 characters are significant.

12.5   Formats: Controlling how data are displayed

Formats describe how a number or string is to be presented. For instance, how is the number
325.24 to be presented? As 325.2, or 325.24, or 325.240, or 3.2524e+02, or 3.25e+02, or some
other way? The *display format* tells Stata exactly how to present such data. You do not have to
specify display formats because Stata always makes reasonable assumptions about how to display a
variable, but you always have the option.

12.5.1   Numeric formats

A Stata numeric format is formed by

first type	%	to indicate the start of the format
then optionally type	-	if you want the result left-aligned
then optionally type	0	if you want to retain leading zeros (1)
then type	a number w	stating the width of the result
then type	.	
then type	a number d	stating the number of digits to follow the decimal point
then type		
either	e	for scientific notation, e.g., 1.00e+03
or	f	for fixed format, e.g., 1000.0
or	g	for general format; Stata chooses based on the number being displayed
then optionally type	c	to indicate comma format (not allowed with e)

(1) Specifying 0 to mean "include leading zeros" will be honored only with the f format.

For example,

%9.0g	general format, 9 columns wide	
	sqrt(2) =	1.414214
	1,000 =	1000
	10,000,000 =	1.00e+07
%9.0gc	general format, 9 columns wide, with commas	
	sqrt(2) =	1.414214
	1,000 =	1,000
	10,000,000 =	1.00e+07
%9.2f	fixed format, 9 columns wide, 2 decimal places	
	sqrt(2) =	1.41
	1,000 =	1000.00
	10,000,000 =	10000000.00
%9.2fc	fixed format, 9 columns wide, 2 decimal places, with commas	
	sqrt(2) =	1.41
	1,000 =	1,000.00
	10,000,000 =	10,000,000.00
%9.2e	exponential format, 9 columns wide	
	sqrt(2) =	1.41e+00
	1,000 =	1.00e+03
	10,000,000 =	1.00e+07

Stata has three numeric format types: e, f, and g. The formats are denoted by a leading percent sign (%) followed by the string $w.d$, where w and d stand for two integers. The first integer, w, specifies the width of the format. The second integer d specifies the number of digits that are to follow the decimal point. d must be less than w. Finally, a character denotes the format type (e, f, or g), and to that may optionally be appended a c indicating that commas are to be included in the result (c is not allowed with e.)

By default, every numeric variable is given a %w.0g format, where w is large enough to display the largest number of the variable's type. The %w.0g format is a set of formatting rules that present the values in as readable a fashion as possible without sacrificing precision. The g format changes the number of decimal places displayed whenever it improves the readability of the current value.

The default formats for each of the numeric variable types are

byte	%8.0g
int	%8.0g
long	%12.0g
float	%9.0g
double	%10.0g

You can change the format of a variable by using the format *varname* %*fmt* command.

In addition to %w.0g, allowed is %w.0gc to display numbers with commas. "One thousand" is displayed as 1000 in %9.0g format and as 1,000 in %9.0gc format.

In addition to using %w.0g and %w.0gc, you can use %w.dg and %w.$d$gc, $d > 0$. For example, %9.4g and %9.4gc. The 4 means to display approximately four significant digits. For instance, the number 3.14159265 in %9.4g format is displayed as 3.142, 31.4159265 as 31.42, 314.159265 as 314.2, and 3141.59265 as 3142. The format is not exactly a significant-digit format because 31415.9265 is displayed as 31416, not as 3.142e+04.

Under the f format, values are always displayed with the same number of decimal places, even if this results in a loss in the displayed precision. Thus the f format is similar to the C f format. Stata's f format is also similar to the Fortran F format, but, unlike the Fortran F format, it switches to g whenever a number is too large to be displayed in the specified f format.

In addition to %w.df, the format %w.$d$fc can display numbers with commas.

The e format is similar to the C e and the Fortran E format. Every value is displayed as a leading digit (with a minus sign, if necessary), followed by a decimal point, the specified number of digits, the letter e, a plus sign or a minus sign, and the power of 10 (modified by the preceding sign) that multiplies the displayed value. When the e format is specified, the width must exceed the number of digits that follow the decimal point by at least seven to accommodate the leading sign and digit, the decimal point, the e, and the signed power of 10.

▷ Example 3

Below we have a 5-observation dataset with three variables: e_fmt, f_fmt, and g_fmt. All three variables have the same values stored in them; only the display format varies. describe shows the display format to the right of the variable type:

```
. use http://www.stata-press.com/data/r11/format
. describe
Contains data from http://www.stata-press.com/data/r11/format.dta
  obs:            5
  vars:           3                            12 Mar 2009 15:18
  size:          80 (99.9% of memory free)
```

variable name	storage type	display format	value label	variable label
e_fmt	float	%9.2e		
f_fmt	float	%10.2f		
g_fmt	float	%9.0g		

```
Sorted by:
```

The formats for each of these variables were set by typing

```
. format e_fmt %9.2e
. format f_fmt %10.2f
```

It was not necessary to set the format for the g_fmt variable because Stata automatically assigned it the %9.0g format. Nevertheless, we could have typed format g_fmt %9.0g if we wished. Listing the data results in

```
. list
```

	e_fmt	f_fmt	g_fmt
1.	2.80e+00	2.80	2.801785
2.	3.96e+06	3962322.50	3962323
3.	4.85e+00	4.85	4.852834
4.	-5.60e-06	-0.00	-5.60e-06
5.	6.26e+00	6.26	6.264982

◁

❑ Technical note

The discussion above is incomplete. There is one other format available that will be of interest to numerical analysts. The %21x format displays base 10 numbers in a hexadecimal (base 16) format. The number is expressed in hexadecimal (base 16) digits; the number aX+b means $a \times 2^b$. For example,

```
. display %21x 1234.75
+1.34b0000000000X+00a
```

Thus the base 10 number 1,234.75 has a base 16 representation of 1.34bX+0a, meaning

$$\left(1 + 3 \cdot 16^{-1} + 4 \cdot 16^{-2} + 11 \cdot 16^{-3}\right) \times 2^{10}$$

Remember, the hexadecimal–decimal equivalents are

hexadecimal	decimal
0	0
1	1
2	2
3	3
4	4
5	5
6	6
7	7
8	8
9	9
a	10
b	11
c	12
d	13
e	14
f	15

See [U] **12.2 Numbers**.

❑

12.5.2   European numeric formats

The three numeric formats e, f, and g will use ',' to indicate the decimal symbol if you specify their width and depth as w,d rather than $w.d$. For instance, the format %9,0g will display what Stata would usually display as 1.5 as 1,5.

If you use the European specification with fc or gc, the "comma" will be presented as a period. For instance, %9,0gc would display what Stata would usually display as 1,000.5 as 1.000,5.

If this way of presenting numbers appeals to you, consider using Stata's set dp comma command. set dp comma tells Stata to interpret nearly all %$w.d${g|f|e} formats as %w,d{g|f|e} formats. Most of Stata is written using a period to represent the decimal symbol, and that means that, even if you set the appropriate %w,d{g|f|e} format for your data, it will affect only displays of the data. For instance, if you type summarize to obtain summary statistics or regress to obtain regression results, the decimal will still be shown as a period.

set dp comma changes that and affects all of Stata. With set dp comma, it does not matter whether your data are formatted %$w.d${g|f|e} or %w,d{g|f|e}. All results will be displayed using a comma as the decimal character:

```
. use http://www.stata-press.com/data/r11/auto
(1978 Automobile Data)

. set dp comma

. summarize mpg weight foreign
```

Variable	Obs	Mean	Std. Dev.	Min	Max
mpg	74	21,2973	5,785503	12	41
weight	74	3019,459	777,1936	1760	4840
foreign	74	,2972973	,4601885	0	1

```
. regress mpg weight foreign
```

Source	SS	df	MS		
Model	1619,2877	2	809,643849		
Residual	824,171761	71	11,608053		
Total	2443,45946	73	33,4720474		

	Number of obs = 74
	F(2, 71) = 69,75
	Prob > F = 0,0000
	R-squared = 0,6627
	Adj R-squared = 0,6532
	Root MSE = 3,4071

mpg	Coef.	Std. Err.	t	P>|t|	[95% Conf. Interval]	
weight	-,0065879	,0006371	-10,34	0,000	-,0078583	-,0053175
foreign	-1,650029	1,075994	-1,53	0,130	-3,7955	,4954422
_cons	41,6797	2,165547	19,25	0,000	37,36172	45,99768

You can switch the decimal character back to a period by typing set dp period.

□ Technical note

set dp comma makes drastic changes inside Stata, and we mention this because some older, user-written programs may not be able to deal with those changes. If you are using an older user-written program, you might set dp comma and then find that the program does not work and instead presents some sort of syntax error.

If, using any program, you do get an unanticipated error, try setting dp back to period. See [D] **format** for more information.

Also understand that set dp comma affects how Stata outputs numbers, not how it inputs them. You must still use the period to indicate the decimal point on all input. Even with set dp comma, you type

```
. replace x=1.5 if x==2
```

□

12.5.3 Date and time formats

Date and time formats are really a numeric format because Stata stores dates as the number of milliseconds, days, weeks, months, quarters, half-years, or years from 01jan1960; see [U] **24 Working with dates and times**.

The syntax of the %t format is

first type	%	to indicate the start of the format
then optionally type	-	if you want the result left-aligned
then type	t	
then type	*character*	to indicate the units
then optionally type	*other characters*	to indicate how the date/time is to be displayed

The letter you type to specify the units is

C	milliseconds from 01jan1960, adjusted for leap seconds
c	milliseconds from 01jan1960, ignoring leap seconds
d	days from 01jan1960
w	weeks from 1960-w1
m	calendar months from jan1960
q	quarters from 1960-q1
h	half years from 1960-h1
g	user-defined units

There are many codes you can type after that to specify exactly how the date/time is to be displayed, but usually, you do not. Most users use the default %tc for date/times and %td for dates. See *Formatting date and time values* in [D] **dates and times** for details.

12.5.4 String formats

The syntax for a string format is

first type	%	to indicate the start of the format
then optionally type	-	if you want the result left-aligned
then type	a number	indicating the width of the result
then type	s	

For instance, %10s represents a string format of width 10.

For str*w*, the default format is %*w*s or %9s, whichever is wider. For example, a str10 variable receives a %10s format. Strings are displayed right-justified in the field, unless the minus sign is coded; %-10s would display the string left-aligned.

▷ Example 4

Our automobile data contain a string variable called make.

```
. use http://www.stata-press.com/data/r11/auto
(1978 Automobile Data)

. describe make

              storage   display   value
variable name   type    format    label     variable label

make            str18   %-18s                Make and Model
. list make in 63/67
```

	make
63.	Mazda GLC
64.	Peugeot 604
65.	Renault Le Car
66.	Subaru
67.	Toyota Celica

These values are left-aligned because make has a display format of %-18s. If we want to right-align the values, we could change the format:

```
. format %18s make
. list make in 63/67
```

	make
63.	Mazda GLC
64.	Peugeot 604
65.	Renault Le Car
66.	Subaru
67.	Toyota Celica

◁

12.6   Dataset, variable, and value labels

Labels are strings used to label elements in Stata, such as labels for datasets, variables, and values.

12.6.1   Dataset labels

Associated with every dataset is an 80-character *dataset label*, which is initially set to blanks. You can use the `label data "text"` command to define the dataset label.

▷ Example 5

We have just entered 1980 state data on marriage rates, divorce rates, and median ages. The `describe` command will describe the data in memory:

```
. describe
Contains data
   obs:            50
   vars:            4
   size:        1,200 (99.8% of memory free)
```

variable name	storage type	display format	value label	variable label
state	str8	%9s		
median_age	float	%9.0g		
marriage_rate	long	%12.0g		
divorce_rate	long	%12.0g		

```
Sorted by:
     Note:  dataset has changed since last saved
```

`describe` shows that there are 50 observations on four variables named `state`, `median_age`, `marriage_rate`, and `divorce_rate`. `state` is stored as a `str8`; `median_age` is stored as a `float`; and `marriage_rate` and `divorce_rate` are both stored as `long`s. Each variable's display format (see [U] **12.5 Formats: Controlling how data are displayed**) is shown. Finally, the data are not in any particular sort order, and the dataset has changed since it was last saved on disk.

We can label the data by typing `label data "1980 state data"`. We type this and then type `describe` again:

```
. label data "1980 state data"

. describe

Contains data
  obs:           50                          1980 state data
  vars:           4
  size:       1,200  (99.7% of memory free)

              storage   display    value
variable name   type    format     label      variable label

state           str8    %9s
median_age      float   %9.0g
marriage_rate   long    %12.0g
divorce_rate    long    %12.0g

Sorted by:
    Note:   dataset has changed since last saved
```

◁

The dataset label is displayed by the describe and use commands.

12.6.2   Variable labels

In addition to the name, every variable has associated with it an 80-character *variable label*. The variable labels are initially set to blanks. You use the label variable *varname* "*text*" command to define a new variable label.

▷ Example 6

We have entered data on four variables: state, median_age, marriage_rate, and divorce_rate. describe portrays the data we entered:

```
. describe

Contains data from states.dta
  obs:           50                          1980 state data
  vars:           4
  size:       1,200  (99.7% of memory free)

              storage   display    value
variable name   type    format     label      variable label

state           str8    %9s
median_age      float   %9.0g
marriage_rate   long    %12.0g
divorce_rate    long    %12.0g

Sorted by:
    Note:   dataset has changed since last saved
```

We can associate labels with the variables by typing

```
. label variable median_age "Median Age"

. label variable marriage_rate "Marriages per 100,000"

. label variable divorce_rate "Divorces per 100,000"
```

From then on, the result of describe will be

```
. describe
Contains data
  obs:            50                          1980 state data
  vars:            4
  size:         1,200 (99.7% of memory free)
```

variable name	storage type	display format	value label	variable label
state	str8	%9s		
median_age	float	%9.0g		Median Age
marriage_rate	long	%12.0g		Marriages per 100,000
divorce_rate	long	%12.0g		Divorces per 100,000

```
Sorted by:
    Note:  dataset has changed since last saved
```
◁

Whenever Stata produces output, it will use the variable labels rather than the variable names to label the results if there is room.

12.6.3 Value labels

Value labels define a correspondence or mapping between numeric data and the words used to describe what those numeric values represent. Mappings are named and defined by the label define *lblname* # "*string*" # "*string*"... command. The maximum length for the *lblname* is 32 characters. # must be an integer or an extended missing value (.a, .b, ..., .z). The maximum length of *string* is 32,000 characters. Named mappings are associated with variables by the label values *varname* *lblname* command.

▷ Example 7

The definition makes value labels sound more complicated than they are in practice. We create a dataset on individuals in which we record a person's sex, coding 0 for males and 1 for females. If our dataset also contained an employee number and salary, it might resemble the following:

```
. use http://www.stata-press.com/data/r11/gxmpl4
(2007 Employee data)

. describe

Contains data from http://www.stata-press.com/data/r11/gxmpl4.dta
  obs:            7                          2007 Employee data
  vars:            3                         11 Feb 2009 15:31
  size:         112 (99.9% of memory free)
```

variable name	storage type	display format	value label	variable label
empno	float	%9.0g		Employee number
sex	float	%9.0g		Sex
salary	float	%8.0fc		Annual salary, exclusive of bonus

```
Sorted by:
```

```
. list
```

	empno	sex	salary
1.	57213	0	34,000
2.	47229	1	37,000
3.	57323	0	34,000
4.	57401	0	34,500
5.	57802	1	37,000
6.	57805	1	34,000
7.	57824	0	32,500

We could create a mapping called `sexlabel` defining 0 as "Male" and 1 as "Female", and then associate that mapping with the variable `sex` by typing

```
. label define sexlabel 0 "Male" 1 "Female"
. label values sex sexlabel
```

From then on, our data would appear as

```
. describe
Contains data from http://www.stata-press.com/data/r11/gxmpl4.dta
  obs:             7                          2007 Employee data
  vars:            3                          11 Feb 2009 15:31
  size:          112 (99.8% of memory free)
```

variable name	storage type	display format	value label	variable label
empno	float	%9.0g		Employee number
sex	float	%9.0g	sexlabel	Sex
salary	float	%8.0fc		Annual salary, exclusive of bonus

```
Sorted by:
. list
```

	empno	sex	salary
1.	57213	Male	34,000
2.	47229	Female	37,000
3.	57323	Male	34,000
4.	57401	Male	34,500
5.	57802	Female	37,000
6.	57805	Female	34,000
7.	57824	Male	32,500

Notice not only that the value label is used to produce words when we `list` the data but also that the association of the variable `sex` with the value label `sexlabel` is shown by the `describe` command.

◁

❏ Technical note

> Value labels and variables may share the same name. For instance, rather than calling the value label `sexlabel` in the example above, we could just as well have named it `sex`. We would then type `label values sex sex` to associate the value label named `sex` with the variable named `sex`.

❏

▷ Example 8

> Stata's `encode` and `decode` commands provide a convenient way to go from string variables to numerically coded variables and back again. Let's pretend that, in the example above, rather than coding 0 for males and 1 for females, we created a string variable recording either `"male"` or `"female"`.

```
. use http://www.stata-press.com/data/r11/gxmpl5
(2007 Employee data)
. describe

Contains data from http://www.stata-press.com/data/r11/gxmpl5
  obs:            7                         2007 Employee data
  vars:           3                         11 Feb 2009 15:37
  size:         126 (99.8% of memory free)
```

variable name	storage type	display format	value label	variable label
empno	float	%9.0g		Employee number
sex	str6	%9s		Sex
salary	float	%8.0fc		Annual salary, exclusive of bonus

```
Sorted by:
. list
```

	empno	sex	salary
1.	57213	male	34,000
2.	47229	female	37,000
3.	57323	male	34,000
4.	57401	male	34,500
5.	57802	female	37,000
6.	57805	female	34,000
7.	57824	male	32,500

We now want to create a numerically encoded variable—we will call it `gender`—from the string variable. We want to do this, say, because we typed `anova salary sex` to perform a one-way ANOVA of salary on sex, and we were told that there were "no observations". We then remembered that all Stata's statistical commands treat string variables as if they contain nothing but missing values. The statistical commands work only with numerically coded data.

```
. encode sex, generate(gender)
. describe
Contains data from http://www.stata-press.com/data/r11/gxmpl5.dta
  obs:             7                          2007 Employee data
  vars:            4                          11 Feb 2009 15:37
  size:          154 (99.8% of memory free)

               storage  display    value
variable name    type   format     label      variable label

empno           float   %9.0g                 Employee number
sex             str6    %9s                    Sex
salary          float   %8.0fc                Annual salary, exclusive of
                                                bonus
gender          long    %8.0g      gender     Sex

Sorted by:
    Note:  dataset has changed since last saved
```

encode adds a new long variable called gender to the data and defines a new value label called
gender. The value label gender maps 1 to the string male and 2 to female, so if we were to list
the data, we could not tell the difference between the gender and sex variables. However, they are
different. Stata's statistical commands know how to deal with gender but do not understand the sex
variable. See [D] **encode**.

❑

❑ Technical note

Perhaps rather than employee data, our data are on persons undergoing sex-change operations.
There would therefore be two sex variables in our data, sex before the operation and sex after the
operation. Assume that the variables are named presex and postsex. We can associate the *same*
value label to each variable by typing

```
. label define sexlabel 0 "Male" 1 "Female"
. label values presex sexlabel
. label values postsex sexlabel
```

❑

❑ Technical note

Stata's input commands (input and infile) can switch from the words in a value label back to
the numeric codes. Remember that encode and decode can translate a string to a numeric mapping
and vice versa, so we can map strings to numeric codes either at the time of input or later.

For example,

```
. label define sexlabel 0 "Male" 1 "Female"
. input empno sex:sexlabel salary, label
        empno       sex      salary
 1. 57213 Male 34000
 2. 47229 Female 37000
 3. 57323 0 34000
 4. 57401 Male 34500
 5. 57802 Female 37000
 6. 57805 Female 34000
 7. 57824 Male 32500
 8. end
```

The `label define` command defines the value label `sexlabel`. `input empno sex:sexlabel salary, label` tells Stata to input three variables from the keyboard (`empno`, `sex`, and `salary`), attach the value label `sexlabel` to the `sex` variable, and look up any words that are typed in the value label to try to convert them to numbers. To prove that it works, we `list` the data that we recently entered:

```
. list
```

	empno	sex	salary
1.	57213	Male	34000
2.	47229	Female	37000
3.	57323	Male	34000
4.	57401	Male	34500
5.	57802	Female	37000
6.	57805	Female	34000
7.	57824	Male	32500

Compare the information we typed for observation 3 with the result listed by Stata. We typed 57323 0 34000. Thus the value of `sex` in the third observation is 0. When Stata listed the observation, it indicated the value is `Male` because we told Stata in our `label define` command that zero is equivalent to `Male`.

Let's now add one more observation to our data:

```
. input, label
          empno          sex        salary
  8. 67223 FEmale 33000
'FEmale' cannot be read as a number
  8. 67223 Female 33000
  9. end
```

At first we typed 67223 FEmale 33000, and Stata responded with "'FEmale' cannot be read as a number". Remember that Stata always respects case, so `FEmale` is not the same as `Female`. Stata prompted us to type the line again, and we did so, this time correctly.

❏

❏ Technical note

Coupled with the `automatic` option, Stata not only can go from words to numbers but also can create the mapping. Let's input the data again, but this time, rather than typing the data, let's read the data from a file. Assume that we have an ASCII file called `employee.raw` stored on our disk that contains

```
57213 Male 34000
47229 Female 37000
57323 Male 34000
57401 Male 34500
57802 Female 37000
57805 Female 34000
57824 Male 32500
```

The `infile` command can read these data and create the mapping automatically:

```
. label list sexlabel
value label sexlabel not found
r(111);
```

```
. infile empno sex:sexlabel salary using employee, automatic
(7 observations read)
```

Our first command, `label list sexlabel`, is only to prove that we had not previously defined the value label `sexlabel`. Stata `infiled` the data without complaint. We now have

```
. list
```

	empno	sex	salary
1.	57213	Male	34000
2.	47229	Female	37000
3.	57323	Male	34000
4.	57401	Male	34500
5.	57802	Female	37000
6.	57805	Female	34000
7.	57824	Male	32500

Of course, `sex` is just another numeric variable; it does not actually take on the values `Male` and `Female`—it takes on numeric codes that have been automatically mapped to `Male` and `Female`. We can find out what that mapping is by using the `label list` command:

```
. label list sexlabel
sexlabel:
           1 Male
           2 Female
```

We discover that Stata attached the codes 1 to `Male` and 2 to `Female`. Anytime we want to see what our data really look like, ignoring the value labels, we can use the `nolabel` option:

```
. list, nolabel
```

	empno	sex	salary
1.	57213	1	34000
2.	47229	2	37000
3.	57323	1	34000
4.	57401	1	34500
5.	57802	2	37000
6.	57805	2	34000
7.	57824	1	32500

❑

12.6.4   Labels in other languages

A dataset can contain labels—data, variable, and value—in up to 100 languages. To discover the languages available for the dataset in memory, type `label language`. You will see this

```
. label language
Language for variable and value labels

    In this dataset, value and variable labels have been defined in only one
    language:  default

To create new language:            . label language <name>, new
To rename current language:        . label language <name>, rename
```

or something like this:

```
. label language
```
Language for variable and value labels
```
      Available languages:
              de
              en
              sp
      Currently set is:              . label language sp
      To select different language:  . label language <name>
      To create new language:        . label language <name>, new
      To rename current language:    . label language <name>, rename
```

Right now, the example dataset is set with sp (Spanish) labels:

```
. describe
Contains data
   obs:              74                      Automóviles, 1978
   vars:             12                      3 Oct 2008 13:53
   size:          3,478 (99.7% of memory free)
```

variable name	storage type	display format	value label	variable label
make	str18	%-18s		Marca y modelo
price	int	%8.0gc		Precio
mpg	int	%8.0g		Consumo de combustible
rep78	int	%8.0g		Historia de reparaciones
headroom	float	%6.1f		Cabeza adelante
trunk	int	%8.0g		Volumen del maletero
weight	int	%8.0gc		Peso
length	int	%8.0g		Longitud
turn	int	%8.0g		Radio de giro
displacement	int	%8.0g		Cilindrada
gear_ratio	float	%6.2f		Relación de cambio
foreign	byte	%8.0g		Extranjero

```
Sorted by:  foreign
```

To create labels in more than one language, you set the new language and then define the labels in the standard way; see [D] **label language**.

12.7   Notes attached to data

A dataset may contain notes, which are nothing more than little bits of text that you define and review with the notes command. Typing note, a colon, and the text defines a note:

```
. note:  Send copy to Bob once verified.
```

You can later display whatever notes you have previously defined by typing notes:

```
. notes
_dta:
   1.  Send copy to Bob once verified.
```

Notes are saved with the data, so once you save your dataset, you can replay this note in the future, too.

You can add more notes:

```
. note: Mary wants a copy, too.

. notes

_dta:
    1.  Send copy to Bob once verified.
    2.  Mary wants a copy, too.
```

The notes you have added so far are attached to the data generically, which is why Stata prefixes them with _dta when it lists them. You can attach notes to variables:

```
. note state: verify values for Nevada.

. note state: what about the two missing values?

. notes

_dta:
    1.  Send copy to Bob once verified.
    2.  Mary wants a copy, too.

state:
    1.  verify values for Nevada.
    2.  what about the two missing values?
```

When you describe your data, you can see whether notes are attached to the dataset or to any of the variables:

```
. describe

Contains data from states.dta
    obs:           50                          1980 state data
    vars:           4
    size:        1,200 (99.3% of memory free)  (_dta has notes)
```

variable name	storage type	display format	value label	variable label
state	str8	%9s	*	
median_age	float	%9.0g		Median Age
marriage_rate	long	%12.0g		Marriages per 100,000
divorce_rate	long	%12.0g		Divorces per 100,000
				* indicated variables have notes

```
Sorted by:
    Note:   dataset has changed since last saved
```

See [D] **notes** for a complete description of this feature.

12.8   Characteristics

Characteristics are an arcane feature of Stata but are of great use to Stata programmers. In fact, the notes command described above was implemented using characteristics.

The dataset itself and each variable within the dataset have associated with them a set of characteristics. Characteristics are named and referred to as *varname* [*charname*], where *varname* is the name of a variable or _dta. The characteristics contain text and are stored with the data in the Stata-format .dta dataset, so they are recalled whenever the data are loaded.

How are characteristics used? The [XT] **xt** commands need to know the name of the panel variable, and some of these commands also need to know the name of the time variable. xtset is used to specify the panel variable and optionally the time variable. Users need xtset their data only once. Stata then remembers this information, even from a different Stata session. Stata does this with characteristics: _dta[iis] contains the name of the panel variable and _dta[tis] contains the name of the time variable. When an xt command is issued, the command checks these characteristics to obtain the panel and time variables' names. If this information is not found, then the data have not previously been xtset and an error message is issued. This use of characteristics is hidden from the user—no mention is made of how the commands remember the identity of the panel variable and the time variable.

As a Stata user, you need understand only how to set and clear a characteristic for the few commands that explicitly reveal their use of characteristics. You set a variable *varname*'s characteristic *charname* to *x* by typing

    . char *varname*[*charname*] *x*

You set the data's characteristic *charname* to be *x* by typing

    . char _dta[*charname*] *x*

You clear a characteristic by typing

    . char *varname*[*charname*]

where *varname* is either a variable name or _dta. You can clear a characteristic, even if it has never been set.

The most important feature of characteristics is that Stata remembers them from one session to the next; they are saved with the data.

❑ Technical note

Programmers will want to know more. A technical description is found in [P] **char**, but for an overview, you may refer to *varname*'s *charname* characteristic by embedding its name in single quotes and typing '*varname*[*charname*]'; see [U] **18.3.13 Referring to characteristics**.

You can fetch the names of all characteristics associated with *varname* by typing

    . local *macname* : char *varname*[ ]

The maximum length of the contents of a characteristic is 8,681 characters for Small Stata and 67,784 characters for Stata/IC, Stata/SE, and Stata/MP. The association of names with characteristics is by convention. If you, as a programmer, wish to create new characteristics for use in your ado-files, do so, but include at least one capital letter in the characteristic name. The current convention reserves all lowercase names for "official" Stata.

❑

12.9   Data Editor and Variables Manager

We have spent most of this chapter writing about data management performed from Stata's command line. However, Stata provides two powerful features in its interface to help you examine and manage your data: the Data Editor and the Variables Manager.

The Data Editor is a spreadsheet-style data editor that allows you to enter new data, edit existing data, safely browse your data in a read-only mode, and perform almost any data-management task you desire in a reproducible manner using a graphical interface. To open the Data Editor, select **Data > Data Editor > Data Editor (Edit)** or **Data > Data Editor > Data Editor (Browse)**. See [GS] **6 Using the Data Editor** (GSM, GSU, or GSW) for a tutorial discussion of the Data Editor. See [D] **edit** for technical details.

The Variables Manager is a tool that lists and allows you to manage all the properties of the variables in your data. Variable properties include the name, label, storage type, format, value label, and notes. The Variables Manager allows you to sort and filter your variables, something that you will find to be very useful if you work with datasets having many variables. The Variables Manager also can be used to create varlists for the Command window. To open the Variables Manager, select **Data > Variables Manager**. See [GS] **7 Using the Variables Manager** (GSM, GSU, or GSW) for a tutorial discussion of the Variables Manager.

Both the Data Editor and Variables Manager submit commands to Stata to perform any changes that you request. This lets you see a log of what changes were made, and it also allows you to work interactively while still building a list of commands you can execute later to reproduce your analysis.

12.10   References

Cox, N. J. 2006. Stata tip 33: Sweet sixteen: Hexadecimal formats and precision problems. *Stata Journal* 6: 282–283.

Long, J. S. 2009. *The Workflow of Data Analysis Using Stata.* College Station, TX: Stata Press.

13 Functions and expressions

Contents

If you have not read [U] **11 Language syntax**, please do so before reading this entry.

13.1 Overview

Examples of expressions include

```
2+2
miles/gallons
myv+2/oth
(myv+2)/oth
ln(income)
age<25 & income>50000
age<25 | income>50000
age==25
name=="M Brown"
fname + " " + lname
substr(name,1,10)
val[_n-1]
L.gnp
```

Expressions like those above are allowed anywhere *exp* appears in a syntax diagram. One example is [D] **generate**:

> generate *newvar* = *exp* $\left[\,if\,\right]$ $\left[\,in\,\right]$

The first *exp* specifies the contents of the new variable, and the optional second expression restricts the subsample over which it is to be defined. Another is [R] **summarize**:

> summarize $\left[\,varlist\,\right]$ $\left[\,if\,\right]$ $\left[\,in\,\right]$

The optional expression restricts the sample over which summary statistics are calculated.

Algebraic and string expressions are specified in a natural way using the standard rules of hierarchy. You may use parentheses freely to force a different order of evaluation.

▷ Example 1

myv+2/oth is interpreted as myv+(2/oth). If you wanted to change the order of the evaluation, you could type (myv+2)/oth.

◁

13.2   Operators

Stata has four different classes of operators: arithmetic, string, relational, and logical. Each type is discussed below.

13.2.1   Arithmetic operators

The *arithmetic operators* in Stata are + (addition), − (subtraction), * (multiplication), / (division), ^ (raise to a power), and the prefix − (negation). Any arithmetic operation on a missing value or an impossible arithmetic operation (such as division by zero) yields a missing value.

▷ Example 2

The expression -(x+y^(x-y))/(x*y) denotes the formula

$$-\frac{x + y^{x-y}}{x \cdot y}$$

and evaluates to *missing* if x or y is missing or zero.

◁

13.2.2   String operators

The + sign is also used as a string operator for the *concatenation* of two strings. Stata determines by context whether + means addition or concatenation. If + appears between two strings, Stata concatenates them. If + appears between two numeric values, Stata adds them.

⊳ Example 3

The expression "this"+"that" results in the string "thisthat", whereas the expression 2+3 results in the number 5. Stata issues the error message "type mismatch" if the arguments on either side of the + sign are not of the same type. Thus the expression 2+"this" is an error, as is 2+"3".

The expressions on either side of the + can be arbitrarily complex:

$$\text{substr(string(20+2),1,1) + upper(substr("rf",1+1,1))}$$

The result of the above expression is the string "2F". See [D] **functions** below for a description of the substr(), string(), and upper() functions.

◁

13.2.3   Relational operators

The *relational operators* are > (greater than), < (less than), >= (greater than or equal), <= (less than or equal), == (equal), and != (not equal). Observe that the relational operator for equality is a pair of equal signs. This convention distinguishes relational equality from the =*exp* assignment phrase.

❏ Technical note

You may use ~ anywhere ! would be appropriate to represent the logical operator "not". Thus the not-equal operator may also be written as ~=.

❏

Relational expressions are either *true* or *false*. Relational operators may be used on either numeric or string subexpressions; thus, the expression 3>2 is *true*, as is "zebra">"cat". In the latter case, the relation merely indicates that "zebra" comes after the word "cat" in the dictionary. All uppercase letters precede all lowercase letters in Stata's book, so "cat">"Zebra" is also *true*.

Missing values may appear in relational expressions. If x were a numeric variable, the expression x>=. is *true* if x is missing and *false* otherwise. A missing value is greater than any nonmissing value; see [U] **12.2.1 Missing values**.

⊳ Example 4

You have data on age and income and wish to list the subset of the data for persons aged 25 years or less. You could type

```
. list if age<=25
```

If you wanted to list the subset of data of persons aged exactly 25, you would type

```
. list if age==25
```

Note the double equal sign. It would be an error to type list if age=25.

◁

Although it is convenient to think of relational expressions as evaluating to *true* or *false*, they actually evaluate to numbers. A result of *true* is defined as 1 and *false* is defined as 0.

▷ Example 5

The definition of *true* and *false* makes it easy to create indicator, or dummy, variables. For instance,

```
generate incgt10k=income>10000
```

creates a variable that takes on the value 0 when `income` is less than or equal to $10,000, and 1 when `income` is greater than $10,000. Because missing values are greater than all nonmissing values, the new variable `incgt10k` will also take on the value 1 when `income` is *missing*. It would be safer to type

```
generate incgt10k=income>10000 if income<.
```

Now, observations in which `income` is *missing* will also contain *missing* in `incgt10k`. See [U] **25 Working with categorical data and factor variables** for more examples.

◁

❑ Technical note

Although you will rarely wish to do so, because arithmetic and relational operators both evaluate to numbers, there is no reason you cannot mix the two types of operators in one expression. For instance, (2==2)+1 evaluates to 2, because 2==2 evaluates to 1, and $1 + 1$ is 2.

Relational operators are evaluated after all arithmetic operations. Thus the expression (3>2)+1 is equal to 2, whereas 3>2+1 is equal to 0. Evaluating relational operators last guarantees the *logical* (as opposed to the *numeric*) interpretation. It should make sense that 3>2+1 is *false*.

❑

13.2.4 Logical operators

The *logical operators* are & (and), | (or), and ! (not). The logical operators interpret any nonzero value (including *missing*) as *true* and zero as *false*.

▷ Example 6

If you have data on `age` and `income` and wish to `list` data for persons making more than $50,000 along with persons under the age of 25 making more than $30,000, you could type

```
list if income>50000 | income>30000 & age<25
```

The & takes precedence over the |. If you were unsure, however, you could have typed

```
list if income>50000 | (income>30000 & age<25)
```

In either case, the statement will also `list` all observations for which `income` is *missing*, because *missing* is greater than 50,000.

◁

❑ Technical note

Like relational operators, logical operators return 1 for *true* and 0 for *false*. For example, the expression 5 & . evaluates to 1. Logical operations, except for !, are performed after all arithmetic and relational operations; the expression 3>2 & 5>4 is interpreted as (3>2) & (5>4) and evaluates to 1.

❑

13.2.5   Order of evaluation, all operators

The order of evaluation (from first to last) of all operators is ! (or ~), ^, − (negation), /, *, − (subtraction), +, != (or ≅), >, <, <=, >=, ==, &, and |.

13.3   Functions

Stata provides mathematical functions, probability and density functions, matrix functions, string functions, functions for dealing with dates and time series, and a set of special functions for programmers. You can find all these documented in [D] **functions**. Stata's matrix programming language, Mata, provides more functions and those are documented in the *Mata Reference Manual*, or online (type `help mata functions`).

Functions are merely a set of rules; you supply the function with arguments, and the function evaluates the arguments according to the rules that define the function. Because functions are essentially subroutines that evaluate arguments and cause no action on their own, functions must be used in conjunction with a Stata command. Functions are indicated by the function name, an open parenthesis, an expression or expressions separated by commas, and a close parenthesis.

For example,

```
. display sqrt(4)
2
```

or

```
. display sqrt(2+2)
2
```

demonstrates the simplest use of a function. Here we have used the mathematical function, `sqrt()`, which takes one number (or expression) as its argument and returns its square root. The function was used with the Stata command `display`. If we had simply typed

```
. sqrt(4)
```

Stata would have returned the error message

```
unrecognized command:  sqrt
r(199);
```

Functions can operate on variables, as well. For example, suppose that you wanted to generate a random variable that has observations drawn from a lognormal distribution. You could type

```
. set obs 5
obs was 0, now 5
. generate y = runiform()
. replace y = invnormal(y)
(5 real changes made)
. replace y = exp(y)
(5 real changes made)
. list
```

	y
1.	.686471
2.	2.380994
3.	.2814537
4.	1.215575
5.	.2920268

You could have saved yourself some typing by typing just

```
. generate y = exp(rnormal())
```

Functions accept expressions as arguments.

All functions are defined over a specified domain and return values within a specified range. Whenever an argument is outside a function's domain, the function will return a missing value or issue an error message, whichever is most appropriate. For example, if you supplied the log() function with an argument of zero, the log(0) would return a missing value because zero is outside the natural logarithm function's domain. If you supplied the log() function with a string argument, Stata would issue a "type mismatch" error because log() is a numerical function and is undefined for strings. If you supply an argument that evaluates to a value that is outside the function's range, the function will return a missing value. Whenever a function accepts a string as an argument, the string must be enclosed in double quotes, unless you provide the name of a variable that has a string storage type.

13.4   System variables (_variables)

Expressions may also contain _variables (pronounced "underscore variables"), which are built-in system variables that are created and updated by Stata. They are called _variables because their names all begin with the underscore character, '_'.

The _variables are

[*eqno*]_b[*varname*] (synonym: [*eqno*]_coef[*varname*]) contains the value (to machine precision) of the coefficient on *varname* from the most recently fitted model (such as ANOVA, regression, Cox, logit, probit, and multinomial logit). See [U] **13.5 Accessing coefficients and standard errors** below for a complete description.

_cons is always equal to the number 1 when used directly and refers to the intercept term when used indirectly, as in _b[_cons].

_n contains the number of the current observation.

_N contains the total number of observations in the dataset or the number of observations in the current by() group.

_rc contains the value of the return code from the most recent capture command.

[*eqno*]_se[*varname*] contains the value (to machine precision) of the standard error of the coefficient on *varname* from the most recently fitted model (such as ANOVA, regression, Cox, logit, probit, and multinomial logit). See [U] **13.5 Accessing coefficients and standard errors** below for a complete description.

13.5   Accessing coefficients and standard errors

After fitting a model, you can access the coefficients and standard errors and use them in subsequent expressions. Also see [R] **predict** (and [U] **20 Estimation and postestimation commands**) for an easier way to obtain predictions, residuals, and the like.

13.5.1 Single-equation models

First, let's consider estimation methods that yield one estimated equation with a one-to-one correspondence between coefficients and variables such as logit, ologit, oprobit, probit, regress, and tobit. _b[*varname*] (synonym _coef[*varname*]) contains the coefficient on *varname* and _se[*varname*] contains its standard error, and both are recorded to machine precision. Thus _b[age] refers to the calculated coefficient on the age variable after typing, say, regress response age sex, and _se[age] refers to the standard error on the coefficient. _b[_cons] refers to the constant and _se[_cons] to its standard error. Thus you might type

```
. regress response age sex
. generate asif = _b[_cons] + _b[age]*age
```

13.5.2 Multiple-equation models

The syntax for referring to coefficients and standard errors in multiple-equation models is the same as in the simple-model case, except that _b[] and _se[] are preceded by an equation number in square brackets. There are, however, many alternatives in how you may type requests. The way that you are supposed to type requests is

$$[eqno]\_b[varname]$$
$$[eqno]\_se[varname]$$

but you may substitute _coef[] for _b[]. In fact, you may omit the _b[] altogether, and most Stata users do:

$$[eqno][varname]$$

You may also omit the second pair of square brackets:

$$[eqno]varname$$

You may retain the _b[] or _se[] and insert a colon between *eqno* and *varname*:

$$\_b[eqno:varname]$$

There are two ways to specify the equation number *eqno*: either as an absolute equation number or as an "indirect" equation number. In the absolute form, the number is preceded by a '#' sign. Thus [#1]displ refers to the coefficient on displ in the first equation (and [#1]_se[displ] refers to its standard error). You can even use this form for simple models, such as regress, if you prefer. regress estimates one equation, so [#1]displ refers to the coefficient on displ, just as _b[displ] does. Similarly, [#1]_se[displ] and _se[displ] are equivalent. The logic works both ways—in the multiple-equation context, _b[displ] refers to the coefficient on displ in the first equation and _se[displ] refers to its standard error. _b[*varname*] (_se[*varname*]) is just another way of saying [#1]*varname* ([#1]_se[*varname*]).

Equations may also be referred to indirectly. [res]displ refers to the coefficient on displ in the equation named res. Equations are often named after the corresponding dependent variable name if there is such a concept in the fitted model, so [res]displ might refer to the coefficient on displ in the equation for variable res.

For multinomial logit (mlogit), multinomial probit (mprobit), and similar commands, equations are named after the levels of the single dependent categorical variable. In these models, there is one dependent variable, and there is an equation corresponding to each of the outcomes (values taken on) recorded in that variable, except for the one that is taken to be the base outcome. [res]displ would be interpreted as the coefficient on displ in the equation corresponding to the outcome res. If outcome res is the base outcome, Stata treats [res]displ as zero (and Stata does the same for [res]_se[displ]).

Continuing with the multinomial outcome case: the outcome variable must be numeric. The syntax [res]displ would be understood only if there were a value label associated with the numeric outcome variable and res were one of the labels. If your data are not labeled, then you can use the usual multiple-equation syntax [##] *varname* and [##] _se[*varname*] to refer to the coefficient and standard error for variable *varname* in the #th equation.

For mlogit, if your data are not labeled, you can also use the syntax [#] *varname* and [#] _se[*varname*] (without the '#') to refer to the coefficient and standard error for *varname* in the equation for outcome #.

13.5.3   Factor variables and time-series operators

We refer to time-series–operated variables exactly as we refer to normal variables. We type the name of the variable, which for time-series–operated variables includes the operators; see [U] **11.4.4 Time-series varlists**. You might type

```
. regress open L.close LD.volume
. display _b[L.close]
. display _b[LD.volume]
```

We cannot refer to factor variables such as i.group in expressions. Assuming that i.group has three levels, i.group represents three virtual indicator variables—1b.group, 2.group, and 3.group. We can refer to the indicator variables in expressions by typing, for example, _b[i2.group] or just _b[2.group]. That is to say, we include the operators and the levels of the factor variables when typing the indicator-variable name. Consider a regression using factor variables:

```
. use http://www.stata-press.com/data/r11/fvex
(Artificial factor variables' data)

. regress y i.sex i.group sex#group age sex#c.age
```

Source	SS	df	MS		
Model	221310.507	7	31615.7868	Number of obs =	3000
Residual	1170122.5	2992	391.083723	F(7, 2992) =	80.84
				Prob > F =	0.0000
				R-squared =	0.1591
				Adj R-squared =	0.1571
Total	1391433.01	2999	463.965657	Root MSE =	19.776

y	Coef.	Std. Err.	t	P>|t|	[95% Conf. Interval]	
1.sex	32.29378	3.782064	8.54	0.000	24.87807	39.70949
group						
2	9.477077	1.624075	5.84	0.000	6.292659	12.66149
3	18.31292	1.776337	10.31	0.000	14.82995	21.79588
sex#group						
1 2	-6.621804	2.021384	-3.28	0.001	-10.58525	-2.658361
1 3	-10.48293	3.209	-3.27	0.001	-16.775	-4.190858
age	-.212332	.0538345	-3.94	0.000	-.3178884	-.1067756
sex#c.age						
1	-.226838	.0745707	-3.04	0.002	-.3730531	-.0806229
_cons	60.48167	2.842955	21.27	0.000	54.90732	66.05601

If we want to use the coefficient for level 2 of group in an expression, we type _b[2.group]; for level 3, we type _b[3.group]. To refer to the coefficient of an interaction of two levels of two factor variables, we specify the interaction operator and the level of each variable. For example, to use the coefficient for sex = 1 and group = 2, we type _b[1.sex#2.group]. When one of the variables in an interaction is continuous, we can either make that explicit, _b[1.sex#c.age], or we can leave off the c., _b[1.sex#age].

Referring to interactions is more challenging than referring to normal variables. It is also more challenging to refer to coefficients from estimators that use multiple equations. If you find it difficult to know what to type for a coefficient, replay your estimation results using the coeflegend option.

```
. regress, coeflegend
```

Source	SS	df	MS
Model	221310.507	7	31615.7868
Residual	1170122.5	2992	391.083723
Total	1391433.01	2999	463.965657

```
Number of obs =    3000
F(  7,  2992) =   80.84
Prob > F      =  0.0000
R-squared     =  0.1591
Adj R-squared =  0.1571
Root MSE      =  19.776
```

y	Coef.	Legend
1.sex	32.29378	_b[1.sex]
group		
2	9.477077	_b[2.group]
3	18.31292	_b[3.group]
sex#group		
1 2	-6.621804	_b[1.sex#2.group]
1 3	-10.48293	_b[1.sex#3.group]
age	-.212332	_b[age]
sex#c.age		
1	-.226838	_b[1.sex#c.age]
_cons	60.48167	_b[_cons]

The Legend column shows you exactly what to type to refer to any coefficient in the estimation.

If your estimation results have both equations and factor variables, nothing changes from what we said in [U] **13.5.2 Multiple-equation models** above. What you type for *varname* is just a little more complicated.

13.6   Accessing results from Stata commands

Most Stata commands—not just estimation commands—save results so that you can access them in subsequent expressions. You do that by referring to e(*name*), r(*name*), s(*name*), or c(*name*).

```
. summarize age
. generate agedev = age-r(mean)
. regress mpg weight
. display "The number of observations used is " e(N)
```

Most commands are categorized as r-class, meaning that they save results in r(). The returned results—such as r(mean)—are available immediately following the command, and if you are going to refer to them, you need to refer to them soon because the next command will probably replace what is in r().

e-class commands are Stata's estimation commands—commands that fit models. Results in e() remain available until the next model is fit.

s-class commands are parsing commands—commands used by programmers to interpret commands you type. Few commands save anything in s().

There are no c-class commands. c() contains values that are always available, such as c(current_date) (today's date), c(pwd) (the current directory), C(N) (the number of observations), and so on. There are many c() values and they are documented in [P] **creturn**.

Every command of Stata is designated r-class, e-class, or s-class, or, if the command saves nothing, n-class. r stands for return as in returned results, e stands for estimation as in estimation results, s stands for string, and, admittedly, this last acronym is weak, n stands for null.

You can find out what is stored where by looking in the *Saved results* section for the particular command in the *Reference* manual. If you know the class of a command—and it is easy enough to guess—you can also see what is stored by typing return list, ereturn list, or sreturn list:

See [R] **saved results** and [U] **18.8 Accessing results calculated by other programs**.

13.7 Explicit subscripting

Individual observations on variables can be referred to by subscripting the variables. Explicit subscripts are specified by following a variable name with square brackets that contain an expression. The result of the subscript expression is truncated to an integer, and the value of the variable for the indicated observation is returned. If the value of the subscript expression is less than 1 or greater than _N, a missing value is returned.

13.7.1 Generating lags and leads

When you type something like

```
. generate y = x
```

Stata interprets it as if you typed

```
. generate y = x[_n]
```

which means that the first observation of y is to be assigned the value from the first observation of x, the second observation of y is to be assigned the value from the second observation on x, and so on. If you instead typed

```
. generate y = x[1]
```

you would set each observation of y equal to the first observation on x. If you typed

```
. generate y = x[2]
```

you would set each observation of y equal to the second observation on x. If you typed

```
. generate y = x[0]
```

Stata would merely copy a missing value into every observation of y because observation 0 does not exist. The same would happen if you typed

```
. generate y = x[100]
```

and you had fewer than 100 observations in your data.

When you type the square brackets, you are specifying explicit subscripts. Explicit subscripting combined with the _variable_ _n can be used to create lagged values on a variable. The lagged value of a variable x can be obtained by typing

```
. generate xlag = x[_n-1]
```

If you are really interested in lags and leads, you probably have time-series data and would be better served by using the time-series operators, such as L.x. Time-series operators can be used with varlists and expressions and they are safer because they account for gaps in the data; see [U] **11.4.4 Time-series varlists** and [U] **13.9 Time-series operators**. Even so, it is important that you understand how the above works.

The built-in underscore variable _n is understood by Stata to mean the observation number of the current observation. That is why

```
. generate y = x[_n]
```

results in observation 1 of x being copied to observation 1 of y and similarly for the rest of the observations. Consider

```
. generate xlag = x[_n-1]
```

_n-1 evaluates to the observation number of the previous observation. For the first observation, _n-1 = 0 and therefore xlag[1] is set to missing. For the second observation, _n-1 = 1 and xlag[2] is set to the value of x[1], and so on.

Similarly, the lead of x can be created by

```
. generate xlead = x[_n+1]
```

Here the last observation on the new variable xlead will be *missing* because _n+1 will be greater than _N (_N is the total number of observations in the dataset).

13.7.2   Subscripting within groups

When a command is preceded by the by *varlist*: prefix, subscript expressions and the underscore variables _n and _N are evaluated relative to the subset of the data currently being processed. For example, consider the following (admittedly not very interesting) data:

```
. use http://www.stata-press.com/data/r11/gxmpl6
. list
```

	bvar	oldvar
1.	1	1.1
2.	1	2.1
3.	1	3.1
4.	2	4.1
5.	2	5.1

To see how _n, _N, and explicit subscripting work, let's create three new variables demonstrating each and then list their values:

```
. generate small_n = _n
. generate big_n = _N
. generate newvar = oldvar[1]
```

```
. list
```

	bvar	oldvar	small_n	big_n	newvar
1.	1	1.1	1	5	1.1
2.	1	2.1	2	5	1.1
3.	1	3.1	3	5	1.1
4.	2	4.1	4	5	1.1
5.	2	5.1	5	5	1.1

small_n (which is equal to _n) goes from 1 to 5, and big_n (which is equal to _N) is 5. This should not be surprising; there are 5 observations in the data, and _n is supposed to count observations, whereas _N is the total number. newvar, which we defined as oldvar[1], is 1.1. Indeed, we see that the first observation on oldvar is 1.1.

Now, let's repeat those same three steps, only this time preceding each step with the prefix by bvar:. First, we will drop the old values of small_n, big_n, and newvar so that we start fresh:

```
. drop small_n big_n newvar
. by bvar, sort: generate small_n=_n
. by bvar: generate big_n =_N
. by bvar: generate newvar=oldvar[1]
. list
```

	bvar	oldvar	small_n	big_n	newvar
1.	1	1.1	1	3	1.1
2.	1	2.1	2	3	1.1
3.	1	3.1	3	3	1.1
4.	2	4.1	1	2	4.1
5.	2	5.1	2	2	4.1

The results are different. Remember that we claimed that _n and _N are evaluated relative to the subset of data in the by-group. Thus small_n (_n) goes from 1 to 3 for bvar = 1 and from 1 to 2 for bvar = 2. big_n (_N) is 3 for the first group and 2 for the second. Finally, newvar (oldvar[1]) is 1.1 and 4.1.

➢ Example 7

You now know enough to do some amazing things.

Suppose that you have data on individual states and you have another variable in your data called region that divides the states into the four census regions. You have a variable x in your data, and you want to make a new variable called avgx to include in your regressions. This new variable is to take on the average value of x for the region in which the state is located. Thus, for California, you will have the observation on x and the observation on the average value in the region, avgx. Here is how:

```
. by region, sort: generate avgx=sum(x)/_n
. by region: replace avgx=avgx[_N]
```

First, by region, we generate avgx equal to the running sum of x divided by the number of observations so far. The , sort ensures that the data are in region order. We have, in effect, created the running average of x within region. It is the last observation of this running average, the overall average within the region, that interests us. So, by region, we replace every avgx observation in a region with the last observation within the region, avgx[_N].

Here is what we will see when we type these commands:

```
. use http://www.stata-press.com/data/r11/gxmpl7, clear
. by region, sort: generate avgx=sum(x)/_n
. by region: replace avgx=avgx[_N]
(46 real changes made)
```

In our example, there are no missing observations on x. If there had been, we would have obtained the wrong answer. When we created the running average, we typed

```
. by region, sort: generate avgx=sum(x)/_n
```

The problem is not with the sum() function. When sum() encounters a missing, it adds zero to the sum. The problem is with _n. Let's assume that the second observation in the first region has recorded a missing for x. When Stata processes the third observation in that region, it will calculate the sum of two elements (remember that one is missing) and then divide the sum by 3 when it should be divided by 2. There is an easy solution:

```
. by region: generate avgx=sum(x)/sum(x<.)
```

Rather than divide by _n, we divide by the total number of nonmissing observations seen on x so far, namely, the sum(x<.).

If our goal were simply to obtain the mean, we could have more easily accomplished it by typing egen avgx=mean(x), by(region); see [D] **egen**. egen, however, is written in Stata, and the above is how egen's mean() function works. The general principles are worth understanding.

◁

➢ Example 8

You have some patient data recording vital signs at various times during an experiment. The variables include patient, an ID number or name of the patient; time, a variable recording the date or time or epoch of the vital-sign reading; and vital, a vital sign. You probably have more than one vital sign, but one is enough to illustrate the concept. Each observation in your data represents a patient-time combination.

Let's assume that you have 1,000 patients and, for every observation on the same patient, you want to create a new variable called orig that records the patient's initial value of this vital sign.

```
. use http://www.stata-press.com/data/r11/gxmpl8, clear
. sort patient time
. by patient: generate orig=vital[1]
```

Observe that vital[1] refers not to the first reading on the first patient but to the first reading on the current patient, because we are performing the generate command by patient.

◁

➢ Example 9

Let's do one more example with these patient data. Suppose that we want to create a new dataset from our patient data that record not only the patient's identification, the time of the reading of the first vital sign, and the first vital sign reading itself, but also the time of the reading of the last vital sign and its value. We want 1 observation per patient. Here's how:

```
. sort patient time
. by patient: generate lasttime=time[_N]
. by patient: generate lastvital=vital[_N]
. by patient: drop if _n!=1
```

◁

13.8   Indicator values for levels of factor variables

Stata's factor-variable features let us access virtual indicator variables for categorical variables and their interactions; see [U] **11.4.3 Factor variables** and [U] **25 Working with categorical data and factor variables**. We can use those virtual indicator variables in expressions just as though the virtual variables existed in our data. If you have not read about factor-variable varlists in [U] **11.4.3 Factor variables**, do so now.

If group is a categorical variable taking on the value 1, 2, or 3, consider the expression

```
. generate group1 = 1.group
```

We have taken the virtual indicator variable that is 1 when group = 1 and 0 when group ≠ 1 and made it into a real variable—group1. That is strictly true only if group is never missing. If group can be missing, we need to add that 1.group is missing when group is missing.

These virtual variables extend to interactions. If we also have a variable, sex, that is 0 for males and 1 for females, then

```
. generate sex0grp2 = 0.sex#2.group
```

creates the variable sex0grp2, which is 1 when sex = 0 and group = 2, . (missing) when sex or group is missing, and 0 otherwise.

Virtual indicator variables can be used in any expression, including if expressions.

13.9   Time-series operators

Time-series operators allow you to refer to the lag of gnp by typing L.gnp, the second lag by typing L2.gnp, etc. There are also operators for lead (F), difference D, and seasonal difference S.

Time-series operators can be used with varlists and with expressions. See [U] **11.4.4 Time-series varlists** if you have not read it already. This section has to do with using time-series operators in expressions such as with generate. You do not have to create new variables; you can use the time-series operated variables directly.

13.9.1   Generating lags, leads, and differences

In a time-series context, referring to L2.gnp is better than referring to gnp[_n-2] because there might be missing observations. Pretend that observation 4 contains data for $t = 25$ and observation 5 data for $t = 27$. L2.gnp will still produce correct answers; L2.gnp for observation 5 will be the value from observation 4 because the time-series operators look at t to find the relevant observation. The more mechanical gnp[_n-2] just goes 2 observations back, which, here, would not produce the desired result.

This same idea holds for differences. In our example, D.gnp will produce a missing value in observation 5 ($t = 27$) because there is no data recorded for $t = 26$, and therefore there is no first difference for $t = 27$.

Time-series operators can be used with varlists or with expressions, so you can type

```
. regress val L.gnp r
```

or

```
. generate gnplagged = L.gnp
. regress val gnplagged
```

Before you can type either one, however, you must use the `tsset` command to tell Stata the identity of the time variable; see [TS] **tsset**. Once you have `tsset` the data, anyplace you see an *exp* in a syntax diagram, you may type time series–operated variables, so you can type

```
. summarize r if F.gnp < gnp
```

or

```
. generate grew = 1 if gnp > L.gnp & L.gnp < .
. replace grew = 0 if grew >= . & L.gnp < .
```

or

```
. generate grew = (gnp > L.gnp) if L.gnp < .
```

13.9.2   Time-series operators and factor variables

As with varlists, factor variables may be combined with the `L.` (lag) and `F.` (lead) time-series operators in expressions. We can generate a variable containing the lag of the level 2 indicator of group (group = 2) by typing

```
. generate lag2group = 2L.group
```

The operators can be combined anywhere expressions are allowed. We can select observations for which the lag of the second level of group is 1 by typing `if i2L.group`.

They can be combined in interactions. We can generate the lag of the interaction of `sex` = 1 with group = 3 by typing

```
. generate lag1sexX3grp = 1L.sex#2L.group
```

See [U] **11.4.3 Factor variables** and [U] **11.4.4 Time-series varlists** for more on factor variables and time-series operators.

13.9.3   Operators within groups

Stata also understands panel or cross-sectional time-series data. For instance, if you type

```
. tsset country time
```

you are declaring that you have time-series data. The time variable is `time`, and you have time-series data for separate countries.

Once you have `tsset` both cross-sectional and time identifiers, you proceed just as you would if you had a simple time series.

```
. generate grew = (gnp > L.gnp) if L.gnp < .
```

would produce correct results. The L. operator will not confuse the observation at the end of one panel with the beginning of the next.

13.10   Label values

If you have not read [U] **12.6 Dataset, variable, and value labels**, please do so. You may use labels in an expression in place of the numeric values with which they are associated. To use a label in this way, type the label in double quotes followed by a colon and the name of the value label.

▷ Example 10

If the value label `yesno` associates the label `yes` with 1 and `no` with 0, then `"yes":yesno` (said aloud as the value of `yes` under `yesno`) is evaluated as 1. If the double-quoted label is not defined in the indicated value label, or if the value label itself is not found, a missing value is returned. Thus the expression `"maybe":yesno` is evaluated as *missing*.

```
. use http://www.stata-press.com/data/r11/gxmpl9, clear
. list
```

	name	answer
1.	Mikulin	no
2.	Gaines	no
3.	Hilbe	yes
4.	DeLeon	no
5.	Cain	no
6.	Wann	yes
7.	Schroeder	no
8.	Cox	no
9.	Bishop	no
10.	Hardin	yes
11.	Lancaster	yes
12.	Poole	no

```
. list if answer=="yes":yesno
```

	name	answer
3.	Hilbe	yes
6.	Wann	yes
10.	Hardin	yes
11.	Lancaster	yes

In the above example, the variable `answer` is not a string variable; it is a numeric variable that has the associated value label `yesno`. Because `yesno` associates `yes` with 1 and `no` with 0, we could have typed `list if answer==1` instead of what we did type. We could not have typed `list if answer=="yes"` because `answer` is not a string variable. If we had, we would have received the error message "type mismatch".

◁

13.11   Precision and problems therein

Examine the following short Stata session:

```
. drop _all
. input x y

            x          y
1. 1 1.1
2. 2 1.2
3. 3 1.3
4. end
. count if x==1
     1
. count if y==1.1
     0
. list
```

	x	y
1.	1	1.1
2.	2	1.2
3.	3	1.3

We created a dataset containing two variables, x and y. The first observation has x equal to 1 and y equal to 1.1. When we asked Stata to count the number of times that the variable x took on the value 1, we were told that it occurred once. Yet when we asked Stata to count the number of times y took on the value 1.1, we were told zero—meaning that it never occurred. What has gone wrong? When we list the data, we see that the first observation has y equal to 1.1.

Despite appearances, Stata has not made a mistake. Stata stores numbers internally in binary form, and the number 1.1 has no exact binary representation—that is, there is no finite string of binary digits that is equal to 1.1.

❏ Technical note

The number 1.1 in binary form is 1.0001100110011 ..., where the period represents the binary point. The problem binary computers have with storing numbers like 1/10 is much like the problem we base-10 users have in precisely writing 1/11, which is 0.0909090909 ....

❏

The number that appears as 1.1 in the listing above is actually 1.1000000238419, which is off by roughly 2 parts in 10^8. Unless we tell Stata otherwise, it stores all numbers as floats, which are also known as *single-precision* or *4-byte reals*. On the other hand, Stata performs all internal calculations in double, which is also known as *double-precision* or *8-byte reals*. This is what leads to the difficulty.

In the above example, we compared the number 1.1, stored as a float, with the number 1.1 stored as a double. The double-precision representation of 1.1 is more accurate than the single-precision representation, but it is also different. Those two numbers are not equal.

There are several ways around this problem. The problem with 1.1 apparently not equaling 1.1 would never arise if the storage precision and the precision of the internal calculations were the same. Thus you could store all your data as doubles. This takes more computer memory, however, and it is unlikely that your data are really that accurate and the extra digits would meaningfully affect any calculated result, even if the data were that accurate.

❑ Technical note

This is unlikely to affect any calculated result because Stata performs all internal calculations in double precision. This is all rather ironic, because the problem would also not arise if we had designed Stata to use single precision for its internal calculations. Stata would be less accurate, but the problem would have been completely disguised from the user, making this entry unnecessary.

❑

Another solution is to use the `float()` function. `float(x)` rounds x to its `float` representation. If we had typed `count if y==float(1.1)` in the above example, we would have been informed that there is one such value.

13.12 References

Cox, N. J. 2006. Stata tip 33: Sweet sixteen: Hexadecimal formats and precision problems. *Stata Journal* 6: 282–283.

Gould, W. W. 2006. Mata Matters: Precision. *Stata Journal* 6: 550–560.

Linhart, J. M. 2008. Mata Matters: Overflow, underflow and the IEEE floating-point format. *Stata Journal* 8: 255–268.

14 Matrix expressions

Contents

14.1   Overview

Stata has two matrix programming languages, one that might be called Stata's older matrix language and another that is called Mata. Stata's Mata is the new one, and there is an uneasy relationship between the two.

Below we discuss Stata's older language and leave the newer one to another manual—the *Mata Reference Manual* ([M])—or you can learn about the newer one by typing `help mata`.

We admit that the newer language is better in almost every way than the older language, but the older one still has a use because it is the one that Stata truly and deeply understands. Even when Mata wants to talk to Stata, matrixwise, it is the older language that Mata must use, so you must learn to use the older language as well as the new.

This is not nearly as difficult, or messy, as you might imagine because Stata's older language is remarkably easy to use, and really, there is not much to learn. Just remember that for heavy-duty programming, it will be worth your time to learn Mata, too.

14.1.1   Definition of a matrix

Stata's definition of a matrix includes a few details that go beyond the mathematics. To Stata, a matrix is a named entity containing an $r \times c$ ($0 < r \leq$ matsize, $0 < c \leq$ matsize) rectangular array of double-precision numbers (including missing values) that is bordered by a row and a column of names.

```
. matrix list A
A[3,2]
     c1  c2
r1    1   2
r2    3   4
r3    5   6
```

Here we have a 3×2 matrix named A containing elements 1, 2, 3, 4, 5, and 6. Row 1, column 2 (written $A_{1,2}$ in math and A[1,2] in Stata) contains 2. The columns are named c1 and c2 and the rows, r1, r2, and r3. These are the default names Stata comes up with when it cannot do better. The names do not play a role in the mathematics, but they are of great help when it comes to labeling the output.

The names are operated on just as the numbers are. For instance,

```
. matrix B=A'*A
. matrix list B
symmetric B[2,2]
      c1  c2
c1  35
c2  44  56
```

We defined $\mathbf{B} = \mathbf{A}'\mathbf{A}$. The row and column names of $\mathbf{B}$ are the same. Multiplication is defined for any $a \times b$ and $b \times c$ matrices, the result being $a \times c$. Thus the row and column names of the result are the row names of the first matrix and the column names of the second matrix. We formed $\mathbf{A}'\mathbf{A}$, using the transpose of $\mathbf{A}$ for the first matrix—which also interchanged the names—and so obtained the names shown.

14.1.2 matsize

Matrices are limited to being no larger than matsize $\times$ matsize. The default value of matsize is 400 for Stata/MP, Stata/SE, and Stata/IC, but you can reset this with the set matsize command; see [R] **matsize**.

The maximum value of matsize is 800 for Stata/IC, so matrices are not suitable for holding many data. This restriction does not prove a limitation because terms that appear in statistical formulas are of the form $(\mathbf{X}'\mathbf{W}\mathbf{Z})$ and Stata provides a command, matrix accum, for efficiently forming such matrices; see [U] **14.6 Creating matrices by accumulating data** below. The maximum value of matsize is 11,000 for Stata/MP and Stata/SE, so performing matrix operations directly on many data is more feasible. The matsize limit does not apply to Mata matrices; see the *Mata Reference Manual*.

14.2 Row and column names

Matrix rows and columns always have names. Stata is smart about setting these names when the matrix is created, and the matrix commands and operators manipulate these names throughout calculations, so the names typically are set correctly at the conclusion of matrix calculations.

For instance, consider the matrix calculation $\mathbf{b} = (\mathbf{X}'\mathbf{X})^{-1}\mathbf{X}'\mathbf{y}$ performed on real data:

```
. use http://www.stata-press.com/data/r11/auto
(1978 Automobile Data)
. matrix accum XprimeX = weight foreign
(obs=74)
. matrix vecaccum yprimeX = mpg weight foreign
. matrix b = invsym(XprimeX)*yprimeX'
. matrix list b
b[3,1]
                mpg
 weight  -.00658789
foreign  -1.6500291
  _cons   41.679702
```

These names were produced without our ever having given a special command to place the names on the result. When we formed matrix XprimeX, Stata produced the result

```
. matrix list XprimeX
symmetric XprimeX[3,3]
             weight    foreign      _cons
 weight   7.188e+08
foreign       50950         22
  _cons      223440         22         74
```

matrix accum forms $\mathbf{X}'\mathbf{X}$ matrices from data and sets the row and column names to the variable names used. The names are correct in the sense that, for instance, the (1,1) element is the sum across the observations of squares of weight and the (2,1) element is the sum of the product of weight and foreign.

Similarly, matrix vecaccum forms $\mathbf{y}'\mathbf{X}$ matrices, and it sets the row and column names to the variable names used, so matrix vecaccum yprimeX = mpg weight foreign resulted in

```
. matrix list yprimeX
yprimeX[1,3]
          weight   foreign     _cons
mpg      4493720       545      1576
```

The final step, matrix b = invsym(XprimeX)*yprimeX', manipulated the names, and, if you think carefully, you can derive the rules for yourself. invsym() (inversion) is much like transposition, so row and column names must be swapped. Here, however, the matrix was symmetric, so that amounted to leaving the names as they were. Multiplication amounts to taking the column names of the first matrix and the row names of the second. The final result is

```
. matrix list b
b[3,1]
                    mpg
 weight   -.00658789
foreign   -1.6500291
  _cons    41.679702
```

and the interpretation is $\text{mpg} = -0.00659\,\text{weight} - 1.65\,\text{foreign} + 41.68 + e$.

Researchers realized long ago that using matrix notation simplifies the description of complex calculations. What they may not have realized is that, corresponding to each mathematical definition of a matrix operator, there is a definition of the operator's effect on the names that can be used to carry the names forward through long and complex matrix calculations.

14.2.1   The purpose of row and column names

Mostly, matrices in Stata are used in programming estimators, and Stata uses row and column names to produce pretty output. Say that we wrote code—interactively or in a program—that produced the following coefficient vector b and covariance matrix V:

```
. matrix list b
b[1,3]
             weight   displacement         _cons
y1       -.00656711     .00528078     40.084522
. matrix list V
symmetric V[3,3]
                     weight   displacement         _cons
      weight      1.360e-06
displacement      -.0000103      .00009741
       _cons      -.00207455     .01188356     4.0808455
```

We could now produce standard estimation output by coding two more lines:

```
. ereturn post b V
. ereturn display
```

	Coef.	Std. Err.	z	P>|z|	[95% Conf.	Interval]
weight	-.0065671	.0011662	-5.63	0.000	-.0088529	-.0042813
displacement	.0052808	.0098696	0.54	0.593	-.0140632	.0246248
_cons	40.08452	2.02011	19.84	0.000	36.12518	44.04387

Stata's `ereturn` command knew to produce this output because of the row and column names on the coefficient vector and variance matrix. Moreover, we usually do nothing special in our code that produces b and V to set the row and column names because, given how matrix names work, they work themselves out.

Also, sometimes row and column names help us detect programming errors. Assume that we wrote code to produce matrices b and V but made a mistake. Sometimes our mistake will result in the wrong row and column names. Rather than the b vector we previously showed you, we might produce

```
. matrix list b
b[1,3]
        weight        c2      _cons
y1  -.00656711     42.23   40.084522
```

If we posted our estimation results now, Stata would refuse because it can tell by the names that there is a problem:

```
. ereturn post b V
name conflict
r(507);
```

Understand, however, that Stata follows the standard rules of matrix algebra; the names are just along for the ride. Matrices are summed by position, meaning that a directive to form $\mathbf{C} = \mathbf{A} + \mathbf{B}$ results in $C_{11} = A_{11} + B_{11}$, regardless of the names, and it is not an error to sum matrices with different names:

```
. matrix list a
symmetric a[3,3]
               c1          c2          c3
   mpg      14419
weight    1221120   1.219e+08
 _cons        545       50950          22
. matrix list b
symmetric b[3,3]
                      c1          c2          c3
displacement    3211055
         mpg     227102       22249
       _cons      12153        1041          52
. matrix c = a + b
. matrix list c
symmetric c[3,3]
                      c1          c2          c3
displacement    3225474
         mpg    1448222   1.219e+08
       _cons      12698       51991          74
```

Matrix row and column names are used to label output; they do not affect how matrix algebra is performed.

14.2.2   Two-part names

Row and column names have two parts separated by a colon: *equation_name*:*opvarname*.

In the examples shown so far, the *equation_name* has been blank and the *opvarname*s have been simple variable names without factor-variable or time-series operators. A blank *equation_name* is typical. Run any single-equation model (such as `regress`, `probit`, or `logistic`), and if you fetch the resulting matrices, you will find that they have row and column names that use only *opvarname*s.

Those who work with time-series data will find matrices with row and column names of the form *opvarname*. For time-series variables, *opvarname* is the variable name prefixed by a time-series operator such as L., D., or L2D.; see [U] **11.4.4 Time-series varlists**. For example,

```
. matrix list example1
symmetric example1[3,3]
                         L.
             rate       rate         _cons
    rate   3.0952534
  L.rate    .0096504    .00007742
   _cons  -2.8413483   -.01821928    4.8578916
```

We obtained this matrix by running a linear regression on `rate` and `L.rate` and then fetching the covariance matrix. Think of the row and column name `L.rate` no differently from how you think of `rate` or, in the previous examples, `r1`, `r2`, `c1`, `c2`, `weight`, and `foreign`.

Those who work with factor variables will also find row and column names of the *opvarname* form. For factor variables, *opvarname* is any factor-variable construct that references a single virtual indicator variable. For example, `3.group` refers to the virtual variable that is 1 when group = 3 and is 0 otherwise, `1.sex#3.group` refers to the virtual variable that is 1 when sex = 1 and group = 3 and is 0 otherwise, and `1.sex#c.age` refers to the virtual variable that takes on the values of age when sex = 1 and is 0 otherwise. For example,

```
. matrix list example2
symmetric example2[5,5]
                        0b.          1.      0b.sex#      1.sex#
                       sex          sex       c.age        c.age        _cons
      0b.sex           0
       1.sex           0    7.7785864
      0b.sex#
       c.age           0     .08350827    .00231307
  1.sex#c.age          0    -.09705697   -1.977e-16    .00223195
       _cons           0    -3.2868185   -.08350827    7.688e-15    3.2868185
```

`1.sex#c.age` is a row name and column name just like `rate` or `L.rate` in the prior example. For details on factor variables and valid factor-variable constructs see [U] **11.4.3 Factor variables**, [U] **25 Working with categorical data and factor variables**, [U] **13.8 Indicator values for levels of factor variables**, and [U] **20.10 Accessing estimated coefficients**.

Factor-variable operators may be combined with the time-series operators L. and F., leading to *opvarname*s such as `1L.sex` (the first lag of the level 1 indicator of `sex`) and `3L2.group` (the second lag of the level 3 indicator of `group`).

Equation names are used to label partitioned matrices and, in estimation, occur in the context of multiple equations. Here is a matrix with *equation_name*s and simple (unoperated) *opvarname*s.

```
. matrix list example3
symmetric example2[5,5]
                       mpg:         mpg:         mpg:         mpg:         mpg:
                    foreign        displ        _cons      foreign        _cons
   mpg:foreign    1.6483972
     mpg:displ     .004747     .00003876
     mpg:_cons   -1.4266352    -.00905773    2.4341021
weight:foreign  -51.208454    -4.665e-19    15.224135    24997.727
 weight:_cons    15.224135     2.077e-17   -15.224135   -7431.7565    7431.7565
```

Here is an example with *equation_names* and operated variable names:

```
. matrix list example4
symmetric example3[5,5]
                       val:         val:         val:      weight:      weight:
                                      L.
                       rate         rate        _cons      foreign        _cons
   val:rate        2.2947268
   val:L.rate       .00385216    .0000309
   val:_cons      -1.4533912    -.0072726     2.2583357
weight:foreign   -163.86684     7.796e-17    49.384526    25351.696
 weight:_cons     49.384526    -1.566e-16   -49.384526   -7640.237    7640.237
```

val:L.rate is a column name, just as, in the previous section, c2 and foreign were column names.

Say that this last matrix is the variance matrix produced by a program we wrote and that our program also produced a coefficient vector, b:

```
. matrix list b
b[1,5]
              val:         val:         val:      weight:      weight:
                            L.
              rate         rate        _cons      foreign        _cons
y1      4.5366753    -.00316923    20.68421   -1008.7968    3324.7059
```

Here is the result of posting and displaying the results:

```
. ereturn post b example4
. ereturn display
```

	Coef.	Std. Err.	z	P>|z|	[95% Conf. Interval]	
val						
rate						
—	4.536675	1.514836	2.995	0.003	1.567652	7.505698
L1	-.0031692	.0055591	-0.570	0.569	-.0140648	.0077264
_cons	20.68421	1.502776	13.764	0.000	17.73882	23.6296
weight						
foreign	-1008.797	159.2222	-6.336	0.000	-1320.866	-696.7271
_cons	3324.706	87.40845	38.036	0.000	3153.388	3496.023

We have been using matrix list to see the row and column names on our matrices because matrix list works on all matrices. There is a better way to see the names when we are working with estimation results because estimation results have the same names on the rows and columns of the variance matrix, and those same names are also the column names for the coefficient vector. That better way is the coeflegend display option available on almost every estimation command. For example,

```
. sureg (y = sex##group) (distance = d.age il2.sex)
  (output omitted )

. sureg, coeflegend
```

Seemingly unrelated regression

Equation	Obs	Parms	RMSE	"R-sq"	chi2	P
y	2998	5	20.03657	0.1343	464.08	0.0000
distance	2998	2	181.3797	0.0005	0.92	0.6314

	Coef.	Legend
y		
1.sex	21.59726	_b[y:1.sex]
group		
2	11.42832	_b[y:2.group]
3	21.6461	_b[y:3.group]
sex#group		
1 2	-4.892653	_b[y:1.sex#2.group]
1 3	-6.220653	_b[y:1.sex#3.group]
_cons	50.5957	_b[y:_cons]
distance		
age		
D1.	.2230927	_b[distance:D.age]
L2.sex		
1	1.300898	_b[distance:1L2.sex]
_cons	57.96172	_b[distance:_cons]

We could have used matrix list e(V) or matrix list e(b) to see the names, but the limited space available to matrix list to write the names would have made the names more difficult to read. With coeflegend, the names are neatly arrayed in their own Legend column. One difference between matrix list and the coeflegend option is that coeflegend brackets the names with _b[]. That is because coeflegend's primary use is to show us how to type coefficients in expressions and postestimation commands; see [U] **13.5 Accessing coefficients and standard errors** and [U] **20.10 Accessing estimated coefficients**. There the _b[] is required.

14.2.3 Setting row and column names

You reset row and column names by using the matrix rownames and matrix colnames commands.

Before resetting the names, use matrix list to verify that the names are not set correctly; often, they already are. When you enter a matrix by hand, however, the row names are unimaginatively set to r1, r2, ..., and the column names to c1, c2, ...

```
. matrix a = (1,2,3\4,5,6)

. matrix list a

a[2,3]
     c1  c2  c3
r1    1   2   3
r2    4   5   6
```

Regardless of the current row and column names, `matrix rownames` and `matrix colnames` reset them:

```
. matrix colnames a = foreign alpha _cons
. matrix rownames a = one two
. matrix list a
a[2,3]
        foreign    alpha    _cons
one           1        2        3
two           4        5        6
```

You may set the *operator* as part of the *opvarname*,

```
. matrix colnames a = foreign l.rate _cons
. matrix list a
a[2,3]
                       L.
        foreign      rate    _cons
one           1        2        3
two           4        5        6
```

The names you specify may be any virtual factor-variable indicators, and those names may include the base (b.) and omitted (o.) operators,

```
. matrix colnames b = 0b.sex 2o.arm 1.sex#c.age 1.sex#3.group#2.arm
. matrix list b
b[2,4]
                                          1.sex#
            0b.        2o.      1.sex#    3.group#
            sex        arm      c.age     2.arm
one           1          2          3         3
two           5          6          7         8
```

See [U] **11.4.3 Factor variables** for more about factor-variable operators.

You may set equation names:

```
. matrix colnames a = this:foreign this:l.rate that:_cons
. matrix list a
a[2,3]
          this:      this:      that:
                       L.
        foreign      rate     _cons
one           1        2          3
two           4        5          6
```

See [P] **matrix rownames** for more information.

14.2.4   Obtaining row and column names

`matrix list` displays the matrix with its row and column names. In a programming context, you can fetch the row and column names into a macro using

```
local ... : rowfullnames matname
local ... : colfullnames matname
local ... : rownames matname
local ... : colnames matname
local ... : roweq matname
local ... : coleq matname
```

rowfullnames and colfullnames return the full names (*equation_name*:*opvarnames*) listed one after the other.

rownames and colnames omit the equations and return *opvarnames*, listed one after the other.

roweq and coleq return the equation names, listed one after the other.

See [P] **macro** and [P] **matrix define** for more information.

14.3   Vectors and scalars

Stata does not have vectors as such—they are considered special cases of matrices and are handled by the matrix command.

Stata does have scalars, although they are not strictly necessary because they, too, could be handled as special cases. See [P] **scalar** for a description of scalars.

14.4   Inputting matrices by hand

You input matrices using

matrix input *matname* = (...)

or

matrix *matname* = (...)

In either case, you enter the matrices by row. You separate one element from the next by using commas (,) and one row from the next by using backslashes (\). If you omit the word input, you are using the expression parser to input the matrix:

```
. matrix a = (1,2\3,4)
. matrix list a
a[2,2]
     c1  c2
r1   1   2
r2   3   4
```

This has the advantage that you can use expressions for any of the elements:

```
. matrix b = (1, 2+3/2 \ cos(_pi), _pi)
. matrix list b
b[2,2]
           c1         c2
r1          1        3.5
r2         -1  3.1415927
```

The disadvantage is that the matrix must be small, say, no more than 50 elements (regardless of the value of matsize).

matrix input has no such restriction, but you may not use subexpressions for the elements:

```
. matrix input c  = (1,2\3,4)
. matrix input d = (1, 2+3/2 \ cos(_pi), _pi)
invalid syntax
r(198);
```

Either way, after inputting the matrix, you will probably want to set the row and column names; see [U] **14.2.3 Setting row and column names** above.

For small matrices, you may prefer entering them in a dialog box. Launch the dialog box from the menu **Data > Matrices, ado language > Input matrix by hand**, or by typing db matrix_input. The dialog box is particularly convenient for small symmetric matrices.

14.5   Accessing matrices created by Stata commands

Some Stata commands—including all estimation commands—leave behind matrices that you can subsequently use. After executing an estimation command, type ereturn list to see what is available:

```
. use http://www.stata-press.com/data/r11/auto
(1978 Automobile Data)
. probit foreign mpg weight
(output omitted)
. ereturn list
scalars:
                e(rank) =   3
                   e(N) =   74
                  e(ic) =   5
                   e(k) =   3
                e(k_eq) =   1
                e(k_dv) =   1
            e(converged) =   1
                  e(rc) =   0
            e(k_autoCns) =   0
                  e(ll) =   -26.84418900579868
            e(k_eq_model) =   1
                e(ll_0) =   -45.03320955699139
                e(df_m) =   2
                e(chi2) =   36.37804110238542
                   e(p) =   1.26069126402e-08
               e(N_cdf) =   0
               e(N_cds) =   0
                e(r2_p) =   .4039023807124773
macros:
            e(cmdline) : "probit foreign mpg weight"
                e(cmd) : "probit"
          e(estat_cmd) : "probit_estat"
            e(predict) : "probit_p"
              e(title) : "Probit regression"
           e(chi2type) : "LR"
                e(opt) : "moptimize"
                e(vce) : "oim"
               e(user) : "mopt__probit_d2()"
           e(crittype) : "log likelihood"
          e(ml_method) : "d2"
      e(singularHmethod) : "m-marquardt"
           e(technique) : "nr"
              e(which) : "max"
             e(depvar) : "foreign"
          e(properties) : "b V"
```

```
matrices:
                    e(b)  :   1 x 3
                    e(V)  :   3 x 3
                  e(mns)  :   1 x 3
                e(rules)  :   1 x 4
                 e(ilog)  :   1 x 20
             e(gradient)  :   1 x 3
functions:
                e(sample)
```

Most estimation commands leave behind e(b) (the coefficient vector) and e(V) (the variance–covariance matrix of the estimator):

```
. matrix list e(b)
e(b)[1,3]
         foreign:      foreign:      foreign:
             mpg        weight         _cons
y1  -.10395033    -.00233554      8.275464
```

You can refer to e(b) and e(V) in any matrix expression:

```
. matrix myb = e(b)
. matrix list myb
myb[1,3]
         foreign:      foreign:      foreign:
             mpg        weight         _cons
y1  -.10395033    -.00233554      8.275464
. matrix c = e(b)*invsym(e(V))*e(b)'
. matrix list c
symmetric c[1,1]
             y1
y1   22.440542
```

14.6 Creating matrices by accumulating data

In programming estimators, matrices of the form $\mathbf{X'X}$, $\mathbf{X'Z}$, $\mathbf{X'WX}$, and $\mathbf{X'WZ}$ often occur, where $\mathbf{X}$ and $\mathbf{Z}$ are data matrices. matrix accum, matrix glsaccum, matrix vecaccum, and matrix opaccum produce such matrices; see [P] **matrix accum**.

We recommend that you not load the data into a matrix and use the expression parser directly to form such matrices, although see [P] **matrix mkmat** if that is your interest. If that is your interest, be sure to read the technical note at the end of [P] **matrix mkmat**. There is much to recommend learning how to use the matrix accum commands.

14.7 Matrix operators

You can create new matrices or replace existing matrices by typing

$$\texttt{matrix } \textit{matname} = \textit{matrix\_expression}$$

For instance,

```
. matrix A = invsym(R*V*R')
. matrix IAR = I(rowsof(A)) - A*R
. matrix beta = b*IAR' + r*A'
. matrix C = -C'
. matrix D = (A, B \ B', A)
. matrix E = (A+B)*C'
. matrix S = (S+S')/2
```

The following operators are provided:

Operator	Symbol
Unary operators	
negation	–
transposition	'
Binary operators	
(lowest precedence)	
row join	\
column join	,
addition	+
subtraction	–
multiplication	*
division by scalar	/
Kronecker product	#
(highest precedence)	

Parentheses may be used to change the order of evaluation.

Note in particular that , and \ are operators; (1,2) creates a 1×2 matrix (vector), and (A,B) creates a rowsof(A) $\times$ colsof(A)+colsof(B) matrix, where rowsof(A) = rowsof(B). (1\2) creates a 2×1 matrix (vector), and (A\B) creates a rowsof(A)+rowsof(B) $\times$ colsof(A) matrix, where colsof(A) = colsof(B). Thus expressions of the form

```
matrix R = (A,B)*Vinv*(A,B)'
```

are allowed.

14.8   Matrix functions

In addition to the functions listed below, see [P] **matrix svd** for singular value decomposition, [P] **matrix symeigen** for eigenvalues and eigenvectors of symmetric matrices, and see [P] **matrix eigenvalues** for eigenvalues of nonsymmetric matrices. For a full description of the matrix functions, see [D] **functions**.

Matrix functions returning matrices:

cholesky(M)	I(n)	nullmat(*matname*)
corr(M)	inv(M)	sweep(M,i)
diag(v)	invsym(M)	vec(M)
get(*systemname*)	J(r,c,z)	vecdiag(M)
hadamard(M,N)	matuniform(r,c)	

Matrix functions returning scalars:

colnumb(M,s)	el(M,i,j)	rownumb(M,s)
colsof(M)	issymmetric(M)	rowsof(M)
det(M)	matmissing(M)	trace(M)
diag0cnt(M)	mreldif(X,Y)	

14.9 Subscripting

1. In matrix and scalar expressions, you may refer to *matname*$[r,c]$, where r and c are scalar expressions, to obtain one element of *matname* as a scalar.

   Examples:
   ```
   matrix A = A / A[1,1]
   generate newvar = oldvar / A[2,2]
   ```

2. In matrix expressions, you may refer to *matname*$[s_r,s_c]$, where s_r and s_c are string expressions, to obtain a submatrix with one element. The element returned is based on searching the row and column names.

   Examples:
   ```
   matrix B = V["price","price"]
   generate sdif = dif / sqrt(V["price","price"])
   ```

3. In matrix expressions, you may mix these two syntaxes and refer to *matname*$[r,s_c]$ or to *matname*$[s_r,c]$.

   Example:
   ```
   matrix b = b * R[1,"price"]
   ```

4. In matrix expressions, you may use *matname*$[r_1..r_2,c_1..c_2]$ to refer to submatrices; r_1, r_2, c_1, and c_2 may be scalar expressions. If r_2 evaluates to missing, it is taken as referring to the last row of *matname*; if c_2 evaluates to missing, it is taken as referring to the last column of *matname*. Thus *matname*$[r_1 \ldots, c_1 \ldots]$ is allowed.

   Examples:
   ```
   matrix S = Z[1..4, 1..4]
   matrix R = Z[5..., 5...]
   ```

5. In matrix expressions, you may refer to *matname*$[s_{r1}..s_{r2},s_{c1}..s_{c2}]$ to refer to submatrices where s_{r1}, s_{r2}, s_{c1}, and s_{c2}, are string expressions. The matrix returned is based on looking up the row and column names.

   If the string evaluates to an equation name only, all the rows or columns for the equation are returned.

   Examples:
   ```
   matrix S = Z["price".."weight", "price".."weight"]
   matrix L = D["mpg:price".."mpg:weight", "mpg:price".."mpg:weight"]
   matrix T1 = C["mpg:", "mpg:"]
   matrix T2 = C["mpg:", "price:"]
   ```

6. In matrix expressions, any of the above syntaxes may be combined.

   Examples:
   ```
   matrix T1 = C["mpg:", "price:weight".."price:displ"]
   matrix T2 = C["mpg:", "price:weight"...]
   matrix T3 = C["mpg:price", 2..5]
   matrix T4 = C["mpg:price", 2]
   ```

7. When defining an element of a matrix, use

$$\texttt{matrix } matname[i,j] \texttt{ = } expression$$

where i and j are scalar expressions. The matrix *matname* must already exist.

Example:
```
matrix A = J(2,2,0)
matrix A[1,2] = sqrt(2)
```

8. To replace a submatrix within a matrix, use the same syntax. If the expression on the right evaluates to a scalar or 1×1 matrix, the element is replaced. If it evaluates to a matrix, the submatrix with top-left element at (i,j) is replaced. The matrix *matname* must already exist.

Example:
```
matrix A = J(4,4,0)
matrix A[2,2] = C'*C
```

14.10   Using matrices in scalar expressions

Scalar expressions are documented as *exp* in the Stata manuals:

```
generate newvar = exp if exp ...
replace  newvar = exp if exp ...
regress ... if exp ...
if exp {... }
while exp {... }
```

Most importantly, scalar expressions occur in `generate` and `replace`, in the `if` *exp* modifier allowed on the end of many commands, and in the `if` and `while` commands for program control.

You will rarely need to refer to a matrix in any of these situations except when using the `if` and `while` commands.

In any case, you may refer to matrices in any of these situations, but the expression cannot require evaluation of matrix expressions returning matrices. Thus you could refer to `trace(A)` but not to `trace(A+B)`.

It can be difficult to predict when an evaluation of an expression requires evaluating a matrix; even experienced users can be surprised. If you get the error message "matrix operators that return matrices not allowed in this context", r(509), you have encountered such a situation.

The solution is to split the line in two. For instance, you would change

```
if trace(A+B)==0 {
    ...
}
```

to

```
matrix AplusB = A+B
if trace(AplusB)==0 {
    ...
}
```

or even to

```
matrix Trace = trace(A+B)
if Trace[1,1]==0 {
    ...
}
```

15 Saving and printing output—log files

Contents

15.1 Overview

Stata can record your session into a file called a log file but does not start a log automatically; you must tell Stata to record your session. By default, the resulting log file contains what you type and what Stata produces in response, recorded in a format called Stata Markup and Control Language (SMCL); see [P] **smcl**. The file can be printed or converted to ASCII text for incorporation into documents you create with your word processor.

To start a log:
    Your session is now being recorded
    in file *filename*.smcl.
	. log using *filename*

To temporarily stop logging:
    Temporarily stop:
    Resume:
	
	. log off
	. log on

To stop logging and close the file:
    You can now print *filename*.smcl or type:
    to create *filename*.log that you can
    load into your word processor.
	. log close
	. translate *filename*.smcl *filename*.log

Alternative ways to start logging:
    append to an existing log:
    replace an existing log:
	
	. log using *filename*, append
	. log using *filename*, replace

Using the GUI:
    To start a log:
    To temporarily stop logging:
    To resume:
    To stop logging and close the file:
    To print previous or current log:
	
	click on the **Log** button
	click on the **Log** button, and choose **Suspend**
	click on the **Log** button, and choose **Resume**
	click on the **Log** button, and choose **Close**
	select **File > View**, choose file,
	        right-click on the Viewer, and select **Print**

Also, cmdlog will produce logs containing solely what you typed—logs that, although not containing your results, are sufficient to recreate the session.

To start a command-only log:	. cmdlog using *filename*
To stop logging and close the file:	. cmdlog close
To recreate your session:	. do *filename*.txt

15.1.1 Starting and closing logs

With great foresight, you begin working in Stata and type log using session (or click on the **Log** button) before starting your work:

```
. log using session

      name:  <unnamed>
       log:  C:\example\session.smcl
  log type:  smcl
 opened on:  17 Mar 2009, 12:35:08
. use http://www.stata-press.com/data/r11/census
(1980 Census data by state)
. tabulate reg [freq=pop]

  Census │
  region │     Freq.     Percent        Cum.
─────────┼─────────────────────────────────────
      NE │ 49,135,283       21.75       21.75
  N Cntrl│ 58,865,670       26.06       47.81
   South │ 74,734,029       33.08       80.89
    West │ 43,172,490       19.11      100.00
─────────┼─────────────────────────────────────
   Total │225,907,472      100.00
. summarize medage

  Variable │      Obs        Mean   Std. Dev.        Min        Max
───────────┼────────────────────────────────────────────────────────
    medage │       50       29.54    1.693445       24.2       34.7
. log close
      name:  <unnamed>
       log:  C:\example\session.smcl
  log type:  smcl
 closed on:  17 Mar 2009, 12:35:38
```

There is now a file named session.smcl on your disk. If you were to look at it in a text editor or word processor, you would see something like this:

```
{smcl}
{com}{sf}{ul off}{txt}{.-}
      name:  {res}<unnamed>
       {txt}log:  {res}C:\example\session.smcl
  {txt}log type:  {res}smcl
  {txt}opened on:  {res}17 Mar 2009, 12:35:08

{com}. use http://www.stata-press.com/data/r11/census
{txt}(1980 Census data by state)

{com}. tabulate reg [freq=pop]

     {txt}Census {c |}
     region {c |}     Freq.     Percent        Cum.
{hline 12}{c +}{hline 35}
        NE {c |}{res} 49,135,283       21.75       21.75
{txt}   N Cntrl {c |}{res} 58,865,670       26.06       47.81
   (output omitted )
```

What you are seeing is SMCL, which Stata understands. Here is the result of typing the file using Stata's **type** command:

```
. type session.smcl
```

```
        name:  <unnamed>
         log:  C:\example\session.smcl
    log type:  smcl
   opened on:  17 Mar 2009, 12:35:08
. use http://www.stata-press.com/data/r11/census
(1980 Census data by state)
. tabulate reg [freq=pop]
     Census |
     region |      Freq.      Percent        Cum.
        NE  |  49,135,283       21.75       21.75
    N Cntrl |  58,865,670       26.06       47.81
      South |  74,734,029       33.08       80.89
       West |  43,172,490       19.11      100.00
      Total | 225,907,472      100.00
. summarize medage
    Variable |       Obs        Mean    Std. Dev.       Min         Max
      medage |        50       29.54    1.693445        24.2        34.7
. log close
        name:  <unnamed>
         log:  C:\example\session.smcl
    log type:  smcl
   closed on:  17 Mar 2009, 12:35:38
```

```
. _
```

What you will see is a perfect copy of what you previously saw. If you use Stata to print the file, you will get a perfect printed copy, too.

SMCL files can be translated to ASCII text, which is a format more useful for inclusion into a word processing document. If you type `translate` *filename*`.smcl` *filename*`.log`, Stata will translate *filename*`.smcl` to ASCII and store the result in *filename*`.log`:

```
. translate session.smcl session.log
```

The resulting file `session.log` looks like this:

```
-------------------------------------------------------------------------------
        name:  <unnamed>
         log:  C:\example\session.smcl
    log type:  smcl
   opened on:  17 Mar 2009, 12:35:08
. use http://www.stata-press.com/data/r11/census
(1980 Census data by state)
. tabulate reg [freq=pop]
     Census |
     region |      Freq.      Percent        Cum.
------------+-----------------------------------
        NE  | 49,135,283       21.75       21.75
    N Cntrl | 58,865,670       26.06       47.81
      South | 74,734,029       33.08       80.89
  (output omitted )
```

When you use `translate` to create *filename*`.log` from *filename*`.smcl`, *filename*`.log` must not already exist:

```
. translate session.smcl session.log
file session.log already exists
r(602);
```

If the file does already exist and you wish to overwrite the existing copy, you can specify the `replace` option:

```
. translate session.smcl session.log, replace
```

See [R] **translate** for more information.

If you prefer, you can skip the SMCL and create ASCII text logs directly, either by specifying that you want the log in `text` format,

```
. log using session, text
```

or by specifying that the file to be created be a `.log` file:

```
. log using session.log
```

15.1.2   Appending to an existing log

Stata never lets you accidentally write over an existing log file. If you have an existing log file and you want to continue logging, you have three choices:

• create a new log file

• append the new log onto the existing log file by typing `log using` *logname*`, append`

• replace the existing log file by typing `log using` *logname*`, replace`

    For example, if you have an existing log file named `session.smcl`, you might type

```
. log using session, append
```

to append the new log to the end of the existing log file, `session.smcl`.

15.1.3   Temporarily suspending and resuming logging

Once you have started logging your session, you can turn logging on and off. When you turn logging off, Stata temporarily stops recording your session but leaves the log file open. When you turn logging back on, Stata continues to record your session, appending the additional record to the end of the file.

Say that the first time something interesting happens, you type `log using results` (or click on **Log** and open `results.smcl`). You then retype the command that produced the interesting result (or double-click on the command in the Review window, or use the *PgUp* key to retrieve the command; see [U] **10 Keyboard use**). You now have a copy of the interesting result saved in the log file.

You are now reasonably sure that nothing interesting will occur, at least for a while. Rather than type `log close`, however, you type `log off`, or you click on **Log** and choose **Suspend**. From now on, nothing goes into the file. The next time something interesting happens, you type `log on` (or click on **Log** and choose **Resume**) and reissue the (interesting) command. After that, you type `log off`. You keep working like this—toggling the log on and off.

15.2   Placing comments in logs

Stata treats lines starting with a "*" as comments and ignores them. Thus, if you are working interactively and wish to make a comment, you can type "*" followed by your comment:

```
. * check that all the spells are completed
. _
```

Stata ignores your comment, but if you have a log going the comment now appears in the file.

❑ Technical note

`log` can be combined with `#review` (see [U] **10 Keyboard use**) to bail you out when you have not adequately planned ahead. Say that you have been working in front of your computer, and you now realize that you have done what you wanted to do. Unfortunately, you are not sure exactly what it is you have done. Did you make a mistake? Could you reproduce the result? Unfortunately, you have not been logging your output. Typing `#review` will allow you to look over what commands you have issued, and, combined with `log`, will allow you to make a record. You can also see the commands that you have issued in the Review window. You can save those commands to a file by right-clicking on the Review window and selecting **Save Review Contents...**.

Type `log using` *filename*. Type `#review` 100. Stata will list the last 100 commands you gave, or however many it has stored. Because `log` is making a record, that list will also be stored in the file. Finally, type `log close`.

❑

15.3   Logging only what you type

Log files record everything that happens during a session, both what you type and what Stata produces in response.

Stata can also produce command log files—files that contain only what you type. These files are perfect for later going back and creating a Stata do-file.

`cmdlog` creates command log files, and its basic syntax is

`cmdlog using` *filename* [`, append replace`]	creates *filename* `.txt`
`cmdlog off`	temporarily suspends command logging
`cmdlog on`	resumes command logging
`cmdlog close`	closes the command log file

See [R] **log** for all the details.

Command logs are plain ASCII text files. If you typed

```
. cmdlog using session
(cmdlog C:\example\session.txt opened)
. use http://www.stata-press.com/data/r11/census
(Census Data)
. tabulate reg [freq=pop]
  (output omitted )
. summarize medage
  (output omitted )
. cmdlog close
(cmdlog C:\example\session.txt closed)
```

file `mycmds.txt` would contain

```
use http://www.stata-press.com/data/r11/census
tabulate reg [freq=pop]
summarize medage
```

You can create both kinds of logs—full session logs and command logs—simultaneously, if you wish. A command log file can later be used as a do-file; see [R] **do**.

15.4   The log-button alternative

The capabilities of the `log` command (but not the `cmdlog` command) are available from Stata's GUI interface; just click on the **Log** button or select **Log** from the **File** menu.

You can use the Viewer to view logs, even logs that are in the process of being created. Just select **File > View**. If you are currently logging, the filename to view will already be filled in with the current log file, and all you need to do is click on **OK**. Periodically, you can click on the **Refresh** button to bring the Viewer up to date.

You can also use the Viewer to view previous logs.

You can access the Viewer by selecting **File > View**, or you can use the `view` command:

```
. view myoldlog.smcl
```

15.5   Printing logs

You print logs from the Viewer. Select **File > View**, or type `view` *logfilename* from the command line to load the log into the Viewer, and then right-click on the Viewer and select **Print**.

You can also print logs by other means; see [R] **translate**.

15.6   Creating multiple log files simultaneously

Programmers or advanced users may wish to create more than one log file simultaneously. For example, you may wish to create a log file of your whole session but also create a separate log file for part of your session.

You can create multiple logs by using `log`'s `name()` option; see [R] **log**.

16 Do-files

Contents

16.1 Description

Rather than typing commands at the keyboard, you can create a text file containing commands and instruct Stata to execute the commands stored in that file. Such files are called *do-files* because the command that causes them to be executed is do.

A do-file is a standard ASCII text file that is executed by Stata when you type do *filename*. You can use any text editor or the built-in Do-file Editor to create do-files; see [GSW] **13 Using the Do-file Editor—automating Stata**. Using do-files rather than typing commands with the keyboard or using dialog boxes offers several advantages. By writing the steps you take to manage and analyze your data in the form of a do-file, you can reproduce your work later. Also, writing a do-file makes the inevitable debugging process much easier. If you decide to change one part of your analysis, changing the relevant commands in your do-file is much easier than having to start back at square one, as is often necessary when working interactively. In this chapter, we describe the mechanics of do-files. Long (2009) cogently argues that do-files should be used in all research projects and offers an abundance of time-tested advice in how to manage data and statistical analysis.

▷ Example 1

You can use do-files to create a batchlike environment in which you place all the commands you want to perform in a file and then instruct Stata to do that file. Assume that you use your text editor or word processor to create a file called myjob.do that contains these three lines:

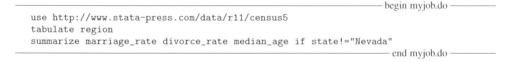

```
─────────────────────────────────── begin myjob.do ───────────
   use http://www.stata-press.com/data/r11/census5
   tabulate region
   summarize marriage_rate divorce_rate median_age if state!="Nevada"
─────────────────────────────────── end myjob.do ───────────
```

181

You then enter Stata and instruct Stata to do the file:

```
. do myjob
. use http://www.stata-press.com/data/r11/census5
(1980 Census data by state)
. tabulate region
```

Census region	Freq.	Percent	Cum.
NE	9	18.00	18.00
N Cntrl	12	24.00	42.00
South	16	32.00	74.00
West	13	26.00	100.00
Total	50	100.00	

```
. summarize marriage_rate divorce_rate median_age if state !="Nevada"
```

Variable	Obs	Mean	Std. Dev.	Min	Max
marriage_r~e	49	.0106791	.0021746	.0074654	.0172704
divorce_rate	49	.0054268	.0015104	.0029436	.008752
median_age	49	29.52653	1.708286	24.2	34.7

You typed only do myjob to produce this output. Because you did not specify the file extension, Stata assumed you meant do myjob.do; see [U] **11.6 File-naming conventions**.

◁

16.1.1 Version

We recommend that the first line in your do-file declare the Stata release you used when you wrote the do-file; myjob.do would read better as

```
───────────────────────────────────── begin myjob.do ─────────
version 11
use http://www.stata-press.com/data/r11/census
tabulate region
summarize marriage_rate divorce_rate median_age if state!="Nevada"
───────────────────────────────────── end myjob.do ─────────
```

We admit that we do not always follow our own advice, as you will see many examples in this manual that do not include the version 11 line.

If you intend to keep the do-file, however, you should include this line because it ensures that your do-file will continue to work with future versions of Stata. Stata is under continual development, and sometimes things change in surprising ways.

For instance, in Stata 3.0, a new syntax for specifying the weights was introduced. If you had an old do-file written for Stata 2.1 that analyzed weighted data and did not have version 2.1 at the top, you would find that today's Stata would flag some of the file's lines as syntax errors. If you had the version 2.1 line, it would work just as it used to.

Skipping ahead to Stata 10, we introduced xtset and declared that, to use the xt commands, you must xtset your data first. Previously, you specified options on the end of each xt command that identified the group and, optionally, the time variables. Despite this change, if you include version 9 or earlier at the top of your do-file, the xt commands will continue to work the old way.

For an overview of versioning and an up-to-date list of the issues that versioning does not address automatically, see help version.

When running an old do-file that includes a `version` statement, you need not worry about setting the version back after it has completed. Stata automatically restores the previous value of `version` when the do-file completes.

16.1.2 Comments and blank lines in do-files

You may freely include blank lines in your do-file. In the previous example, the do-file could just as well have read

―――――――――――――――――――――――― begin myjob.do ―――――――
```
version 11
use http://www.stata-press.com/data/r11/census
tabulate region
summarize marriage_rate divorce_rate median_age if state!="Nevada"
```
――――――――――――――――――――――――――――――― end myjob.do ―――――――

There are four ways to include comments in a do-file.

1. Begin the line with a '`*`'; Stata ignores such lines. `*` cannot be used within Mata.

2. Place the comment in `/* */` delimiters.

3. Place the comment after two forward slashes, i.e., `//`. Everything after the `//` to the end of the current line is considered a comment (unless the `//` is part of `http://`...).

4. Place the comment after three forward slashes, i.e., `///`. Everything after the `///` to the end of the current line is considered a comment. However, when you use `///`, the next line joins with the current line. `///` lets you split long lines across multiple lines in the do-file.

❏ Technical note

The `/* */`, `//`, and `///` comment indicators can be used in do-files and ado-files only; you may not use them interactively. You can, however, use the '`*`' comment indicator interactively.

❏

`myjob.do` then might read

―――――――――――――――――――――――― begin myjob.do ―――――――
```
* a sample analysis job
version 11
use http://www.stata-press.com/data/r11/census
/* obtain the summary statistics: */
tabulate region
summarize marriage_rate divorce_rate median_age if state!="Nevada"
```
――――――――――――――――――――――――――――――― end myjob.do ―――――――

or equivalently,

―――――――――――――――――――――――― begin myjob.do ―――――――
```
// a sample analysis job
version 11
use http://www.stata-press.com/data/r11/census
// obtain the summary statistics:
tabulate region
summarize marriage_rate divorce_rate median_age if state!="Nevada"
```
――――――――――――――――――――――――――――――― end myjob.do ―――――――

The style of comment indicator you use is up to you. One advantage of the `/* */` method is that it can be put at the end of lines:

─────────────────────────────── begin myjob.do ───────────

```
* a sample analysis job
version 11

use http://www.stata-press.com/data/r11/census

tabulate region                 /* obtain summary statistics */
summarize marriage_rate divorce_rate median_age if state!="Nevada"
```
─────────────────────────────────────── end myjob.do ───────────

In fact, /* */ can be put anywhere, even in the middle of a line:

─────────────────────────────── begin myjob.do ───────────

```
* a sample analysis job
version 11

use /* confirm this is latest */ http://www.stata-press.com/data/r11/census

tabulate region                 /* obtain summary statistics */
summarize marriage_rate divorce_rate median_age if state!="Nevada"
```
─────────────────────────────────────── end myjob.do ───────────

You can achieve the same results with the // and /// methods:

─────────────────────────────── begin myjob.do ───────────

```
// a sample analysis job
version 11

use http://www.stata-press.com/data/r11/census

tabulate region                 // obtain summary statistics
summarize marriage_rate divorce_rate median_age if state!="Nevada"
```
─────────────────────────────────────── end myjob.do ───────────

or

─────────────────────────────── begin myjob.do ───────────

```
// a sample analysis job
version 11

use /// confirm this is latest
http://www.stata-press.com/data/r11/census

tabulate region                 // obtain summary statistics
summarize marriage_rate divorce_rate median_age if state!="Nevada"
```
─────────────────────────────────────── end myjob.do ───────────

16.1.3   Long lines in do-files

When you use Stata interactively, you press *Enter* to end a line and tell Stata to execute it. If you need to type a line that is wider than the screen, you simply do it, letting it wrap or scroll.

You can follow the same procedure in do-files—if your editor or word processor will let you—but you can do better. You can change the end-of-line delimiter to ';' by using #delimit, you can comment out the line break by using /* */ comment delimiters, or you can use the /// line-join indicator.

▷ Example 2

In the following fragment of a do-file, we temporarily change the end-of-line delimiter:

```
──────────────────────────────────── fragment of example.do ──────────
use mydata
#delimit ;
summarize weight price displ headroom rep78 length turn gear_ratio
        if substr(company,1,4)=="Ford" |
            substr(company,1,2)=="GM", detail ;
gen byte ford = substr(company,1,4)=="Ford" ;
#delimit cr
gen byte gm = substr(company,1,2)=="GM"
──────────────────────────────────── fragment of example.do ──────────
```

Once we change the line delimiter to semicolon, all lines, even short ones, must end in semicolons. Stata treats carriage returns as no different from blanks. We can change the delimiter back to carriage return by typing #delimit cr.

The #delimit command is allowed only in do-files—it is not allowed interactively. You need not remember to set the delimiter back to carriage return at the end of a do-file because Stata will reset it automatically.

◁

▷ Example 3

The other way around long lines is to comment out the carriage return by using /* */ comment brackets or to use the /// line-join indicator. Thus our code fragment could also read

```
──────────────────────────────────── fragment of example.do ──────────
use mydata
summarize weight price displ headroom rep78 length turn gear_ratio /*
    */  if substr(company,1,4)=="Ford" |    /*
    */      substr(company,1,2)=="GM", detail
gen byte ford = substr(company,1,4)=="Ford"
gen byte gm = substr(company,1,2)=="GM"
──────────────────────────────────── fragment of example.do ──────────
```

or

```
──────────────────────────────────── fragment of example.do ──────────
use mydata
summarize weight price displ headroom rep78 length turn gear_ratio ///
        if substr(company,1,4)=="Ford" |    ///
            substr(company,1,2)=="GM", detail
gen byte ford = substr(company,1,4)=="Ford"
gen byte gm = substr(company,1,2)=="GM"
──────────────────────────────────── fragment of example.do ──────────
```

◁

(*Continued on next page*)

16.1.4   Error handling in do-files

A do-file stops executing when the end of the file is reached, an `exit` is executed, or an error (nonzero *return code*) occurs. If an error occurs, the remaining commands in the do-file are not executed.

If you press *Break* while executing a do-file, Stata responds as though an error has occurred, stopping the do-file. This happens because the return code is nonzero; see [U] **8 Error messages and return codes** for an explanation of return codes.

▷ Example 4

Here is what happens when we execute a do-file and then press *Break*:

```
. do myjob2
. version 11
. use census
(Census data)
. tabulate region

    Census
    region │    Freq.      Percent        Cum.
—Break—
r(1);

end of do-file
—Break—
r(1);

. _
```

When we pressed *Break*, Stata responded by typing —Break— and showed a return code of 1. Stata seemingly repeated itself, typing first "end of do-file", and then —Break— and the return code of 1 again. Do not worry about the repeated messages. The first message indicates that Stata was stopping the `tabulate` because you pressed *Break*, and the second message indicates that Stata is stopping the do-file for the same reason.

◁

▷ Example 5

Let's try our example again, but this time, let's introduce an error. We change the file `myjob2.do` to read

```
──────────────────────────────────────── begin myjob2.do ────────────
    version 11
    use censas
    tabulate region
    summarize marriage_rate divorce_rate median_age if state!="Nevada"
──────────────────────────────────────── end myjob2.do ──────────
```

To introduce a subtle typographical error, we typed `use censas` when we meant `use census`. We assume that there is no file called `censas.dta`, so now we have an error. Here is what happens when you instruct Stata to do the file:

```
. do myjob2

. version 11

. use censas
file censas.dta not found
r(601);

end of do-file
r(601);

. _
```

When Stata was told to use censas, it responded with "file censas.dta not found" and a return code of 601. Stata then typed "end of do-file" and repeated the return code of 601. The repeated message occurred for the same reason it did when we pressed *Break* in the previous example. The use resulted in a return code of 601, so the do-file itself resulted in the same return code. The important thing to understand is that Stata stopped executing the file because there was an error.

◁

❑ Technical note

We can tell Stata to continue executing the file even if there are errors by typing do *filename*, nostop. Here is the result:

```
. do myjob2, nostop

. version 11

. use censas
file censas.dta not found
r(601);

. tabulate region
no variables defined
r(111);

summarize marriage_rate divorce_rate median_age if state!="Nevada"
no variables defined
r(111);

end of do-file

. _
```

None of the commands worked because the do-file's first command failed. That is why Stata ordinarily stops. However, if our file had contained anything that could work, it would have worked. In general, we do not recommend coding in this manner, as unintended consequences can result when errors do not stop execution.

❑

16.1.5   Logging the output of do-files

You log the output of do-files just as you would an interactive session; see [U] **15 Saving and printing output—log files**.

Many users include the commands to start and stop the logging in the do-file itself:

```
─────────────────────────────────────────── begin myjob3.do ───────────
  version 11
  log using myjob3, replace
  * a sample analysis job
  use census
  tabulate region                    // obtain summary statistics
  summarize marriage_rate divorce_rate median_age if state!="Nevada"
  log close
─────────────────────────────────────────────── end myjob3.do ─────────
```

We chose to open with `log using myjob3, replace`, the important part being the `replace` option. Had we omitted the option, we could not easily rerun our do-file. If `myjob3.smcl` had already existed and `log` was not told that it is okay to replace the file, the do-file would have stopped and instead reported that "file myjob3.smcl already exists". We could get around that, of course, by erasing the log file before running the do-file.

16.1.6 Preventing –more– conditions

Assume that you are running a do-file and logging the output so that you can look at it later. Then Stata's feature of pausing every time the screen is full is just an irritation: it means that you have to sit and watch the do-file run so you can clear the —more—.

The way around this is to include the line `set more off` in your do-file. Setting more to `off`, as explained in [U] **7 –more– conditions**, prevents Stata from ever issuing a —more—.

16.2 Calling other do-files

Do-files may call other do-files. Say that you wrote `makedata.do`, which infiles your data, generates a few variables, and saves `step1.dta`. Say that you wrote `anlstep1.do`, which performed a little analysis on `step1.dta`. You could then create a third do-file,

```
─────────────────────────────────────────── begin master.do ───────────
  version 11
  do makedata
  do anlstep1
─────────────────────────────────────────────── end master.do ─────────
```

and so in effect combine the two do-files.

Do-files may call other do-files, which, in turn, call other do-files, and so on. Stata allows do-files to be nested 64 deep.

Be not confused: `master.do` above could call 1,000 do-files one after the other, and still the level of nesting would be only two.

16.3   Creating and running do-files

16.3.1   Creating and running do-files for Windows

1. You can execute do-files by typing do followed by the filename, as we did above.

2. You can execute do-files by selecting **File > Do...**.

3. You can use the Do-file Editor to compose, save, and execute do-files; see [GSW] **13 Using the Do-file Editor—automating Stata**. To use the Do-file Editor, click on the **Do-file Editor** button, or type doedit in the Command window.

4. You can double-click on the icon for the do-file to launch Stata and open the do-file in the Do-file Editor.

5. You can run the do-file in batch mode. See [GSW] **C.6 Stata batch mode** for details, but the short explanation is that you open a Window command window and type

       C:\data> "C:\Program Files\Stata11\Stata" /s do myjob

   or

       C:\data> "C:\Program Files\Stata11\Stata" /b do myjob

to run in batch mode, assuming that you have installed Stata in the folder C:\Program Files\Stata11. /b and /s determine the kind of log produced, but put that aside for a second. When you start Stata in these ways, Stata will run in the background. When the do-file completes, the Stata icon on the taskbar will flash. You can then click on it to close Stata. If you want to stop the do-file before it completes, click on the Stata icon on the taskbar, and Stata will ask you if you want to cancel the job. If you want Stata to exit when the do-file is complete rather than flashing on the taskbar, also specify /e on the command line.

To log the output, you can start the log before executing the do-file or you can include the log using and log close in your do-file.

When you run Stata in these ways, Stata takes the following actions:

   a. Stata automatically opens a log. If you specified /s, Stata will open a SMCL log; if you specified /b, Stata will open an ASCII text log. If your do-file is named *xyz*.do, the log will be called *xyz*.smcl (/s) or *xyz*.log (/b) in the same directory.

   b. If your do-file explicitly opens another log, Stata will save two copies of the output.

   c. Stata ignores —more— conditions and anything else that would cause the do-file to stop were it running interactively.

16.3.2   Creating and running do-files for Mac

1. You can execute do-files by typing do followed by the filename, as we did above.

2. You can execute do-files by selecting **File > Do...**.

3. With Stata running, you can go to the Desktop and double-click on the do-file.

4. You can use the Do-file Editor to compose, save, and execute do-files; see [GSM] **13 Using the Do-file Editor—automating Stata**. Click on the **Do-file Editor** button, or type doedit in the Command window.

5. If Stata is not running, you can double-click on the icon for the do-file to launch Stata and run the do-file. When the do-file completes, Stata will prompt you for the next command just as if you had started Stata the normal way. If you want Stata to exit instead, include `exit, STATA clear` as the last line of your do-file.

6. You can run the do-file in batch mode. See [GSM] **C.4 Stata batch mode** for details, but the short explanation is that you open a Terminal window and type

   ```
   % /Applications/Stata/Stata.app/Contents/MacOS/Stata -s do myjob
   ```

   or

   ```
   % /Applications/Stata/Stata.app/Contents/MacOS/Stata -b do myjob
   ```

   to run in batch mode, assuming that you have installed Stata/IC in the folder `/Applications/Stata`. `-b` and `-s` determine the kind of log produced, but put that aside for a second. When you start Stata in these ways, Stata will run in the background. When the do-file completes, the Stata icon on the Dock will bounce until you put Stata into the foreground. You can then exit Stata. If you want to stop the do-file before it completes, right-click on the Stata icon on the Dock, and select **Quit**.

To log the output, you can start the log before executing the do-file or you can include the `log using` and `log close` in your do-file.

When you run Stata in these ways, Stata takes the following actions:

   a. Stata automatically opens a log. If you specified `-s`, Stata will open a SMCL log; if you specified `-b`, Stata will open an ASCII text log. If your do-file is named *xyz*.do, the log will be called *xyz*.smcl (`-s`) or *xyz*.log (`-b`) in the same directory.

   b. If your do-file explicitly opens another log, Stata will save two copies of the output.

   c. Stata ignores —more— conditions and anything else that would cause the do-file to stop were it running interactively.

16.3.3 Creating and running do-files Unix

1. You can execute do-files by typing `do` followed by the filename, as we did above.

2. You can execute do-files by selecting **File > Do...**.

3. You can use the Do-file Editor to compose, save, and execute do-files; see [GSW] **13 Using the Do-file Editor—automating Stata**. Click on the **Do-file Editor** button, or type `doedit` in the Command window.

4. At the Unix prompt, you can type
       $ `xstata` do *filename*
   or
       $ `stata` do *filename*
   to launch Stata and run the do-file. When the do-file completes, Stata will prompt you for the next command just as if you had started Stata the normal way. If you want Stata to exit instead, include `exit, STATA clear` as the last line of your do-file.

To log the output, you can start the log before executing the do-file or you can include the `log using` and `log close` in your do-file.

5. At the Unix prompt, you can type

> $ stata -s do *filename* &

or

> $ stata -b do *filename* &

to run the do-file in the background. The above two examples both involve the use of stata, not xstata. Type stata, even if you usually use the GUI version of Stata, xstata. The examples differ only in that one specifies the -s option and the other, the -b option, which determines the kind of log that will be produced. In the above examples, Stata takes the following actions:

> a. Stata automatically opens a log. If you specified -s, Stata will open a SMCL log; if you specified -b, Stata will open an ASCII text log. If your do-file is named *xyz*.do, the log will be called *xyz*.smcl (-s) or *xyz*.log (-b) in the current directory (the directory from which you issued the stata command).

> b. If your do-file explicitly opens another log, Stata will save two copies of the output.

> c. Stata ignores —more— conditions and anything else that would cause the do-file to stop were it running interactively.

To reiterate: one way to run a do-file in the background and obtain an ASCII text log is by typing

> $ stata -b do myfile &

Another way uses standard redirection:

> $ stata < myfile.do > myfile.log &

The first way is slightly more efficient. Either way, Stata knows it is in the background and ignores —more— conditions and anything else that would cause the do-file to stop if it were running interactively. However, if your do-file contains either the #delimit command or the comment characters (/* at the end of one line and */ at the beginning of the next), the second method will not work. We recommend that you use the first method: stata -b do myfile &.

The choice between stata -b do myfile & and stata -s do myfile & is more personal. We prefer obtaining SMCL logs (-s) because they look better when printed, and, in any case, they can always be converted to ASCII text format with translate; see [R] **translate**.

16.4   Programming with do-files

This is an advanced topic, and we are going to refer to concepts not yet explained; see [U] **18 Programming Stata** for more information.

16.4.1   Argument passing

Do-files accept arguments, just as Stata programs do; this is described in [U] **18 Programming Stata** and [U] **18.4 Program arguments**. In fact, the logic Stata follows when invoking a do-file is the same as when invoking a program: the local macros are saved, and new ones are defined. Arguments are stored in the local macros '1', '2', and so on. When the do-file completes, the previous definitions are restored, just as with programs.

Thus, if you wanted your do-file to

1. use a dataset of your choosing,

2. tabulate a variable named region, and

3. summarize variables marriage_rate and divorce_rate,

you could write the do-file

```
──────────────────────────────────────────── begin myxmpl.do ────────
use `1'
tabulate region
summarize marriage_rate divorce_rate
────────────────────────────────────────────── end myxmpl.do ────────
```

and you could run this do-file by typing, for instance,

```
. do myxmpl census
  (output omitted)
```

The first command—use `1'—would be interpreted as use census because census was the first argument you typed after do myxmpl.

An even better version of the do-file would read

```
──────────────────────────────────────────── begin myxmpl.do ────────
args dsname
use `dsname'
tabulate region
summarize marriage_rate divorce_rate
────────────────────────────────────────────── end myxmpl.do ────────
```

The args command merely assigns a better name to the argument passed. args dsname does not verify that what we type following do myxmpl is a filename—we would have to use the syntax command if we wanted to do that—but substituting `dsname' for `1' does make the code more readable.

If our program were to receive two arguments, we could refer to them as `1' and `2', or we could put an `args dsname other' at the top of our do-file and then refer to `dsname' and `other'.

To learn more about argument passing, see [U] **18.4 Program arguments**. Baum (2009) provides many examples and tips related to do-files.

16.4.2 Suppressing output

There is an alternative to typing do *filename*; it is run *filename*. run works in the same way as do, except that neither the instructions in the file nor any of the output caused by those instructions is shown on the screen or in the log file.

For instance, with the above myxmpl.do, typing run myxmpl census results in

```
. run myxmpl census

.  _
```

All the instructions were executed, but none of the output was shown.

This is not useful here, but if the do-file contained only the definitions of Stata programs—see [U] **18 Programming Stata**—and you merely wanted to load the programs without seeing the code, run would be useful.

16.5   References

Baum, C. F. 2009. *An Introduction to Stata Programming*. College Station, TX: Stata Press.

Long, J. S. 2009. *The Workflow of Data Analysis Using Stata*. College Station, TX: Stata Press.

17 Ado-files

Contents

17.1 Description

Stata is programmable, and even if you never write a Stata program, Stata's programmability is still important. Many of Stata's features are implemented as Stata programs, and new features are implemented every day, both by StataCorp and by others.

1. You can obtain additions from the *Stata Journal.* You subscribe to the printed journal, but the software additions are available free over the Internet.

2. You can obtain additions from the Stata listserver, Statalist, where an active group of users advise each other on how to use Stata, and often, in the process, trade programs. Visit the Stata web site, http://www.stata.com, for instructions on how to subscribe; subscribing to the listserver is free.

3. The Boston College Statistical Software Components Archive (SSC) is a distributed database making available a large and constantly growing number of Stata programs. You can browse and search the archive, and you can find links to the archive from http://www.stata.com. Importantly, Stata knows how to access the archive and other places, as well. You can search for additions by using Stata's search, net command; see [R] **search**. You can immediately install materials you find with search, net by using the hyperlinks that will be displayed by search in the Results window or by using the net command. A specialized command, ssc, has several options available to help you find and install the user-written commands that are available from this site; see [R] **ssc**.

4. You can write your own additions to Stata.

This chapter is written for people who want to use ado-files. All users should read it. If you later decide you want to write ado-files, see [U] **18.11 Ado-files**.

17.2   What is an ado-file?

An ado-file defines a Stata command, but not all Stata commands are defined by ado-files.

When you type `summarize` to obtain summary statistics, you are using a command built into Stata.

When you type `ci` to obtain confidence intervals, you are running an ado-file. The results of using a built-in command or an ado-file are indistinguishable.

An ado-file is an ASCII text file that contains a Stata program. When you type a command that Stata does not know, it looks in certain places for an ado-file of that name. If Stata finds it, Stata loads and executes it, so it appears to you as if the ado-command is just another command built into Stata.

We just told you that Stata's `ci` command is implemented as an ado-file. That means that, somewhere, there is a file named `ci.ado`.

Ado-files usually come with help files. When you type `help ci` (or select **Help > Stata Command...**, and type `ci`), Stata looks for `ci.sthlp`, just as it looks for `ci.ado` when you use the `ci` command. A help file is also an ASCII text file that tells Stata's help system what to display.

17.3   How can I tell if a command is built in or an ado-file?

You can use the `which` command to determine whether a file is built in or implemented as an ado-file. For instance, `logistic` is an ado-file, and here is what happens when you type `which logistic`:

```
. which logistic
C:\Program Files\Stata11\ado\base\l\logistic.ado
*! version 3.4.7   25jun2009
```

`summarize` is a built-in command:

```
. which summarize
built-in command:  summarize
```

17.4   How can I look at an ado-file?

Certainly. When you type `which` followed by an ado-command, Stata reports where the file is stored:

```
. which logistic
C:\Program Files\Stata11\ado\base\l\logistic.ado
*! version 3.4.7   25jun2009
```

Ado-files are just ASCII text files containing the Stata program, so you can type them or view them in Stata's Viewer (or even look at them in your editor or word processor):

```
. type "C:\Program Files\Stata11\ado\base\l\logistic.ado"
*! version 3.4.7   25jun2009
program define logistic, eclass prop(or svyb svyj svyr swml mi) byable(onecall)
        version 6.0, missing
  (output omitted )
end
```

or

```
. viewsource logistic.ado
*! version 3.4.7  25jun2009
program define logistic, eclass prop(or svyb svyj svyr swml mi) byable(onecall)
        version 6.0, missing
  (output omitted )
end
```

The `type` command displays the contents of a file. The `viewsource` command searches for a file along the ado directories and displays the file in the Viewer. You can also look at the corresponding help file in raw form if you wish. If there is a help file, it is stored in the same place as the ado-file:

```
. type "C:\Program Files\Stata11\ado\base\l\logistic.sthlp", asis
{smcl}
{* *! version 1.2.9  26jun2009}{...}
{cmd:help logistic}{right:dialogs:  {dialog logistic}  {dialog logistic,
> message(-svy-) name(svy_logistic):svy: logistic}}
{right:also see:  {help logistic postestimation}}
{hline}
  (output omitted )
```

or

```
. viewsource logistic.sthlp
{smcl}
{* *! version 1.2.9  26jun2009}{...}
{cmd:help logistic}{right:dialogs:  {dialog logistic}  {dialog logistic,
> message(-svy-) name(svy_logistic):svy: logistic}}
{right:also see:  {help logistic postestimation}}
{hline}
  (output omitted )
```

17.5   Where does Stata look for ado-files?

Stata looks for ado-files in seven places, which can be categorized in three ways:

I. The official ado directories:
  1. (UPDATES), the official updates directory containing updated ado-files from StataCorp
  2. (BASE), the official base directory containing the ado-files shipped with your version of Stata

II. Your personal ado-directories:
  3. (SITE), the directory for ado-files your site might have installed
  4. (PLUS), the directory for ado-files you personally might have installed
  5. (PERSONAL), the directory for ado-files you might have written
  6. (OLDPLACE), the directory where Stata users used to save their personally written ado-files

III. The current directory:
  7. (.), the ado-files you have written just this instant or for just this project

The location of these directories varies from computer to computer, but Stata's `sysdir` command will tell you where they are on your computer:

```
. sysdir
    STATA:  C:\Program Files\Stata11\
  UPDATES:  C:\Program Files\Stata11\ado\updates\
     BASE:  C:\Program Files\Stata11\ado\base\
     SITE:  C:\Program Files\Stata11\ado\site\
     PLUS:  C:\ado\plus\
 PERSONAL:  C:\ado\personal\
 OLDPLACE:  C:\ado\
```

17.5.1 Where are the official ado-directories?

These are the directories listed as BASE and UPDATES by sysdir:

```
. sysdir
    STATA:  C:\Program Files\Stata11\
  UPDATES:  C:\Program Files\Stata11\ado\updates\
     BASE:  C:\Program Files\Stata11\ado\base\
     SITE:  C:\Program Files\Stata11\ado\site\
     PLUS:  C:\ado\plus\
 PERSONAL:  C:\ado\personal\
 OLDPLACE:  C:\ado\
```

1. BASE contains the ado-files we originally shipped to you.

2. UPDATES contains any updates you might have installed since then. You can install these updates by using the update command or by selecting **Help > Official Updates**; see [U] **17.8 How do I install official updates?**.

17.5.2 Where is my personal ado-directory?

These are the directories listed as PERSONAL, PLUS, SITE, and OLDPLACE by sysdir:

```
. sysdir
    STATA:  C:\Program Files\Stata11\
  UPDATES:  C:\Program Files\Stata11\ado\updates\
     BASE:  C:\Program Files\Stata11\ado\base\
     SITE:  C:\Program Files\Stata11\ado\site\
     PLUS:  C:\ado\plus\
 PERSONAL:  C:\ado\personal\
 OLDPLACE:  C:\ado\
```

1. PERSONAL is for ado-files you have written. Store your private ado-files here; see [U] **17.7 How do I add my own ado-files?**.

2. PLUS is for ado-files you personally installed but did not write. Such ado-files are usually obtained from the SJ, but they are sometimes found in other places, too. You find and install such files by using Stata's net command, or you can select **Help > SJ and User-written Programs**; see [U] **17.6 How do I install an addition?**.

3. SITE is really the opposite of a personal ado directory—it is a public directory corresponding to PLUS. If you are on a networked computer, the site administrator can install ado-files here, and all Stata users will then be able to use them just as if they all found and installed them in their PLUS directory for themselves. Site administrators find and install the ado-files just as you would, using Stata's net command, but they specify an option when they install something that tells Stata to write the files into SITE rather than PLUS; see [R] **net**.

4. OLDPLACE is for old-time Stata users. Prior to Stata 6, all "personal" ado-files, whether personally written or just personally installed, were written in the same directory—OLDPLACE. So that the old-time Stata users do not have to go back and rearrange what they have already done, Stata still looks in OLDPLACE.

17.6   How do I install an addition?

Additions come in four types:

1. User-written additions, which you might find in the SJ, etc.

2. Updates to user-written additions
   See [U] **17.9 How do I install updates to user-written additions?**.

3. Ado-files you have written
   See [U] **17.7 How do I add my own ado-files?** If you have an ado-file obtained from the Stata listserver or a friend, treat it as belonging to this case.

4. Official updates provided by StataCorp
   See [U] **17.8 How do I install official updates?**.

User-written additions you might find in the *Stata Journal* (SJ), etc., are obtained over the Internet. To access them on the Internet,

1. select **Help > SJ and User-written Programs**, and click on one of the links

or

2. type `net from http://www.stata.com`.

What to do next will be obvious, but, in case it is not, see [GSW] **19 Updating and extending Stata—Internet functionality**, [GSM] **19 Updating and extending Stata—Internet functionality**, or [GSU] **19 Updating and extending Stata—Internet functionality**. Also see [U] **28 Using the Internet to keep up to date**, [R] **net**, and [R] **adoupdate**.

17.7   How do I add my own ado-files?

You write a Stata program (see [U] **18 Programming Stata**), store it in a file ending in `.ado`, perhaps write a help file, and copy everything to the directory `sysdir` lists as PERSONAL:

```
. sysdir
    STATA:  C:\Program Files\Stata11\
  UPDATES:  C:\Program Files\Stata11\ado\updates\
     BASE:  C:\Program Files\Stata11\ado\base\
     SITE:  C:\Program Files\Stata11\ado\site\
     PLUS:  C:\ado\plus\
 PERSONAL:  C:\ado\personal\
 OLDPLACE:  C:\ado\
```

Here we would copy the files to `C:\ado\personal`.

While you are writing your ado-file, it is sometimes convenient to store the pieces in the current directory. Do that if you wish; you can move them to your personal ado-directory when the program is debugged.

17.8   How do I install official updates?

Updates are available over the Internet:

1. select **Help > Official Updates**, and then click on **http://www.stata.com**

or

2. type `update query`.

What to do next should be obvious, but in case it is not, see [GSW] **19 Updating and extending Stata—Internet functionality**, [GSM] **19 Updating and extending Stata—Internet functionality**, or [GSU] **19 Updating and extending Stata—Internet functionality**. Also see [U] **28 Using the Internet to keep up to date** and [R] **net**.

The official updates include bug fixes and new features but do not change the syntax of an existing command or change the way Stata works.

Once you have installed the updates, you can enter Stata and type help whatsnew (or select **Help > What's New?**) to learn about what has changed.

17.9   How do I install updates to user-written additions?

If you have previously installed user-written additions, you can check for updates to them by typing adoupate. If updates are available, you can install them by typing adoupdate, update. See [R] **adoupdate**.

17.10   Reference

Cox, N. J. 2006. Stata tip 30: May the source be with you. *Stata Journal* 6: 149–150.

18 Programming Stata

Contents

Stata programming is an advanced topic. Some Stata users live productive lives without ever programming Stata. After all, you do not need to know how to program Stata to input data, create new variables, and fit models. On the other hand, programming Stata is not difficult—at least if the problem is not difficult—and Stata's programmability is one of its best features. The real power of Stata is not revealed until you program it.

If you are uncertain whether to read this chapter, we recommend that you start reading and then bail out when it gets too arcane for you. You will learn things about Stata that you may find useful even if you never write a Stata program.

If you want even more, we offer courses over the Internet on Stata programming; see [U] **3.7.1 Net-Courses**. Baum (2009) provides a wealth of practical knowledge related to Stata programming.

18.1   Description

When you type a command that Stata does not recognize, Stata first looks in its memory for a program of that name. If Stata finds it, Stata executes the program.

There is no Stata command named `hello`,

```
. hello
unrecognized command
r(199);
```

but there could be if you defined a program named `hello`, and after that, the following might happen when you typed `hello`:

```
. hello
hi there
. _
```

This would happen if, beforehand, you had typed

```
. program hello
  1. display "hi there"
  2. end
. _
```

That is how programming works in Stata. A program is defined by

> program *progname*
> > *Stata commands*
> end

and it is executed by typing *progname* at Stata's dot prompt.

18.2   Relationship between a program and a do-file

Stata treats programs the same way it treats do-files. Below we will discuss passing arguments, consuming results from Stata commands, and other topics, but everything we say applies equally to do-files and programs.

Programs and do-files differ in the following ways:

1. You invoke a do-file by typing do *filename*. You invoke a program by simply typing the program's name.

2. Programs must be defined (loaded) before they are used, whereas all that is required to run a do-file is that the file exist. There are ways to make programs load automatically, however, so this difference is of little importance.

3. When you type do *filename*, Stata displays the commands it is executing and the results. When you type *progname*, Stata shows only the results, not the display of the underlying commands. This is an important difference in outlook: in a do-file, how it does something is as important as what it does. In a program, the how is no longer important. You might think of a program as a new feature of Stata.

Let's now mention some of the similarities:

1. Arguments are passed to programs and do-files in the same way.

2. Programs and do-files both contain Stata commands. Any Stata command you put in a do-file can be put in a program.

3. Programs may call other programs. Do-files may call other do-files. Programs may call do-files (this rarely happens), and do-files may call programs (this often happens). Stata allows programs (and do-files) to be nested up to 64 deep.

Now here is the interesting thing: programs are typically defined in do-files (or in a variant of do-files called ado-files; we will get to that later).

You can define a program interactively, and that is useful for pedagogical purposes, but in real applications, you will compose your program in a text editor and store its definition in a do-file.

You have already seen your first program:

```
program hello
        display "hi there"
end
```

You could type those commands interactively, but if the body of the program were more complicated, that would be inconvenient. So instead, suppose that you typed the commands into a do-file:

```
─────────────────────────────────────── begin hello.do ─────────
program hello
        display "hi there"
end
─────────────────────────────────────── end hello.do ─────────
```

Now returning to Stata, you type

```
. do hello

. program hello
  1.        display "hi there"
  2. end

.
end of do-file
```

Do you see that typing do `hello` did nothing but load the program? Typing do `hello` is the same as typing out the program's definition because that is all the do-file contains. The do-file was executed, but the statements in the do-file only defined the program `hello`; they did not execute it. Now that the program is loaded, we can execute it interactively:

```
. hello
hi there
```

So, that is one way you could use do-files and programs together. If you wanted to create new commands for interactive use, you could

1. Write the command as a `program ... end` in a do-file.

2. `do` the do-file before you use the new command.

3. Use the new command during the rest of the session.

There are more convenient ways to do this that would automatically load the do-file, but put that aside. The above method would work.

Another way we could use do-files and programs together is to put the definition of the program and its execution together into a do-file:

```
──────────────────────────────────────────── begin hello.do ─────────
program hello
        display "hi there"
end
hello
──────────────────────────────────────────── end hello.do ─────────
```

Here is what would happen if we executed this do-file:

```
. do hello

. program hello
  1.        display "hi there"
  2. end

. hello
hi there

.

end of do-file
```

Do-files and programs are often used in such combinations. Why? Say that program `hello` is long and complicated and you have a problem where you need to do it twice. That would be a good reason to write a program. Moreover, you may wish to carry forth this procedure as a step of your analysis and, being cautious, do not want to perform this analysis interactively. You never intended program `hello` to be used interactively—it was just something you needed in the midst of a do-file—so you defined the program and used it there.

Anyway, there are many variations on this theme, but few people actually sit in front of Stata and interactively type `program` and then compose a program. They instead do that in front of their text editor. They compose the program in a do-file and then execute the do-file.

There is one other (minor) thing to know: once a program is defined, Stata does not allow you to redefine it:

```
. program hello
hello already defined
r(110);
```

Thus, in our most recent do-file that defines and executes `hello`, we could not rerun it in the same Stata session:

```
. do hello

. program hello
hello already defined
r(110);

end of do-file
r(110);
```

That problem is solved by typing `program drop hello` before redefining it. We could do that interactively, or we could modify our do-file:

```
─────────────────────────────────────── begin hello.do ───────────
program drop hello
program hello
        display "hi there"
end
hello
─────────────────────────────────────── end hello.do ───────────
```

There is a problem with this solution. We can now rerun our do-file, but the first time we tried to run it in a Stata session, it would fail:

```
. do hello

. program drop hello
hello not found
r(111);

end of do-file
r(111);
```

The way around this conundrum is to modify the do-file:

```
─────────────────────────────────────── begin hello.do ───────────
capture program drop hello
program hello
        display "hi there"
end
hello
─────────────────────────────────────── end hello.do ───────────
```

`capture` in front of a command makes Stata indifferent to whether the command works; see [P] **capture**. In real do-files containing programs, you will often see `capture program drop` before the program's definition.

To learn about the `program` command itself, see [P] **program**. It manipulates programs. `program` can define programs, drop programs, and show you a directory of programs that you have defined.

A program can contain any Stata command, but certain Stata commands are of special interest to program writers; see the *Programming* heading in the subject table of contents in the *Quick Reference and Index*.

18.3 Macros

Before we can begin programming, we must discuss macros, which are the variables of Stata programs.

A *macro* is a string of characters, called the *macroname*, that stands for another string of characters, called the *macro contents*.

Macros can be local or global. We will start with local macros because they are the most commonly used, but nothing really distinguishes one from the other at this stage.

18.3.1   Local macros

Local macro names can be up to 31 (not 32) characters long.

One sets the contents of a local macro with the `local` command. In fact, we can do this interactively. We will begin by experimenting with macros in this way to learn about them. If we type

```
. local shortcut "myvar thisvar thatvar"
```

then `‘shortcut’` is a synonym for "`myvar thisvar thatvar`". Note the single quotes around shortcut. We said that sentence exactly the way we meant to because

> if you type   `‘shortcut’`,
> i.e.,   left-single-quote `shortcut` right-single-quote,
> Stata hears   `myvar thisvar thatvar`.

To access the contents of the macro, we use a left single quote (located at the upper left on most keyboards), the macro name, and a right single quote (located under the " on the right side of most keyboards).

The single quotes bracketing the macroname `shortcut` are called the macro-substitution characters. `shortcut` means `shortcut`. `‘shortcut’` means `myvar thisvar thatvar`.

So, if you typed

```
. list ‘shortcut’
```

the effect would be exactly as if you typed

```
. list myvar thisvar thatvar
```

Macros can be used anywhere in Stata. For instance, if we also defined

```
. local cmd "list"
```

we could type

```
. ‘cmd’ ‘shortcut’
```

to mean `list myvar thisvar thatvar`.

For another example, consider the definitions

```
. local prefix "my"
. local suffix "var"
```

Then

```
. ‘cmd’ ‘prefix’‘suffix’
```

would mean `list myvar`.

One other important note is on the way we use left and right single quotes within Stata, which you will especially deal with when working with macros (see [U] **18.3 Macros**). Single quotes (and double quotes, for that matter) may look different on your keyboard, your monitor, and our printed documentation, making it difficult to determine which key to press on your keyboard to replicate what we have shown you.

For the left single quote, we use the grave accent, which occupies a key by itself on most computer keyboards. On U.S. keyboards, the grave accent is located at the top left, next to the numeral 1. On some non-U.S. keyboards, the grave accent is produced by a dead key. For example, pressing the grave accent dead key followed by the letter a would produce à; to get the grave accent by itself, you would press the grave accent dead key followed by a space. This accent mark appears in our printed documentation as ‘.

For the right single quote, we use the standard single quote, or apostrophe. On U.S. keyboards, the single quote is located on the same key as the double quote, on the right side of the keyboard next to the *Enter* key.

18.3.2   Global macros

Let's put aside why Stata has two kinds of macros—local and global—and focus right now on how global macros work.

Global macros can have names that are up to 32 (not 31) characters long. You set the contents of a global macro by using the `global` rather than the `local` command:

```
. global shortcut "alpha beta"
```

You obtain the contents of a global macro by prefixing its name with a dollar sign: `$shortcut` is equivalent to "alpha beta".

In the previous section, we defined a local macro named `shortcut`, which is a different macro. `'shortcut'` is still "myvar thisvar thatvar".

Local and global macros may have the same names, but even if they do, they are unrelated and are still distinguishable.

Global macros are just like local macros except that you set their contents with `global` rather than `local`, and you substitute their contents by prefixing them with a `$` rather than enclosing them in ` ' `.

18.3.3   The difference between local and global macros

The difference between local and global macros is that local macros are private and global macros are public.

Say that you have written a program

```
program myprog
        code using local macro alpha
end
```

The local macro `alpha` in `myprog` is private in that no other program can modify or even look at `alpha`'s contents. To make this point absolutely clear, assume that your program looks like this:

```
program myprog
        code using local macro alpha
        mysub
        more code using local macro alpha
end
program mysub
        code using local macro alpha
end
```

`myprog` calls `mysub`, and both programs use a local macro named `alpha`. Even so, the local macros in each program are different. `mysub`'s `alpha` macro may contain one thing, but that has nothing to do with what `myprog`'s `alpha` macro contains. Even when `mysub` begins execution, its `alpha` macro is different from `myprog`'s. It is not that `mysub`'s inherits `myprog`'s `alpha` macro contents but is then free to change it. It is that `myprog`'s `alpha` and `mysub`'s `alpha` are entirely different things.

When you write a program using local macros, you need not worry that some other program has been written using local macros with the same names. Local macros are just that: local to your program.

Global macros, on the other hand, are available to all programs. If both myprog and mysub use the global macro beta, they are using the same macro. Whatever the contents of $beta are when mysub is invoked, those are the contents when mysub begins execution, and, whatever the contents of $beta are when mysub completes, those are the contents when myprog regains control.

18.3.4 Macros and expressions

From now on, we are going to use local and global macros according to whichever is convenient; whatever is said about one applies to the other.

Consider the definitions

```
. local one 2+2
. local two = 2+2
```

(which we could just as well have illustrated using the global command). In any case, note the equal sign in the second macro definition and the lack of the equal sign in the first. Formally, the first should be

```
. local one "2+2"
```

but Stata does not mind if we omit the double quotes in the local (global) statement.

local one 2+2 (with or without double quotes) copies the string 2+2 into the macro named one.

local two = 2+2 evaluates the expression 2+2, producing 4, and stores 4 in the macro named two.

That is, you type

local *macname contents*

if you want to copy *contents* to *macname*, and you type

local *macname = expression*

if you want to evaluate *expression* and store the result in *macname*.

In the second form, *expression* can be numeric or string. 2+2 is a numeric expression. As an example of a string expression,

```
. local res = substr("this",1,2) + "at"
```

stores that in res.

Because the expression can be either numeric or string, what is the difference between the following statements?

```
. local a "example"
. local b = "example"
```

Both statements store example in their respective macros. The first does so by a simple copy operation, whereas the second evaluates the expression "example", which is a string expression because of the double quotes that, here, evaluates to itself.

There is, however, a difference. Stata's expression parser is limited to handling strings of 244 characters. Strings longer than that are truncated.

The copy operation of the first syntax is not limited—it can copy up to the maximum length of a macro, which is currently 165,200 characters for Stata/IC and 8,681 for Small Stata. For Stata/MP and Stata/SE, the limit is $33 * c(\text{max\_k\_theory}) + 200$ characters, which for the default setting of 5,000 is 165,200 characters.

To a programmer, the length limit for string expressions may seem restrictive, but it is not, because of another feature discussed in [U] **18.3.6 Extended macro functions**.

There are some other issues of using macros and expressions that look a little strange to programmers coming from other languages, at least the first time they see them. Say that the macro 'i' contains 5. How would you increment i so that it contains $5 + 1 = 6$? The answer is

```
local i = 'i' + 1
```

Do you see why the single quotes are on the right but not the left? Remember, 'i' refers to the contents of the local macro named i, which, we just said, is 5. Thus, after expansion, the line reads

```
local i = 5 + 1
```

which is the desired result.

There is a another way to increment local macros that will be more familiar to some programmers, especially C programmers:

```
local ++i
```

As C programmers would expect, `local ++i` is more efficient (executes more quickly) than `local i = i+1`, but in terms of outcome, it is equivalent. You can decrement a local macro by using

```
local --i
```

`local --i` is equivalent to `local i = i-1` but executes more quickly. Finally,

```
local i++
```

will *not* increment the local macro i but instead redefines the local macro i to contain ++. There is, however, a context in which i++ (and i--) do work as expected; see [U] **18.3.7 Macro increment and decrement functions**.

18.3.5 Double quotes

Consider another local macro, 'answ', which might contain yes or no. In a program that was supposed to do something different on the basis of answ's content, you might code

```
if "'answ'" == "yes" {
        . . .
}
else {
        . . .
}
```

Note the odd-looking "'answ'", and now think about the line after substitution. The line reads either

```
if "yes" == "yes" {
```

or

```
if "no" == "yes" {
```

either of which is the desired result. Had we omitted the double quotes, the line would have read

```
if no == "yes" {
```

(assuming `answ` contains no), and that is not at all the desired result. As the line reads now, no would not be a string but would be interpreted as a variable in the data.

The key to all this is to think of the line after substitution.

Double quotes are used to enclose strings: "yes", "no", "my dir\my file", "`answ`" (meaning that the contents of local macro answ, treated as a string), and so on. Double quotes are used with macros,

```
local a "example"
if "`answ`" == "yes" {
        ...
}
```

and double quotes are used by many Stata commands:

```
. regress lnwage age ed if sex=="female"
. gen outa = outcome if drug=="A"
. use "person file"
```

Do not omit the double quotes just because you are using a "quoted" macro:

```
. regress lnwage age ed if sex=="`x`"
. gen outa = outcome if drug=="`firstdrug`"
. use "`filename`"
```

Stata has two sets of double-quote characters, of which "" is one. The other is `""`. They both work the same way:

```
. regress lnwage age ed if sex==`"female"`
. gen outa = outcome if drug==`"A"`
. use `"person file"`
```

No rational user would use `""` (called compound double quotes) instead of "" (called simple double quotes), but smart programmers do use them:

```
local a `"example"`
if `""`answ`""` == `"yes"` {
        ...
}
```

Why is `"example"` better than "example", `""`answ`""` better than "`answ`", and `"yes"` better than "yes"? The answer is that only `""`answ`""` is better than "`answ`"; `"example"` and `"yes"` are no better—and no worse—than "example" and "yes".

`""`answ`""` is better than "`answ`" because the macro answ might itself contain (simple or compound) double quotes. The really great thing about compound double quotes is that they nest. Say that `answ` contained the string "I "think" so". Then,

Stata would find	if "`answ`"=="yes"
confusing because it would expand to	if "I "think" so"=="yes"
Stata would not find	if `""`answ`""`==`"yes"`
confusing because it would expand to	if `""I "think" so"`==`"yes"`

Open and close double quote in the simple form look the same; open quote is " and so is close quote. Open and close double quote in the compound form are distinguishable; open quote is `" and close quote is "`, and so Stata can pair the close with the corresponding open double quote. `"I "think" so"` is easy for Stata to understand, whereas "I "think" so" is a hopeless mishmash. (If you disagree, consider what "A"B"C" might mean. Is it the quoted string A"B"C, or is it quoted string A, followed by B, followed by quoted string C?)

Because Stata can distinguish open from close quotes, even nested compound double quotes are understandable: `‘"I ‘"think"’ so"’`. (What does `"A"B"C"` mean? Either it means `‘"A‘"B"’C"’` or it means `‘"A"’B‘"C"’`.)

Yes, compound double quotes make you think that your vision is stuttering, especially when combined with the macro substitution `‘ ’` characters. That is why we rarely use them, even when writing programs. You do not have to use exclusively one or the other style of quotes. It is perfectly acceptable to code

```
local a "example"
if ‘"‘answ’"’ == "yes" {
        ...
}
```

using compound double quotes where it might be necessary (`‘"‘answ’"’`) and using simple double quotes in other places (such as `"yes"`). It is also acceptable to use simple double quotes around macros (e.g., `"‘answ’"`) if you are certain that the macros themselves do not contain double quotes or (more likely) if you do not care what happens if they do.

Sometimes careful programmers should use compound double quotes. Later you will learn that Stata's `syntax` command interprets standard Stata syntax and so makes it easy to write programs that understand things like

```
. myprog mpg weight if strpos(make,"VW")!=0
```

`syntax` works—we are getting ahead of ourselves—by placing the if *exp* typed by the user in the local macro if. Thus `‘if’` will contain "if strpos(make,"VW")!=0" here. Now say that you are at a point in your program where you want to know whether the user specified an if *exp*. It would be natural to code

```
if ‘"‘if’"’ != "" {
        // the if exp was specified
        ...
}
else {
        // it was not
        ...
}
```

We used compound double quotes around the macro `‘if’`. The local macro `‘if’` might contain double quotes, so we placed compound double quotes around it.

18.3.6   Extended macro functions

In addition to allowing =*exp*, `local` and `global` provide *extended functions*. The use of an extended function is denoted by a colon (`:`) following the macro name, as in

```
local       lbl : variable label myvar
local filenames : dir "." files "*.dta"
local       xi : word ‘i’ of ‘list’
```

Some macro extended functions access a piece of information. In the first example, the variable label associated with variable `myvar` will be stored in macro `lbl`. Other macro extended functions perform operations to gather the information. In the second example, macro `filenames` will contain the names of all the `.dta` datasets in the current directory. Still other macro extended functions perform an operation on their arguments and return the result. In the third example, `xi` will contain the `‘i’`th word (element) of `‘list’`. See [P] **macro** for a list of the macro extended functions.

Another useful source of information is c(), documented in [P] **creturn**:

```
local  today "`c(current_date)'"
local curdir "`c(pwd)'"
local   newn = c(N)+1
```

c() refers to a prerecorded list of values, which may be used directly in expressions or which may be quoted and the result substituted anywhere. c(current_date) returns today's date in the form *"dd MON yyyy"*. Thus the first example stores in macro today that date. c(pwd) returns the current directory, such as C:\data\proj. Thus the second example stores in macro curdir the current directory. c(N) returns the number of observations of the data in memory. Thus the third example stores in macro newn that number, plus one.

Note the use of quotes with c(). We could just as well have coded the first two examples as

```
local  today = c(current_date)
local curdir = c(pwd)
```

c() is a Stata function in the same sense that sqrt() is a Stata function. Thus we can use c() directly in expressions. It is a special property of macro expansion, however, that you may use the c() function inside macro-expansion quotes. The same is not true of sqrt().

In any case, whenever you need a piece of information, whether it be about the dataset or about the environment, look in [P] **macro** and [P] **creturn**. It is likely to be in one place or the other, and sometimes, it is in both. You can obtain the current directory by using

```
local curdir = c(pwd)
```

or by using

```
local curdir : pwd
```

When information is in both, it does not matter which source you use.

18.3.7 Macro increment and decrement functions

We mentioned incrementing macros in [U] **18.3.4 Macros and expressions**. The construct

```
command that makes reference to `i'
local ++i
```

occurs so commonly in Stata programs that it is convenient (and faster when executed) to collapse both lines of code into one and to increment (or decrement) i at the same time that it is referred to. Stata allows this:

```
while (`++i' < 1000) {
        ...
}
while (`i++' < 1000) {
        ...
}
while (`--i' > 0) {
        ...
}
while (`i--' > 0) {
        ...
}
```

Above we have chosen to illustrate this by using Stata's `while` command, but `++` and `--` can be used anyplace in any context, just so long as it is enclosed in macro-substitution quotes.

When the `++` or `--` appears before the name, the macro is first incremented or decremented, and then the result is substituted.

When the `++` or `--` appears after the name, the current value of the macro is substituted and then the macro is incremented or decremented.

❑ Technical note

Do not use the inline `++` or `--` operators when a part of the line might not be executed. Consider

```
if (‘i’==0) local j = ‘k++’
```

versus

```
if (‘i’==0) {
        local j = ‘k++’
}
```

The first will not do what you expect because macros are expanded before the line is interpreted. Thus the first will result in k always being incremented, whereas the second increments k only when `‘i’==0`.

❑

18.3.8 Macro expressions

Typing

> *command that makes reference to* `‘=exp’`

is equivalent to

> `local` *macroname* `=` *exp*
> *command that makes reference to* `‘macroname’`

although the former runs faster and is easier to type. When you use `‘=exp’` within some larger command, *exp* is evaluated by Stata's expression evaluator, and the results are inserted as a literal string into the larger command. Then the command is executed. For example,

```
summarize u4
summarize u‘=2+2’
summarize u‘=4*(cos(0)==1)’
```

all do the same thing. *exp* can be any valid Stata expression and thus may include references to variables, matrices, scalars, or even other macros. In the last case, just remember to enclose the submacros in quotes:

```
replace ‘var’ = ‘group’[‘=‘j’+1’]
```

Also, typing

> *command that makes reference to* `‘:extended macro function’`

is equivalent to

> `local` *macroname* `:` *extended macro function*
> *command that makes reference to* `‘macroname’`

Thus one might code

```
format y ':format x'
```

to assign to variable y the same format as the variable x.

❏ Technical note

There is another macro expansion operator, . (called dot), which is used in conjunction with Stata's class system; see [P] **class** for more information.

There is also a macro expansion function, macval(), which is for use when expanding a macro—'macval(*name*)'—which confines the macro expansion to the first level of *name*, thereby suppressing the expansion of any embedded references to macros within *name*. Only two or three Stata users have or will ever need this, but, if you suspect you are one of them, see [P] **macro** and then see [P] **file** for an example.

❏

18.3.9 Advanced local macro manipulation

This section is really an aside to help test your understanding of macro substitution. The tricky examples illustrated below sometimes occur in real programs.

1. Say that you have macros x1, x2, x3, and so on. Obviously, 'x1' refers to the contents of x1, 'x2' to the contents of x2, etc. What does 'x'i'' refer to? Suppose that 'i' contains 6.

   The rule is to expand the inside first:

   'x'i''   expands to   'x6'
   'x6'   expands to   the contents of local macro x6

   So, there you have a vector of macros.

2. We have already shown adjoining expansions: 'alpha''beta' expands to myvar if 'alpha' contains my and 'beta' contains var. What does 'alpha''gamma''beta' expand to when gamma is undefined?

   Stata does not mind if you refer to a nonexistent macro. A nonexistent macro is treated as a macro with no contents. If local macro gamma does not exist, then

   'gamma'   expands to   nothing

   It is not an error. Thus 'alpha''gamma''beta' expands to myvar.

3. You clear a local macro by setting its contents to nothing:

   ```
          local macname
   or     local macname ""
   or     local macname = ""
   ```

[U] 18.3 Macros   215

18.3.10   Advanced global macro manipulation

Global macros are rarely used, and when they are used, it is typically for communication between programs. You should never use a global macro where a local macro would suffice.

1. Constructions like xi are expanded sequentially. If $x contained this and $i 6, then xi expands to this6. If $x was undefined, then xi is just 6 because undefined global macros, like undefined local macros, are treated as containing nothing.

2. You can nest macro expansion by including braces, so if $i contains 6, ${x$i} expands to ${x6}, which expands to the contents of $x6 (which would be nothing if $x6 is undefined).

3. You can mix global and local macros. Assume that local macro j contains 7. Then, ${x`j'} expands to the contents of $x7.

4. You also use braces to force the contents of global macros to run up against the succeeding text. For instance, assume that the macro drive contains "b:". If drive were a local macro, you could type

    `drive'myfile.dta

    to obtain b:myfile.dta. Because drive is a global macro, however, you must type

    ${drive}myfile.dta

    You could not type

    $drive myfile.dta

    because that would expand to b: myfile.dta. You could not type

    $drivemyfile.dta

    because that would expand to .dta.

5. Because Stata uses $ to mark global-macro expansion, printing a real $ is sometimes tricky. To display the string $22.15 with the display command, you can type display "\$22.15", although you can get away with display "$22.15" because Stata is rather smart. Stata would not be smart about display "$this" if you really wanted to display $this and not the contents of the macro this. You would have to type display "\$this". Another alternative would be to use the SMCL code for a dollar sign when you wanted to display it: display "{c S|}this"; see [P] **smcl**.

6. Real dollar signs can also be placed into the contents of macros, thus postponing substitution. First, let's understand what happens when we do not postpone substitution; consider the following definitions:

    ```
    global baseset "myvar thatvar"
    global bigset "$baseset thisvar"
    ```

    $bigset is equivalent to "myvar thatvar thisvar". Now say that we redefine the macro baseset:

    ```
    global baseset "myvar thatvar othvar"
    ```

    The definition of bigset has not changed—it is still equivalent to "myvar thatvar thisvar". It has not changed because bigset used the definition of baseset that was current at the time it was defined. bigset no longer knows that its contents are supposed to have any relation to baseset.

    Instead, let's assume that we had defined bigset as

    ```
    global bigset "\$baseset thisvar"
    ```

at the outset. Then `$bigset` is equivalent to "`$baseset thisvar`", which in turn is equivalent to "`myvar thatvar othvar thisvar`". Because `bigset` explicitly depends upon `baseset`, anytime we change the definition of `baseset`, we will automatically change the definition of `bigset` as well.

18.3.11   Constructing Windows filenames by using macros

Stata uses the \ character to tell its parser not to expand macros.

Windows uses the \ character as the directory path separator.

Mostly, there is no problem using a \ in a filename. However, if you are writing a program that contains a Windows path in macro `path` and a filename in `fname`, do not assemble the final result as

> `'path'\'fname'`

because Stata will interpret the \ as an instruction to not expand `'fname'`. Instead, assemble the final result as

> `'path'/'fname'`

Stata understands / as a directory separator on all platforms.

18.3.12   Accessing system values

Stata programs often need access to system parameters and settings, such as the value of π, the current date and time, or the current working directory.

System values are accessed via Stata's c-class values. The syntax works much the same as if you were referring to a local macro. For example, a reference to the c-class value for π, `'c(pi)'`, will expand to a literal string containing 3.141592653589793 and could be used to do

```
. display sqrt(2*'c(pi)')
2.5066283
```

You could also access the current time

```
. display "'c(current_time)'"
11:34:57
```

C-class values are designed to provide one all-encompassing way to access system parameters and settings, including system directories, system limits, string limits, memory settings, properties of the data currently in memory, output settings, efficiency settings, network settings, and debugging settings.

See [P] **creturn** for a detailed list of what is available. Typing

```
. creturn list
```

will give you the list of current settings.

18.3.13   Referring to characteristics

Characteristics—see [U] **12.8 Characteristics**—are like macros associated with variables. They have names of the form *varname*[*charname*]—such as `mpg[comment]`—and you quote their names just as you do macro names to obtain their contents:

> To substitute the value of *varname*[*charname*], type   `'varname[charname]'`
> For example,   `'mpg[comment]'`

You set the contents using the `char` command:

$$\text{char } varname\,[charname]\ \ [["]text["]]$$

This is similar to the `local` and `global` commands, except that there is no =*exp* variation. You clear a characteristic by setting its contents to nothing just as you would with a macro:

Type	`char` *varname*[*charname*]
or	`char` *varname*[*charname*] `""`

What is unique about characteristics is that they are saved with the data, meaning that their contents survive from one session to the next, and they are associated with variables in the data, so if you ever drop a variable, the associated characteristics disappear, too. (Also, _dta[*charname*] is associated with the data but not with any variable in particular.)

All the standard rules apply: characteristics may be referred to by quotation in any context, and the characteristic's contents are substituted for the quoted characteristic name. As with macros, referring to a nonexistent characteristic is not an error; it merely substitutes to nothing.

18.4 Program arguments

When you invoke a program or do-file, what you type following the program or do-file name are the arguments. For instance, if you have a program called `xyz` and type

```
. xyz mpg weight
```

then `mpg` and `weight` are the program's arguments, `mpg` being the first argument and `weight` the second.

Program arguments are passed to programs via local macros:

Macro	Contents
'0'	what the user typed exactly as the user typed it, odd spacing, double quotes, and all
'1'	the first argument (first word of '0')
'2'	the second argument (second word of '0')
'3'	the third argument (third word of '0')
...	...
'*'	the arguments '1', '2', '3', ..., listed one after the other and with one blank in between; similar to but different from '0' because odd spacing and double quotes are removed

That is, what the user types is passed to you in three different ways:

1. It is passed in '0' exactly as the user typed it, meaning quotes, odd spacing, and all.

2. It is passed in '1', '2', ... broken out into arguments on the basis of blanks (but with quotes used to force binding; we will get to that).

3. It is passed in '*' as "'1' '2' '3' ...", which is a crudely cleaned up version of '0'.

You will probably not use all three forms in one program.

We recommend that you ignore '*', at least for receiving arguments; it is included so that old Stata programs will continue to work.

Operating directly with '0' takes considerable programming sophistication, although Stata's `syntax` command makes interpreting '0' according to standard Stata syntax easy. That will be covered in [U] **18.4.4 Parsing standard Stata syntax** below.

The easiest way to receive arguments, however, is to deal with the positional macros '1', '2', ...

At the start of this section, we imagined an `xyz` program invoked by typing `xyz mpg weight`. Then '1' would contain `mpg`, '2' would contain `weight`, and '3' would contain nothing.

Let's write a program to report the correlation between two variables. Of course, Stata already has a command that can do this—`correlate`—and, in fact, we will implement our program in terms of `correlate`. It is silly, but all we want to accomplish right now is to show how Stata passes arguments to a program.

Here is our program:

```
program xyz
        correlate '1' '2'
end
```

Once the program is defined, we can try it:

```
. use http://www.stata-press.com/data/r11/auto
(1978 Automobile Data)

. xyz mpg weight
(obs=74)
```

	mpg	weight
mpg	1.0000	
weight	-0.8072	1.0000

See how this works? We typed `xyz mpg weight`, which invoked our `xyz` program with '1' being `mpg` and '2' being `weight`. Our program gave the command `correlate '1' '2'`, and that expanded to `correlate mpg weight`.

Stylistically, this is not a good example of the use of positional arguments, but realistically, there is nothing wrong with it. The stylistic problem is that if `xyz` is really to report the correlation between two variables, it ought to allow standard Stata syntax, and that is not a difficult thing to do. Realistically, the program works.

Positional arguments, however, play an important role, even for programmers who care about style. When we write a subroutine—a program to be called by another program and not intended for direct human use—we often pass information by using positional arguments.

Stata forms the positional arguments '1', '2', . . . by taking what the user typed following the command (or do-file), parsing it on white space with double quotes used to force binding, and stripping the quotes. The arguments are formed on the basis of words, but double-quoted strings are kept together as one argument but with the quotes removed.

Let's create a program to illustrate these concepts. Although we would not normally define programs interactively, this program is short enough that we will:

```
. program listargs
  1.   display "The 1st argument you typed is: '1'"
  2.   display "The 2nd argument you typed is: '2'"
  3.   display "The 3rd argument you typed is: '3'"
  4.   display "The 4th argument you typed is: '4'"
  5.   end
```

The `display` command simply types the double-quoted string following it; see [P] **display**.

Let's try our program:

```
. listargs
The 1st argument you typed is:
The 2nd argument you typed is:
The 3rd argument you typed is:
The 4th argument you typed is:
```

We type `listargs`, and the result shows us what we already know—we typed nothing after the word `listargs`. There are no arguments. Let's try it again, this time adding `this is a test`:

```
. listargs this is a test
The 1st argument you typed is:  this
The 2nd argument you typed is:  is
The 3rd argument you typed is:  a
The 4th argument you typed is:  test
```

We learn that the first argument is 'this', the second is 'is', and so on. Blanks always separate arguments. You can, however, override this feature by placing double quotes around what you type:

```
. listargs "this is a test"
The 1st argument you typed is:  this is a test
The 2nd argument you typed is:
The 3rd argument you typed is:
The 4th argument you typed is:
```

This time we typed only one argument, 'this is a test'. When we place double quotes around what we type, Stata interprets whatever we type inside the quotes to be one argument. Here '1' contains 'this is a test' (the double quotes were removed).

We can use double quotes more than once:

```
. listargs "this is" "a test"
The 1st argument you typed is:  this is
The 2nd argument you typed is:  a test
The 3rd argument you typed is:
The 4th argument you typed is:
```

The first argument is 'this is' and the second argument is 'a test'.

18.4.1   Named positional arguments

Positional arguments can be named: in your code, you do not have to refer to '1', '2', '3', ...; you can instead refer to more meaningful names, such as n, a, and b; numb, alpha, and beta; or whatever else you find convenient. You want to do this because programs coded in terms of '1', '2', ... are hard to read and therefore are more likely to contain errors.

You obtain better-named positional arguments by using the `args` command:

```
program progname
        args argnames
        . . .
end
```

For instance, if your program received four positional arguments and you wanted to call them varname, n, oldval, and newval, you would code

```
program progname
        args varname n oldval newval
        . . .
end
```

varname, n, oldval, and newval become new local macros, and `args` simply copies '1', '2', '3', and '4' to them. It does not change '1', '2', '3', and '4'—you can still refer to the numbered macros if you wish—and it does not verify that your program receives the right number of arguments. If our example above were invoked with just two arguments, 'oldval' and 'newval' would contain nothing. If it were invoked with five arguments, the fifth argument would still be out there, stored in local macro '5'.

Let's make a command to create a dataset containing n observations on x ranging from a to b. Such a command would be useful, for instance, if we wanted to graph some complicated mathematical function and experiment with different ranges. It is convenient if we can type the range of x over which we wish to make the graph rather than concocting the range by hand. (In fact, Stata already has such a command—range—but it will be instructive to write our own.)

Before writing this program, we had better know how to proceed, so here is how you could create a dataset containing n observations with x ranging from a to b:

1. `drop _all`
   to clear whatever data are in memory.

2. `set obs` n
   to make a dataset of n observations on no variables; if n were 100, we would type `set obs 100`.

3. `gen x = (_n-1)/(`n`-1)*(`b`-`a`)+`a
   because the built-in variable _n is 1 in the first observation, 2 in the second, and so on; see [U] **13.4 System variables (_variables)**.

So, the first version of our program might read

```
program rng                          // arguments are n a b
        drop _all
        set obs '1'
        generate x = (_n-1)/(_N-1)*('3'-'2')+'2'
end
```

The above is just a direct translation of what we just said. '1' corresponds to n, '2' corresponds to a, and '3' corresponds to b. This program, however, would be far more understandable if we changed it to read

```
program rng
        args n a b
        drop _all
        set obs 'n'
        generate x = (_n-1)/(_N-1)*('b'-'a')+'a'
end
```

18.4.2   Incrementing through positional arguments

Some programs contain k arguments, where k varies, but it does not much matter because the same thing is done to each argument. One such program is summarize: type `summarize mpg` to obtain summary statistics on mpg, and type `summarize mpg weight` to obtain first summary statistics on mpg and then summary statistics on weight.

```
program ...
        local i = 1
        while "''i''" != "" {
                logic stated in terms of ''i''
                local ++i
        }
end
```

Equivalently, if the logic that uses ''i'' contains only one reference to ''i'',

```
program ...
        local i = 1
        while "''i''" != "" {
                logic stated in terms of ''i++''
        }
end
```

Note the tricky construction ''i'', which then itself is placed in double quotes—"''i''"—for the while loop. To understand it, say that i contains 1 or, equivalently, 'i' is 1. Then ''i'' is '1' is the name of the first variable. "''i''" is the name of the first variable in quotes. The while asks if the name of the variable is nothing and, if it is not, executes. Now 'i' is 2, and "''i''" is the name of the second variable, in quotes. If that name is not "", we continue. If the name is "", we are done.

Say that you were writing a subroutine that was to receive k variables, but the code that processes each variable needs to know (while it is processing) how many variables were passed to the subroutine. You need first to count the variables (and so derive k) and then, knowing k, pass through the list again.

```
program progname
        local k = 1                  // count the number of arguments
        while "''k''" != "" {
                local ++k
        }
        local --k                    // k contains one too many
                                     // now pass through again
        local i = 1
        while 'i' <= 'k' {
                code in terms of ''i'' and 'k'
                local ++i
        }
end
```

In the above example, we have used while, Stata's all-purpose looping command. Stata has two other looping commands, foreach and forvalues, and they sometimes produce code that is more readable and executes more quickly. We direct you to read [P] **foreach** and [P] **forvalues**, but at this point, there is nothing they can do that while cannot do. Above we coded

```
local i = 1
while 'i' <= 'k' {
        code in terms of ''i'' and 'k'
        local ++i
}
```

to produce logic that looped over the values 'i' = 1 to 'k'. We could have instead coded

```
forvalues i = 1(1)'k' {
        code in terms of ''i'' and 'k'
}
```

Similarly, at the beginning of this subsection, we said that you could use the following code in terms of while to loop over the arguments received:

```
program ...
        local i = 1
        while "''i''" != "" {
                logic stated in terms of ''i''
                local ++i
        }
end
```

Equivalent to the above would be

```
program ...
        foreach x of local 0 {
                logic stated in terms of `x'
        }
end
```

See [P] **foreach** and [P] **forvalues**.

You can combine `args` and incrementing through an unknown number of positional arguments. Say that you were writing a subroutine that was to receive `varname`, the name of some variable; n, which is some sort of count; and at least one and maybe 20 variable names. Perhaps you are to sum the variables, divide by n, and store the result in the first variable. What the program does is irrelevant; here is how we could receive the arguments:

```
program progname
        args varname n
        local i 3
        while "``i''" != "" {
                logic stated in terms of ``i''
                local ++i
        }
end
```

18.4.3   Using macro shift

Another way to code the repeat-the-same-process problem for each argument is

```
program ...
        while "`1'" != "" {
                logic stated in terms of `1'
                macro shift
        }
end
```

`macro shift` shifts `1', `2', `3', ..., one to the left: what was `1' disappears, what was `2' becomes `1', what was `3' becomes `2', and so on.

The outside `while` loop continues the process until macro `1' contains nothing.

`macro shift` is an older construct that we no longer advocate using. Instead, we recommend that you use the techniques described in the previous subsection, that is, references to ``i'' and foreach/forvalues.

There are two reasons we make this recommendation: `macro shift` destroys the positional macros `1', `2', which must then be reset using `tokenize` should you wish to pass through the argument list again, and (more importantly) if the number of arguments is large (which in Stata/MP and Stata/SE is more likely), `macro shift` can be incredibly slow.

❏ Technical note

`macro shift` can do one thing that would be difficult to do by other means.

`*', the result of listing the contents of the numbered macros one after the other with one blank between, changes with `macro shift`. Say that your program received a list of variables and that the first variable was the dependent variable and the rest were independent variables. You want to save the first variable name in `lhsvar' and all the rest in `rhsvars'. You could code

```
program progname
        local lhsvar "`1'"
        macro shift 1
        local rhsvars "`*'"
        ...
end
```

Now suppose that one macro contains a list of variables and you want to split the contents of the macro in two. Perhaps 'varlist' is the result of a syntax command (see [U] **18.4.4 Parsing standard Stata syntax**), and you now wish to split 'varlist' into 'lhsvar' and 'rhsvars'. tokenize will reset the numbered macros:

```
program progname
        ...
        tokenize `varlist'
        local lhsvar "`1'"
        macro shift 1
        local rhsvars "`*'"
        ...
end
```

❏

18.4.4   Parsing standard Stata syntax

Let's now switch to '0' from the positional arguments '1', '2', ...

You can parse '0' (what the user typed) according to standard Stata syntax with one command. Remember that standard Stata syntax is

$$\left[\text{by } varlist:\right] \quad command \quad \left[varlist\right] \quad \left[=exp\right] \quad \left[\text{using } filename\right] \quad \left[if\right] \quad \left[in\right] \quad \left[weight\right]$$

$$\left[, \ options\right]$$

See [U] **11 Language syntax**.

The syntax command parses standard syntax. You code what amounts to the syntax diagram of your command in your program, and then syntax looks at '0' (it knows to look there) and compares what the user typed with what you are willing to accept. Then one of two things happens: either syntax stores the pieces in an easily processable way or, if what the user typed does not match what you specified, syntax issues the appropriate error message and stops your program.

Consider a program that is to take two or more variable names along with an optional if *exp* and in *range*. The program would read

```
program ...
        syntax varlist(min=2) [if] [in]
        ...
    end
```

You will have to read [P] **syntax** to learn how to specify the syntactical elements, but the command is certainly readable, and it will not be long until you are guessing correctly about how to fill it in. And yes, the square brackets really do indicate optional elements, and you just use them with syntax in the natural way.

The one syntax command you code encompasses the parsing process. Here, if what the user typed matches "two or more variables and an optional if and in", syntax defines new local macros:

> `'varlist'`   the two or more variable names
> `'if'`   the if *exp* specified by the user (or nothing)
> `'in'`   the in *range* specified by the user (or nothing)

To see that this works, experiment with the following program:

```
program tryit
        syntax varlist(min=2) [if] [in]
        display "varlist now contains |'varlist'|"
        display '"if now contains |'if'|"'
        display "in now contains |'in'|"
end
```

Below we experiment:

```
. tryit mpg weight
varlist now contains |mpg weight|
if now contains ||
in now contains ||
. tryit mpg weight displ if foreign==1
varlist now contains |mpg weight displ|
if now contains |if foreign==1|
in now contains ||
. tryit mpg wei in 1/10
varlist now contains |mpg weight|
if now contains ||
in now contains |in 1/10|
. tryit mpg
too few variables specified
r(102);
```

In our third try we abbreviated the weight variable as `wei`, yet, after parsing, `syntax` unabbreviated the variable for us.

If this program were next going to step through the variables in the varlist, the positional macros '1', '2', ... could be reset by coding

```
tokenize 'varlist'
```

See [P] **tokenize**. `tokenize 'varlist'` resets '1' to be the first word of 'varlist', '2' to be the second word, and so on.

18.4.5   Parsing immediate commands

Immediate commands are described in [U] **19 Immediate commands**—they take numbers as arguments. By convention, when you name immediate commands, you should make the last letter of the name *i*. Assume that `mycmdi` takes as arguments two numbers, the first of which must be a positive integer, and allows the options `alpha` and `beta`. The basic structure is

```
program mycmdi
        gettoken n 0 : 0, parse(" ,")         /* get first number */
        gettoken x 0 : 0, parse(" ,")         /* get second number */
        confirm integer number 'n'            /* verify first is integer */
        confirm number 'x'                    /* verify second is number */

        if 'n'<=0 error 2001                  /* check that n is positive */
        place any other checks here

        syntax [, Alpha Beta]                 /* parse remaining syntax */
        make calculation and display output
end
```

See [P] **gettoken**.

18.4.6   Parsing nonstandard syntax

If you wish to interpret nonstandard syntax and positional arguments are not adequate for you, you know that you face a formidable programming task. The key to the solution is the gettoken command.

gettoken can pull one token from the front of a macro according to the parsing characters you specify and, optionally, define another macro or redefine the initial macro to contain the remaining (unparsed) characters. That is,

Say that '0' contains	"this is what the user typed"
After gettoken,	
new macro 'token' could contain	"this"
and '0' could still contain	"this is what the user typed"
or	
new macro 'token' could contain	"this"
and new macro 'rest' could contain	" is what the user typed"
and '0' could still contain	"this is what the user typed"
or	
new macro 'token' could contain	"this"
and '0' could contain	" is what the user typed"

A simplified syntax of gettoken is

> gettoken *emname1* [*emname2*] : *emname3* [, parse(*pchars*) quotes
>
>   match(*lmacname*) bind]

where *emname1*, *emname2*, *emname3*, and *lmacname* are the names of local macros. (Stata provides a way to work with global macros, but in practice that is seldom necessary; see [P] **gettoken**.)

gettoken pulls the first token from *emname3* and stores it in *emname1*, and if *emname2* is specified, stores the remaining characters from *emname3* in *emname2*. Any of *emname1*, *emname2*, and *emname3* may be the same macro. Typically, gettoken is coded

> gettoken *emname1*   : 0 [, *options*]
>
> gettoken *emname1* 0 : 0 [, *options*]

because '0' is the macro containing what the user typed. The first coding is used for token lookahead, should that be necessary, and the second is used for committing to taking the token.

gettoken's options are

parse("*string*")	for specifying parsing characters
	the default is parse(" "), meaning to parse on white space
	it is common to specify parse('"" "'), meaning to parse on white space and double quote
	('"" "' is the string double-quote-space in compound double quotes)
quotes	to specify that outer double quotes *not* be stripped
match(*lmacname*)	to bind on parentheses and square brackets
	lmacname will be set to contain "(", "[", or nothing, depending on whether *emname1* was bound on parentheses or brackets or if match() turned out to be irrelevant
	emname1 will have the outside parentheses or brackets removed

gettoken binds on double quotes whenever a (simple or compound) double quote is encountered at the beginning of *emname3*. Specifying parse('"" "') ensures that double-quoted strings are isolated.

quote specifies that double quotes not be removed from the source in defining the token. For instance, in parsing ""this is" a test", the next token is "this is" if quote is not specified and is ""this is"" if quote is specified.

match() specifies that parentheses and square brackets be matched in defining tokens. The outside level of parentheses or brackets is stripped. In parsing "(2+3)/2", the next token is "2+3" if match() is specified. In practice, match() might be used with expressions, but it is more likely to be used to isolate bound varlists and time-series varlists.

18.5 Scalars and matrices

In addition to macros, scalars and matrices are provided for programmers; see [U] **14 Matrix expressions**, [P] **scalar** and [P] **matrix**.

As far as scalar calculations go, you can use macros or scalars. Remember, macros can hold numbers. Stata's scalars are, however, slightly faster and are a little more accurate than macros. The speed issue is so slight as to be nearly immeasurable. Macros are accurate to a minimum of 12 decimal digits, and scalars are accurate to roughly 16 decimal digits. Which you use makes little difference except in iterative calculations.

Stata also has a serious matrix programming language called Mata, which is the subject of another manual. Mata can be used to write subroutines that are called by Stata programs. See the *Mata Reference Manual*, and in particular, [M-1] **ado**.

18.6 Temporarily destroying the data in memory

It is sometimes necessary to modify the data in memory to accomplish a particular task. A well-behaved program, however, ensures that the user's data are always restored. The preserve command makes this easy:

```
code before the data need changing
preserve
code that changes data freely
```

When you give the preserve command, Stata makes a copy of the user's data on disk. When your program terminates—no matter how—Stata restores the data and erases the temporary file; see [P] **preserve**.

18.7 Temporary objects

If you write a substantial program, it will invariably require the use of temporary variables in the data, or temporary scalars, matrices, or files. Temporary objects are necessary while the program is making its calculations, and once the program completes they are discarded.

Stata provides three commands to create temporary objects: tempvar creates names for variables in the dataset, tempname creates names for scalars and matrices, and tempfile creates names for files. All are described in [P] **macro**, and all have the same syntax:

{ tempvar | tempname | tempfile } *macname* [*macname* ...]

The commands create local macros containing names you may use.

18.7.1 Temporary variables

Say that, in making a calculation, you need to add variables sum_y and sum_z to the data. You might be tempted to code

```
. . .
gen sum_y = . . .
gen sum_z = . . .
. . .
```

but that would be poor because the dataset might already have variables named sum_y and sum_z in it and you will have to remember to drop the variables before your program concludes. Better is

```
. . .
tempvar sum_y
gen 'sum_y' = . . .
tempvar sum_z
gen 'sum_z' = . . .
. . .
```

or

```
. . .
tempvar sum_y sum_z
gen 'sum_y' = . . .
gen 'sum_z' = . . .
. . .
```

It is not necessary to explicitly drop 'sum_y' and 'sum_z' when you are finished, although you may if you wish. Stata will automatically drop any variables with names assigned by tempvar. After issuing the tempvar command, you must refer to the names with the enclosing quotes, which signifies macro expansion. Thus, after typing tempvar sum_y—the one case where you do not put single quotes around the name—refer thereafter to the variable 'sum_y', with quotes. tempvar does not create temporary variables. Instead tempvar creates names that may later be used to create new variables that will be temporary, and tempvar stores that name in the local macro whose name you provide.

A full description of tempvar can be found in [P] **macro**.

18.7.2 Temporary scalars and matrices

tempname works just like tempvar. For instance, a piece of your code might read

```
tempname YXX XXinv
matrix accum 'YXX' = price weight mpg
matrix 'XXinv' = invsym('YXX'[2..., 2...])
tempname b
matrix 'b' = 'XXinv'*'YXX'[1..., 1]
```

The above code solves for the coefficients of a regression on price on weight and mpg; see [U] **14 Matrix expressions** and [P] **matrix** for more information on the matrix commands.

As with temporary variables, temporary scalars and matrices are automatically dropped at the conclusion of your program.

18.7.3 Temporary files

In cases where you ordinarily might think you need temporary files, you may not because of Stata's ability to preserve and automatically restore the data in memory; see [U] **18.6 Temporarily destroying the data in memory** above.

For more complicated programs, Stata does provide temporary files. A code fragment might read

```
preserve                          /* save original data */
tempfile males females
keep if sex==1
save "'males'"
restore, preserve                 /* get back original data */
keep if sex==0
save "'females'"
```

As with temporary variables, scalars, and matrices, it is not necessary to delete the temporary files when you are through with them; Stata automatically erases them when your program ends.

18.8 Accessing results calculated by other programs

Stata commands that report results also save the results where they can be subsequently used by other commands or programs. This is documented in the *Saved results* section of the particular command in the reference manuals. Commands save results in one of three places:

1. r-class commands, such as `summarize`, save their results in `r()`; most commands are r-class.

2. e-class commands, such as `regress`, save their results in `e()`; e-class commands are Stata's model estimation commands.

3. s-class commands (there are no good examples) save their results in `s()`; this is a rarely used class that programmers sometimes find useful to help parse input.

Commands that do not save results are called n-class commands. More correctly, these commands require that you state where the result is to be saved, as in `generate` *newvar* = ...

▷ Example 1

You wish to write a program to calculate the standard error of the mean, which is given by the formula $\sqrt{s^2/n}$, where s^2 is the calculated variance. (You could obtain this statistic by using the `ci` command, but we will pretend that is not true.) You look at [R] **summarize** and learn that the mean is stored in `r(mean)`, the variance in `r(Var)`, and the number of observations in `r(N)`. With that knowledge, you write the following program:

```
program meanse
        quietly summarize '1'
        display "     mean = " r(mean)
        display "SE of mean = " sqrt(r(Var)/r(N))
end
```

The result of executing this program is

```
. meanse mpg
     mean = 21.297297
SE of mean = .67255109
```

◁

If you run an r-class command and type `return list` or run an e-class command and type `ereturn list`, Stata will summarize what was saved:

```
. use http://www.stata-press.com/data/r11/auto
(1978 Automobile Data)
. regress mpg weight displ
 (output omitted )
. ereturn list
scalars:
                 e(N) =  74
              e(df_m) =  2
              e(df_r) =  71
                 e(F) =  66.78504752026517
                e(r2) =  .6529306984682528
              e(rmse) =  3.45606176570828
               e(mss) =  1595.409691543724
               e(rss) =  848.0497679157351
              e(r2_a) =  .643154098425105
                e(ll) =  -195.2397979466294
              e(ll_0) =  -234.3943376482347
              e(rank) =  3
macros:
           e(cmdline) : "regress mpg weight displ"
             e(title) : "Linear regression"
         e(marginsok) : "XB default"
               e(vce) : "ols"
            e(depvar) : "mpg"
               e(cmd) : "regress"
        e(properties) : "b V"
           e(predict) : "regres_p"
             e(model) : "ols"
         e(estat_cmd) : "regress_estat"
matrices:
                 e(b) :  1 x 3
                 e(V) :  3 x 3
functions:
            e(sample)
. summarize mpg if foreign
```

Variable	Obs	Mean	Std. Dev.	Min	Max
mpg	22	24.77273	6.611187	14	41

```
. return list
scalars:
                 r(N) =  22
             r(sum_w) =  22
              r(mean) =  24.77272727272727
               r(Var) =  43.70779220779221
                r(sd) =  6.611186898567625
               r(min) =  14
               r(max) =  41
               r(sum) =  545
```

In the example above, we ran `regress` followed by `summarize`. As a result, `e(N)` records the number of observations used by `regress` (equal to 74), and `r(N)` records the number of observations used by `summarize` (equal to 22). `r(N)` and `e(N)` are not the same.

If we now ran another r-class command—say, `tabulate`—the contents of `r()` would change, but those in `e()` would remain unchanged. You might, therefore, think that if we then ran another e-class command, say, `probit`, the contents of `e()` would change, but `r()` would remain unchanged.

Although it is true that e() results remain in place until the next e-class command is executed, do not depend on r() remaining unchanged. If an e-class or n-class command were to use an r-class command as a subroutine, that would cause r() to change. Anyway, most commands are r-class, so the contents of r() change often.

❑ Technical note

It is, therefore, of great importance that you access results stored in r() immediately after the command that sets them. If you need the mean and variance of the variable '1' for subsequent calculation, do *not* code

```
summarize '1'
...
... r(mean) ... r(Var) ...
```

Instead, code

```
summarize '1'
local mean = r(mean)
local var = r(Var)
...
... 'mean' ... 'var' ...
```

or

```
tempname mean var
summarize '1'
scalar 'mean' = r(mean)
scalar 'var' = r(Var)
...
... 'mean' ... 'var' ...
```

❑

Saved results, whether in r() or e(), come in three types: scalars, macros, and matrices. If you look back at the ereturn list and return list output, you will see that regress saves examples of all three, whereas summarize saves just scalars. (regress also saves the "function" e(sample), as do all the other e-class commands; see [U] **20.6 Specifying the estimation subsample**.)

Regardless of the type of e(*name*) or r(*name*), you can just refer to e(*name*) or r(*name*). That was the rule we gave in [U] **13.6 Accessing results from Stata commands**, and that rule is sufficient for most uses. There is, however, another way to refer to saved results. Rather than referring to r(*name*) and e(*name*), you can embed the reference in macro-substitution characters ' ' to produce 'r(*name*)' and 'e(*name*)'. The result is the same as macro substitution; the saved result is evaluated, and then the evaluation is substituted:

```
. display "You can refer to " e(cmd) " or to 'e(cmd)'"
You can refer to regress or to regress
```

This means, for instance, that typing 'e(cmd)' is the same as typing regress because e(cmd) contains "regress":

```
. 'e(cmd)'
      Source |       SS       df       MS              Number of obs =      74
-------------+------------------------------           F(  2,    71) =   66.79
       Model | 1595.40969        2  797.704846         Prob > F      = 0.0000
    (remaining output omitted)
```

In the ereturn list, e(cmd) was listed as a macro, and when you place a macro's name in single quotes, the macro's contents are substituted, so this is hardly a surprise.

What is surprising is that you can do this with scalar and even matrix saved results. e(N) is a scalar equal to 74 and may be used as such in any expression such as "display e(mss)/e(N)" or "local meanss = e(mss)/e(N)". 'e(N)' substitutes to the string "74" and may be used in any context whatsoever, such as "local val'e(N)' = e(N)" (which would create a macro named val74). The rules for referring to saved results are

1. You may refer to r(*name*) or e(*name*) without single quotes in any expression and only in an expression. (Referring to s-class s(*name*) without single quotes is not allowed.)

    1.1 If *name* does not exist, missing value (.) is returned; it is not an error to refer to a nonexistent saved result.

    1.2 If *name* is a scalar, the full double-precision value of *name* is returned.

    1.3 If *name* is a macro, it is examined to determine whether its contents can be interpreted as a number. If so, the number is returned; otherwise, the first 80 characters of *name* are returned.

    1.4 If *name* is a matrix, the full *matrix* is returned.

2. You may refer to 'r(*name*)', 'e(*name*)', or 's(*name*)'—note the presence of quotes indicating macro substitution—in any context whatsoever.

    2.1 If *name* does not exist, nothing is substituted; it is not an error to refer to a nonexistent saved result. The resulting line is the same as if you had never typed 'r(*name*)', 'e(*name*)', or 's(*name*)'.

    2.2 If *name* is a scalar, a string representation of the number accurate to no less than 12 digits of precision is substituted.

    2.3 If *name* is a macro, the full contents are substituted.

    2.4 If *name* is a matrix, the word matrix is substituted.

In general, you should refer to scalar and matrix saved results without quotes—r(*name*) and e(*name*)—and to macro saved results with quotes—'r(*name*)', 'e(*name*)', and 's(*name*)'—but it is sometimes convenient to switch. Say that returned result r(example) contains the number of periods patients are observed, and assume that r(example) was saved as a macro and not as a scalar. You could still refer to r(example) without the quotes in an expression context and obtain the expected result. It would have made more sense for you to have stored r(example) as a scalar, but really it would not matter, and the user would not even have to know how the saved result was stored.

Switching the other way is sometimes useful, too. Say that returned result r(N) is a scalar that contains the number of observations used. You now want to use some other command that has an option n(#) that specifies the number of observations used. You could not type n(r(N)) because the syntax diagram says that the n() option expects its argument to be a literal number. Instead, you could type n('r(N)').

18.9   Accessing results calculated by estimation commands

Estimation results are saved in e(), and you access them in the same way you access any saved result; see [U] **18.8 Accessing results calculated by other programs** above. In summary,

1. Estimation commands—regress, logistic, etc.—save results in e().

2. Estimation commands save their name in e(cmd). For instance, regress saves "regress" and poisson saves "poisson" in e(cmd).

3. Estimation commands save the command they executed in e(cmdline). For instance, if you typed reg mpg displ, saved in e(cmdline) would be "reg mpg displ".

4. Estimation commands save the number of observations used in e(N), and they identify the estimation subsample by setting e(sample). You could type, for instance, summarize if e(sample) to obtain summary statistics on the observations used by the estimator.

5. Estimation commands save the entire coefficient vector and variance–covariance matrix of the estimators in e(b) and e(V). These are matrices, and they may be manipulated like any other matrix:

```
. matrix list e(b)
e(b)[1,3]
          weight        displ       _cons
y1  -.00656711    .00528078    40.084522
. matrix y = e(b)*e(V)*e(b)'
. matrix list y
symmetric y[1,1]
           y1
y1   6556.982
```

6. Estimation commands set _b[*name*] and _se[*name*] as convenient ways to use coefficients and their standard errors in expressions; see [U] **13.5 Accessing coefficients and standard errors**.

7. Estimation commands may set other e() scalars, macros, or matrices containing more information. This is documented in the *Saved results* section of the particular command in the command reference.

▷ Example 2

If you are writing a command for use after regress, early in your code you should include the following:

```
if "`e(cmd)'" != "regress" {
        error 301
}
```

This is how you verify that the estimation results that are stored have been set by regress and not by some other estimation command. Error 301 is Stata's "last estimates not found" error.

◁

18.10   Saving results

If your program calculates something, it should save the results of the calculation so that other programs can access them. In this way your program not only can be used interactively but also can be used as a subroutine for other commands.

Saving results is easy:

1. On the program line, specify the rclass, eclass, or sclass option according to whether you intend to return results in r(), e(), or s().

2. Code
```
          return scalar name = exp      (same syntax as scalar without the return)
          return local  name ...        (same syntax as local without the return)
          return matrix name matname    (moves matname to r(name))
```
to save results in r().

3. Code

ereturn *name* = *exp*	(same syntax as `scalar` without the ereturn)
ereturn local *name* ...	(same syntax as `local` without the ereturn)
ereturn matrix *name matname*	(moves *matname* to e(*name*))

to save results in e(). You do not save the coefficient vector and variance matrix e(b) and e(V) in this way; instead you use ereturn post.

4. Code

> sreturn local *name* ...   (same syntax as `local` without the sreturn)

to save results in s(). (The s-class has only macros.)

A program must be exclusively r-class, e-class, or s-class.

18.10.1 Saving results in r()

In [U] **18.8 Accessing results calculated by other programs**, we showed an example that reported the mean and standard error of the mean. A better version would save in r() the results of its calculations and would read

```
program meanse, rclass
        quietly summarize '1'
        local mean = r(mean)
        local sem  = sqrt(r(Var)/r(N))
        display "     mean = " 'mean'
        display "SE of mean = " 'sem'
        return scalar mean = 'mean'
        return scalar se = 'sem'
end
```

Running meanse now sets r(mean) and r(se):

```
. meanse mpg
      mean = 21.297297
SE of mean = .67255109

. return list

scalars:
        r(se)      =  .6725510870764975
        r(mean)    =  21.2972972972973
```

In this modification, we added the rclass option to the program statement, and we added two return commands to the end of the program.

Although we placed the return statements at the end of the program, they may be placed at the point of calculation if that is more convenient. A more concise version of this program would read

```
program meanse, rclass
        quietly summarize '1'
        return scalar mean = r(mean)
        return scalar se = sqrt(r(Var)/r(N))
        display "     mean = " return(mean)
        display "SE of mean = " return(se)
end
```

The `return()` function is just like the `r()` function, except that `return()` refers to the results that this program *will* return rather than to the saved results that currently *are* returned (which here are due to `summarize`). That is, when you code the `return` command, the result is not immediately posted to `r()`. Rather, Stata holds onto the result in `return()` until your program concludes, and then it copies the contents of `return()` to `r()`. While your program is active, you may use the `return()` function to access results you have already "returned". (`return()` works just like `r()` works after your program returns, meaning that you may code '`return()`' to perform macro substitution.)

18.10.2   Saving results in e()

Saving in `e()` is in most ways similar to saving in `r()`: you add the `eclass` option to the `program` statement, and then you use `ereturn` ... just as you used `return` ... to store results. There are, however, some significant differences:

1. Unlike `r()`, estimation results are saved in `e()` the instant you issue an `ereturn scalar`, `ereturn local`, or `ereturn matrix` command. Estimation results can consume considerable memory, and Stata does not want to have multiple copies of the results floating around. That means you must be more organized and post your results at the end of your program.

2. In your code when you have your estimates and are ready to begin posting, you will first clear the previous estimates, set the coefficient vector `e(b)` and corresponding variance matrix `e(V)`, and set the estimation-sample function `e(sample)`. How you do this depends on how you obtained your estimates:

   2.1 If you obtained your estimates by using Stata's likelihood maximizer `ml`, this is automatically handled for you; skip to step 3.

   2.2 If you obtained estimates by "stealing" an existing estimator, `e(b)`, `e(V)`, and `e(sample)` already exist, and you will not want to clear them; skip to step 3.

   2.3 If you write your own code from start to finish, you use the `ereturn post` command; see [P] **ereturn**. You will code something like "`ereturn post 'b' 'V', esample('touse')`", where '`b`' is the name of the coefficient vector, '`V`' is the name of the corresponding variance matrix, and '`touse`' is the name of a variable containing 1 if the observation was used and 0 if it was ignored. `ereturn post` clears the previous estimates and moves the coefficient vector, variance matrix, and variable into `e(b)`, `e(V)`, and `e(sample)`.

   2.4 A variation on (2.3) is when you use an existing estimator to produce the estimates but do not want all the other `e()` results stored by the estimator. Then you code

```
tempvar touse
tempname b V
matrix 'b' = e(b)
matrix 'V' = e(V)
qui gen byte 'touse' = e(sample)
ereturn post 'b' 'V', esample('touse')
```

3. You now save anything else in `e()` that you wish by using the `ereturn scalar`, `ereturn local`, or `ereturn matrix` command.

4. Save `e(cmdline)` by coding

```
ereturn local cmdline '"'0'"'
```

   This is not required, but it is considered good style.

5. You code `ereturn local cmd "`*cmdname*`"`. Stata does not consider estimation results complete until this command is posted, and Stata considers the results to be complete when this is posted, so you must remember to do this and to do this last. If you set `e(cmd)` too early and the user pressed *Break*, Stata would consider your estimates complete when they are not.

Say that you wish to write the estimation command with syntax

> `myest` *depvar* *var*$_1$ *var*$_2$ [if *exp*] [in *range*], *optset1* *optset2*

where *optset1* affects how results are displayed and *optset2* affects the estimation results themselves. One important characteristic of estimation commands is that, when typed without arguments, they redisplay the previous estimation results. The outline is

```
program myest, eclass
        local options "optset1"
        if replay() {
                if "`e(cmd)'"!="myest" {
                        error 301           /* last estimates not found      */
                }
                syntax [, `options']
        }
        else {
                syntax varlist [if] [in] [, `options' optset2]
                marksample touse
Code contains either this,
                tempnames b V
                commands for performing estimation
                assume produces `b' and `V'
                ereturn post `b' `V', esample(`touse')
                ereturn local depvar "`depv'"
or this,
                ml model ... if `touse' ...
and regardless, concludes,
                perhaps other ereturn commands appear here
                ereturn local cmdline `"`0'"'
                ereturn local cmd "myest"
        }
                                            /* (re)display results ...       */
code typically reads
        code to output header above coefficient table
                ereturn display             /* displays coefficient table    */
or
        ml display                          /* displays header and coef. table */
end
```

Here is a list of the commonly saved `e()` results. Of course, you may create any `e()` results that you wish.

`e(N)` (scalar)
   Number of observations.

`e(df_m)` (scalar)
   Model degrees of freedom.

`e(df_r)` (scalar)
   "Denominator" degrees of freedom if estimates are nonasymptotic.

`e(r2_p)` (scalar)
   Value of the pseudo-R^2 if it is calculated. (If a "real" R^2 is calculated as it would be in linear regression, it is stored in (scalar) `e(r2)`.)

e(F) (scalar)
   Test of the model against the constant-only model, if relevant, and if results are nonasymptotic.

e(11) (scalar)
   Log-likelihood value, if relevant.

e(11_0) (scalar)
   Log-likelihood value for constant-only model, if relevant.

e(N_clust) (scalar)
   Number of clusters, if any.

e(chi2) (scalar)
   Test of the model against the constant-only model, if relevant, and if results are asymptotic.

e(rank) (scalar)
   Rank of e(V).

e(cmd) (macro)
   Name of the estimation command.

e(cmdline) (macro)
   Command as typed.

e(depvar) (macro)
   Names of the dependent variables.

e(wtype) and e(wexp) (macros)
   If weighted estimation was performed, e(wtype) contains the weight type (fweight, pweight, etc.) and e(wexp) contains the weighting expression.

e(title) (macro)
   Title in estimation output.

e(clustvar) (macro)
   Name of the cluster variable, if any.

e(vcetype) (macro)
   Text to appear above standard errors in estimation output; typically Robust, Bootstrap, Jack-knife, or "".

e(vce) (macro)
   vcetype specified in vce().

e(chi2type) (macro)
   LR or Wald or other depending on how e(chi2) was performed.

e(crittype) (macro)
   Type of optimization criterion used, such as log likelihood or deviance.

e(properties) (macro)
   Typically contains b V.

e(predict) (macro)
   Name of the command that predict is to use; if this is blank, predict uses the default _predict.

e(b) and e(V) (matrices)
   The coefficient vector and corresponding variance matrix. Saved when you coded ereturn post.

e(sample) (function)

 This function was defined by ereturn post's esample() option if you specified it. You specified a variable containing 1 if you used an observation and 0 otherwise. ereturn post stole the variable and created e(sample) from it.

18.10.3   Saving results in s()

S is a strange class because, whereas the other classes allow scalars, macros, and matrices, s allows only macros.

S is seldom used and is for subroutines that you might write to assist in parsing the user's input prior to evaluating any user-supplied expressions.

Here is the problem s solves: say that you create a nonstandard syntax for some command so that you have to parse through it yourself. The syntax is so complicated that you want to create subroutines to take pieces of it and then return information to your main routine. Assume that your syntax contains expressions that the user might type. Now say that one of the expressions the user types is, e.g., r(mean)/sqrt(r(Var))—perhaps the user is using results left behind by summarize.

If, in your parsing step, you call subroutines that return results in r(), you will wipe out r(mean) and r(Var) before you ever get around to seeing them, much less evaluating them. So, you must be careful to leave r() intact until your parsing is complete; you must use no r-class commands, and any subroutines you write must not touch r(). You must use s-class subroutines because s-class routines return results in s() rather than r(). S-class provides macros only because that is all you need to solve parsing problems.

To create an s-class routine, specify the sclass option on the program line and then use sreturn local to return results.

S-class results are posted to s() at the instant you issue the sreturn() command, so you must organize your results. Also, s() is never automatically cleared, so occasionally coding sreturn clear at appropriate points in your code is a good idea.

Few programs need s-class subroutines.

18.11   Ado-files

Ado-files were introduced in [U] **17 Ado-files**.

When a user types '*gobbledygook*', Stata first asks itself if *gobbledygook* is one of its built-in commands. If so, the command is executed. Otherwise, it asks itself if *gobbledygook* is a defined program. If so, the program is executed. Otherwise, Stata looks in various directories for *gobbledygook*.ado. If there is no such file, the process ends with the "unrecognized command" error.

If Stata finds the file, it quietly issues to itself the command 'run *gobbledygook*.ado' (specifying the path explicitly). If that runs without error, Stata asks itself again if *gobbledygook* is a defined program. If not, Stata issues the "unrecognized command" error. (Here somebody wrote a bad ado-file.) If the program is defined, as it should be, Stata executes it.

Thus you can arrange for programs you write to be loaded automatically. For instance, if you were to create hello.ado containing

```
                                                    begin hello.ado
program hello
        display "hi there"
end
                                                    end hello.ado
```

and store the file in your current directory or your personal directory (see [U] **17.5.2 Where is my personal ado-directory?**), you could type `hello` and be greeted by a reassuring

```
. hello
hi there
```

You could, at that point, think of `hello` as just another part of Stata.

There are two places to put your personal ado-files. One is the current directory, and that is a good choice when the ado-file is unique to a project. You will want to use it only when you are in that directory. The other place is your *personal ado-directory*, which is probably something like `C:\ado\personal` if you use Windows, `~/ado/personal` if you use Unix, and `~/ado/personal` if you use a Mac. We are guessing.

To find your personal ado-directory, enter Stata and type

```
. personal
```

❏ Technical note

Stata looks in various directories for ado-files, defined by the c-class value `c(adopath)`, which contains

```
UPDATES;BASE;SITE;.;PERSONAL;PLUS;OLDPLACE
```

The words in capital letters are codenames for directories, and the mapping from codenames to directories can be obtained by typing the `sysdir` command. Here is what `sysdir` shows on one particular Windows computer:

```
. sysdir
    STATA:  C:\Program Files\Stata11\
  UPDATES:  C:\Program Files\Stata11\ado\updates\
     BASE:  C:\Program Files\Stata11\ado\base\
     SITE:  C:\Program Files\Stata11\ado\site\
     PLUS:  C:\ado\plus\
 PERSONAL:  C:\ado\personal\
 OLDPLACE:  C:\ado\
```

Even if you use Windows, your mapping might be different because it all depends on where you installed Stata. That is the point of the codenames. They make it possible to refer to directories according to their logical purposes rather than their physical location.

The c-class value `c(adopath)` is the search path, so in looking for an ado-file, Stata first looks in UPDATES then in BASE, and so on, until it finds the file. Actually, Stata not only looks in UPDATES but also takes the first letter of the ado-file it is looking for and looks in the lettered subdirectory. For files with the extension `.style`, Stata will look in a subdirectory named `style` rather than a lettered subdirectory. Say that Stata was looking for gobbledygook.ado. Stata would look up UPDATES (`C:\Program Files\Stata11\ado\updates` in our example) and, if the file were not found there, it would look in the g subdirectory of UPDATES (`C:\Program Files\Stata11\ado\updates\g`) before looking in BASE, whereupon it would follow the same rules. If Stata were looking for gobbledygook.style, Stata would look up UPDATES (`C:\Program Files\Stata11\ado\updates` in our example) and, if the file were not found there, it would look in the `style` subdirectory of UPDATES (`C:\Program Files\Stata11\ado\updates\style`) before looking in BASE, whereupon it would follow the same rules.

Why the extra complication? We distribute hundreds of ado-files, help files, and other file types with Stata, and some operating systems have difficulty dealing with so many files in the same directory. All operating systems experience at least a performance degradation. To prevent this, the ado-directory we ship is split 28 ways (letters *a–z*, underscore, and `style`). Thus the Stata command `ci`, which is implemented as an ado-file, can be found in the subdirectory c of BASE.

If you write ado-files, you can structure your personal ado-directory this way, too, but there is no reason to do so until you have more than, say, 250 files in one directory.

❏

❏ Technical note

After finding and running *gobbledygook*.ado, Stata calculates the total size of all programs that it has automatically loaded. If this exceeds adosize (see [P] **sysdir**), Stata begins discarding the oldest automatically loaded programs until the total is less than adosize. Oldest here is measured by the time last used, not the time loaded. This discarding saves memory and does not affect you, because any program that was automatically loaded could be automatically loaded again if needed.

It does, however, affect performance. Loading the program takes time, and you will again have to wait if you use one of the previously loaded-and-discarded programs. Increasing adosize reduces this possibility, but at the cost of memory. The set adosize command allows you to change this parameter; see [P] **sysdir**. The default value of adosize is 1,000. A value of 1,000 for adosize means that up to 1,000 K can be allocated to autoloaded programs. Experimentation has shown that this is a good number—increasing it does not improve performance much.

❏

18.11.1   Version

We recommend that the first line following program in your ado-file declare the Stata release under which you wrote the program; hello.ado would read better as

```
                                                      ── begin hello.ado ────────
    program hello
            version 11
            display "hi there"
    end
                                                      ── end hello.ado ──────────
```

We introduced the concept of version in [U] **16.1.1 Version**. In regular do-files, we recommend that the version line appear as the first line of the do-file. For ado-files, the line appears after the program because loading the ado-file is one step and executing the program is another. It is when Stata executes the program defined in the ado-file that we want to stipulate the interpretation of the commands.

The inclusion of the version line is of more importance in ado-files than in do-files because ado-files have longer lives than do-files, so it is more likely that you will use an ado-file with a later release and ado-files tend to use more of Stata's features, increasing the probability that any change to Stata will affect them.

18.11.2   Comments and long lines in ado-files

Comments in ado-files are handled the same way as in do-files: you enclose the text in /* comment */ brackets, or you begin the line with an asterisk (*), or you interrupt the line with //; see [U] **16.1.2 Comments and blank lines in do-files**.

Logical lines longer than physical lines are also handled as they are in do-files: either you change the delimiter to a semicolon (;) or you comment out the new line by using /// at the end of the previous physical line.

18.11.3 Debugging ado-files

Debugging ado-files is a little tricky because it is Stata and not you that controls when the ado-file is loaded.

Assume that you wanted to change `hello` to say "Hi, Mary". Assume that your editor is called `vi` and that you are in the habit of calling your editor from Stata, so you do this,

```
. !vi hello.ado
```

and make the obvious change to the program. Equivalently, you can pretend that you are using a windowed operating system and jump out of Stata—leaving it running—to modify the `hello.ado` file. Anyway, you change `hello.ado` to read

```
─────────────────────────────────────────────── begin hello.ado ───────────
program hello
        version 11
        display "hi, Mary"
end
─────────────────────────────────────────── end hello.ado ───────────
```

Back in Stata, you try it:

```
. hello
hi there
```

Stata ran the old copy of `hello`—the copy it still has in its memory. Stata wants to be fast about executing ado-files, so when it loads one, it keeps it around a while—waiting for memory to get short—before clearing it from its memory. Naturally, Stata can drop `hello` anytime because it can always reload it from disk.

You changed the copy on disk, but Stata still has the old copy loaded into memory. You type `discard` to tell Stata to forget these automatically loaded things and to force itself to get new copies of the ado-files from disk:

```
. discard
. hello
hi, Mary
```

You had to type `discard` only because you changed the ado-file while Stata was running. Had you exited Stata and returned later to use `hello`, the `discard` would not have been necessary because Stata forgets things between sessions anyway.

18.11.4 Local subroutines

An ado-file can contain more than one `program`, and if it does, the other programs defined in the ado-file are assumed to be subroutines of the main program. For example,

```
─────────────────────────────────────────────── begin decoy.ado ───────────
program decoy
        ...
        duck ...
        ...
end
program  duck
        ...
end
─────────────────────────────────────────── end decoy.ado ───────────
```

duck is considered a local subroutine of decoy. Even after decoy.ado was loaded, if you typed duck, you would be told "unrecognized command". To emphasize what *local* means, assume that you have also written an ado-file named duck.ado:

―――――――――――――――――――――――――――――――――――――― begin duck.ado ――――――――
```
program duck
        . . .
    end
```
―――――――――――――――――――――――――――――――――――――― end duck.ado ――――――――

Even so, when decoy called duck, it would be the program duck defined in decoy.ado that was called. To further emphasize what *local* means, assume that decoy.ado contains

―――――――――――――――――――――――――――――――――――――― begin decoy.ado ――――――――
```
program decoy
        . . .
        manic . . .
        . . .
        duck . . .
        . . .
    end
program duck
        . . .
    end
```
―――――――――――――――――――――――――――――――――――――― end decoy.ado ――――――――

and that manic.ado contained

―――――――――――――――――――――――――――――――――――――― begin manic.ado ――――――――
```
program manic
        . . .
        duck . . .
        . . .
    end
```
―――――――――――――――――――――――――――――――――――――― end manic.ado ――――――――

Here is what would happen when you executed decoy:

1. decoy in decoy.ado would begin execution. decoy calls manic.

2. manic in manic.ado would begin execution. manic calls duck.

3. duck in duck.ado (yes) would begin execution. duck would do whatever and return.

4. manic regains control and eventually returns.

5. decoy is back in control. decoy calls duck.

6. duck in decoy.ado would execute, complete, and return.

7. decoy would regain control and return.

When manic called duck, it was the global ado-file duck.ado that was executed, yet when decoy called duck, it was the local program duck that was executed.

Stata does not find this confusing and neither should you.

18.11.5   Development of a sample ado-command

Below we demonstrate how to create a new Stata command. We will program an influence measure for use with linear regression. It is an interesting statistic in its own right, but even if you are not interested in linear regression and influence measures, the focus here is on programming, not on the particular statistic chosen.

Belsley, Kuh, and Welsch (1980, 24) present a measure of influence in linear regression defined as

$$\frac{\text{Var}\left(\widehat{y}_i^{(i)}\right)}{\text{Var}(\widehat{y}_i)}$$

which is the ratio of the variance of the ith fitted value based on regression estimates obtained by omitting the ith observation to the variance of the ith fitted value estimated from the full dataset. This ratio is estimated using

$$\text{FVARATIO}_i \equiv \frac{n-k}{n-(k+1)} \left\{ 1 - \frac{d_i^2}{1-h_{ii}} \right\} (1-h_{ii})^{-1}$$

where n is the sample size; k is the number of estimated coefficients; $d_i^2 = e_i^2/\mathbf{e}'\mathbf{e}$ and e_i is the ith residual; and h_{ii} is the ith diagonal element of the hat matrix. The ingredients of this formula are all available through Stata, so, after estimating the regression parameters, we can easily calculate FVARATIO_i. For instance, we might type

```
. regress mpg weight displ
. predict hii if e(sample), hat
. predict ei if e(sample), resid
. quietly count if e(sample)
. scalar nreg = r(N)
. gen eTe = sum(ei*ei)
. gen di2 = (ei*ei)/eTe[_N]
. gen FVi = (nreg - 3) / (nreg - 4) * (1 - di2/(1-hii)) / (1-hii)
```

The number 3 in the formula for `FVi` represents k, the number of estimated parameters (which is an intercept plus coefficients on `weight` and `displ`), and the number 4 represents $k+1$.

❏ Technical note

Do you understand why this works? `predict` can create h_{ii} and e_i, but the trick is in getting $\mathbf{e}'\mathbf{e}$—the sum of the squared e_is. Stata's `sum()` function creates a running sum. The first observation of eTe thus contains e_1^2; the second, $e_1^2 + e_2^2$; the third, $e_1^2 + e_2^2 + e_3^2$; and so on. The last observation, then, contains $\sum_{i=1}^{N} e_i^2$, which is $\mathbf{e}'\mathbf{e}$. (We specified if e(sample) on our predict commands to restrict calculations to the estimation subsample, so `hii` and `eii` might have missing values, but that does not matter because `sum()` treats missing values as contributing zero to the sum.) We use Stata's explicit subscripting feature and then refer to eTe[_N], the last observation. (See [U] **13.3 Functions** and [U] **13.7 Explicit subscripting**.) After that, we plug into the formula to obtain the result.

❏

Assuming that we often wanted this influence measure, it would be easier and less prone to error if we canned this calculation in a program. Our first draft of the program reflects exactly what we would have typed interactively:

```
───────────────────────────────────── begin fvaratio.ado, version 1 ─────────
program fvaratio
        version 11
        predict hii if e(sample), hat
        predict ei if e(sample), resid
        quietly count if e(sample)
        scalar nreg = r(N)
        gen eTe = sum(ei*ei)
        gen di2 = (ei*ei)/eTe[_N]
        gen FVi = (nreg - 3) / (nreg - 4) * (1 - di2/(1-hii)) / (1-hii)
        drop hii ei eTe di2
end
───────────────────────────────────── end fvaratio.ado, version 1 ─────────
```

All we have done is to enter what we would have typed into a file, bracketing it with `program fvaratio` and `end`. Because our command is to be called `fvaratio`, the file must be named `fvaratio.ado` and must be stored in either the current directory or our personal ado-directory (see [U] **17.5.2 Where is my personal ado-directory?**).

Now when we type `fvaratio`, Stata will be able to find it, load it, and execute it. In addition to copying the interactive lines into a program, we added the line 'drop hii ...' to eliminate the working variables we had to create along the way.

So, now we can interactively type

```
. regress mpg weight displ
. fvaratio
```

and add the new variable `FVi` to our data.

Our program is not general. It is suitable for use after fitting a regression model on two, and only two, independent variables because we coded a 3 in the formula for k. Stata statistical commands such as `regress` store information about the problem and answer in `e()`. Looking in *Saved results* in [R] **regress**, we find that `e(df_m)` contains the model degrees of freedom, which is $k - 1$, assuming that the model has an intercept. Also, the sample size of the dataset used in the regression is stored in `e(N)`, eliminating our need to count the observations and define a scalar containing this count. Thus the second draft of our program reads

```
───────────────────────────────────── begin fvaratio.ado, version 2 ─────────
program fvaratio
        version 11
        predict hii if e(sample), hat
        predict ei if e(sample), resid
        gen eTe = sum(ei*ei)
        gen di2 = (ei*ei)/eTe[_N]
        gen FVi = (e(N)-(e(df_m)+1)) / (e(N)-(e(df_m)+2)) *      /// changed this
                (1 - di2/(1-hii)) / (1-hii)                      // version
        drop hii ei eTe di2
end
───────────────────────────────────── end fvaratio.ado, version 2 ─────────
```

In the formula for `FVi`, we substituted `(e(df_m)+1)` for the literal number 3, `(e(df_m)+2)` for the literal number 4, and `e(N)` for the sample size.

Back to the substance of our problem, `regress` also saves the residual sum of squares in `e(rss)`, so calculating `eTe` is not really necessary:

```
──────────────────────────────────────── begin fvaratio.ado, version 3 ────────
program fvaratio
        version 11
        predict hii if e(sample), hat
        predict ei if e(sample), resid
        gen di2 = (ei*ei)/e(rss)                          // changed this version
        gen FVi = (e(N)-(e(df_m)+1)) / (e(N)-(e(df_m)+2)) *     ///
                  (1 - di2/(1-hii)) / (1-hii)
        drop hii ei di2
end
──────────────────────────────────────────── end fvaratio.ado, version 3 ──────
```

Our program is now shorter and faster, and it is completely general. This program is probably good enough for most users; if you were implementing this solely for your own occasional use, you could stop right here. The program does, however, have the following deficiencies:

1. When we use it with data with missing values, the answer is correct, but we see messages about the number of missing values generated. (These messages appear when the program is generating the working variables.)

2. We cannot control the name of the variable being produced—it is always called FVi. Moreover, when FVi already exists (say, from a previous regression), we get an error message that FVi already exists. We then have to drop the old FVi and type fvaratio again.

3. If we have created any variables named hii, ei, or di2, we also get an error that the variable already exists, and the program refuses to run.

Fixing these problems is not difficult. The fix for problem 1 is easy; we embed the entire program in a quietly block:

```
──────────────────────────────────────── begin fvaratio.ado, version 4 ────────
program fvaratio
        version 11
        quietly {                                         // new this version
                predict hii if e(sample), hat
                predict ei if e(sample), resid
                gen di2 = (ei*ei)/e(rss)
                gen FVi = (e(N)-(e(df_m)+1)) / (e(N)-(e(df_m)+2)) *     ///
                          (1 - di2/(1-hii)) / (1-hii)
                drop hii ei di2
        }                                                 // new this version
end
──────────────────────────────────────────── end fvaratio.ado, version 4 ──────
```

The output for the commands between the quietly { and } is now suppressed—the result is the same as if we had put quietly in front of each command.

Solving problem 2—that the resulting variable is always called FVi—requires use of the syntax command. Let's put that off and deal with problem 3—that the working variables have nice names like hii, ei, and di2, and so prevent users from using those names in their data.

One solution would be to change the nice names to unlikely names. We could change hii to MyHiiVaR, which would not guarantee the prevention of a conflict but would certainly make it unlikely. It would also make our program difficult to read, an important consideration should we want to change it in the future. There is a better solution. Stata's tempvar command (see [U] **18.7.1 Temporary variables**) places names into local macros that are guaranteed to be unique:

```
 ─────────────────────────────────── begin fvaratio.ado, version 5 ───────────
program fvaratio
        version 11
        tempvar hii ei di2                                  // new this version
        quietly {
                predict 'hii' if e(sample), hat    // changed, as are other lines
                predict 'ei' if e(sample), resid
                gen 'di2' = ('ei'*'ei')/e(rss)
                gen FVi = (e(N)-(e(df_m)+1)) / (e(N)-(e(df_m)+2)) *      ///
                        (1 - 'di2'/(1-'hii')) / (1-'hii')
        }
end
 ─────────────────────────────────────── end fvaratio.ado, version 5 ─────────
```

At the beginning of our program, we declare the temporary variables. (We can do it outside or inside the quietly—it makes no difference—and we do not have to do it at the beginning or even all at once; we could declare them as we need them, but at the beginning is prettiest.) When we refer to a temporary variable, we do not refer directly to it (such as by typing hii); we refer to it indirectly by typing open and close single quotes around the name ('hii'). And at the end of our program, we no longer bother to drop the temporary variables—temporary variables are dropped automatically by Stata when a program concludes.

❏ Technical note

Why do we type single quotes around the names? tempvar creates local macros containing the real temporary variable names. hii in our program is now a local macro, and 'hii' refers to the contents of the local macro, which is the variable's actual name.

❏

We now have an excellent program—its only fault is that we cannot specify the name of the new variable to be created. Here is the solution to that problem:

```
 ─────────────────────────────────── begin fvaratio.ado, version 6 ───────────
program fvaratio
        version 11
        syntax newvarname                                   // new this version
        tempvar hii ei di2
        quietly {
                predict 'hii' if e(sample), hat
                predict 'ei' if e(sample), resid
                gen 'di2' = ('ei'*'ei')/e(rss)
                gen 'typlist' 'varlist' = ///              changed this version
                        (e(N)-(e(df_m)+1)) / (e(N)-(e(df_m)+2)) *      ///
                        (1 - 'di2'/(1-'hii')) / (1-'hii')
        }
end
 ─────────────────────────────────────── end fvaratio.ado, version 6 ─────────
```

It took a change to one line and the addition of another to obtain the solution. This magic all happens because of syntax (see [U] **18.4.4 Parsing standard Stata syntax** above).

'syntax newvarname' specifies that one new variable name must be specified (had we typed 'syntax [newvarname]', the new varname would have been optional; had we typed 'syntax newvarlist', the user would have been required to specify at least one new variable and allowed to specify more). In any case, syntax compares what the user types to what is allowed. If what the user types does not match what we have declared, syntax will issue the appropriate error message and stop our program. If it does match, our program will continue, and what the user typed will be broken out and stored in local macros for us. For a newvarname, the new name typed by the user is placed in the local macro varlist, and the type of the variable (float, double, ...) is placed in typlist (even if the user did not specify a storage type, in which case the type is the current default storage type).

This is now an excellent program. There are, however, two more improvements we could make. First, we have demonstrated that, by the use of 'syntax newvarname', we can allow the user to define not only the name of the created variable but also the storage type. However, when it comes to the creation of intermediate variables, such as 'hii' and 'di2', it is good programming practice to keep as much precision as possible. We want our final answer to be precise as possible, regardless of how we ultimately decide to store it. Any calculation that uses a previously generated variable would benefit if the previously generated variable were stored in double precision. Below we modify our program appropriately:

```
────────────────────────────────────────── begin fvaratio.ado, version 7 ──────────
program fvaratio
        version 11
        syntax newvarname
        tempvar hii ei di2
        quietly {
                predict double 'hii' if e(sample), hat         // changed, as are
                predict double 'ei' if e(sample), resid        // other lines
                gen double 'di2' = ('ei'*'ei')/e(rss)
                gen 'typlist' 'varlist' = ///
                        (e(N)-(e(df_m)+1)) / (e(N)-(e(df_m)+2)) *      ///
                        (1 - 'di2'/(1-'hii')) / (1-'hii')
        }
end
────────────────────────────────────────── end fvaratio.ado, version 7 ──────────
```

As for the second improvement we could make, fvaratio is intended to be used sometime after regress. How do we know the user is not misusing our program and executing it after, say, logistic? e(cmd) will tell us the name of the last estimation command; see [U] **18.9 Accessing results calculated by estimation commands** and [U] **18.10.2 Saving results in e()** above. We should change our program to read

```
────────────────────────────────────────── begin fvaratio.ado, version 8 ──────────
program fvaratio
        version 11
        if "'e(cmd)'"!="regress" {                              // new this version
                error 301
        }
        syntax newvarname
        tempvar hii ei di2
        quietly {
                predict double 'hii' if e(sample), hat
                predict double 'ei' if e(sample), resid
                gen double 'di2' = ('ei'*'ei')/e(rss)
                gen 'typlist' 'varlist' = ///
                        (e(N)-(e(df_m)+1)) / (e(N)-(e(df_m)+2)) *      ///
                        (1 - 'di2'/(1-'hii')) / (1-'hii')
        }
end
────────────────────────────────────────── end fvaratio.ado, version 8 ──────────
```

The error command issues one of Stata's prerecorded error messages and stops our program. Error 301 is "last estimates not found"; see [P] **error**. (Try typing error 301 at the command line.)

In any case, this is a perfect program.

❑ Technical note

You do not have to go to all the trouble we did to program the FVARATIO measure of influence or any other statistic that appeals to you. Whereas version 1 was not really an acceptable solution—it was too specialized—version 2 was acceptable. Version 3 was better, and version 4 better yet, but the improvements were of less and less importance.

Putting aside the details of Stata's language, you should understand that final versions of programs do not just happen—they are the results of drafts that have been refined. How much refinement depends on how often and who will be using the program. In this sense, the "official" ado-files that come with Stata are poor examples. They have been subject to substantial refinement because they will be used by strangers with no knowledge of how the code works. When writing programs for yourself, you may want to stop refining at an earlier draft.

❑

18.11.6 Writing online help

When you write an ado-file, you should also write a help file to go with it. This file is a standard ASCII text file, named *command*.sthlp, that you place in the same directory as your ado-file *command*.ado. This way, when users type help followed by the name of your new command (or pulls down **Help**), they will see something better than "help for ... not found".

You can obtain examples of help files by examining the .sthlp files in the official ado-directory; type "sysdir" and look in the lettered subdirectories of the directory defined as BASE:

```
. sysdir
    STATA:  C:\Program Files\Stata11\
  UPDATES:  C:\Program Files\Stata11\ado\updates\
     BASE:  C:\Program Files\Stata11\ado\base\
     SITE:  C:\Program Files\Stata11\ado\site\
     PLUS:  C:\ado\plus\
 PERSONAL:  C:\ado\personal\
 OLDPLACE:  C:\ado\
```

Here you would find examples of .sthlp files in the a, b, ... subdirectories of C:\Program Files\Stata11\ado\base.

Help files are physically written on the disk in ASCII text format, but their contents are Stata Markup and Control Language (SMCL). For the most part, you can ignore that. If the file contains a line that reads

```
    Also see help for the finishup command
```

it will display in just that way. However, SMCL contains many special directives, so that if the line in the file were to read

```
    Also see {hi:help} for the {help finishup} command
```

what would be displayed would be

Also see **help** for the **finishup** command

and moreover, **finishup** would appear as a hypertext link, meaning that if users clicked on it, they would see help on finishup.

You can read about the details of SMCL in [P] **smcl**. The following is a SMCL help file:

─── begin examplehelpfile.sthlp ───────────

```
{smcl}
{* *! version 1.1.0  14feb2009}{...}
{cmd:help whatever}
{hline}

{title:Title}

{phang}
{bf:whatever} {hline 2}  Calculate whatever statistic


{title:Syntax}

{p 8 17 2}
{cmdab:wh:atever}
[{varlist}]
{ifin}
{weight}
[{cmd:,}
{it:options}]

{synoptset 20 tabbed}{...}
{synopthdr}
{synoptline}
{syntab:Main}
{synopt:{opt d:etail}}display additional statistics{p_end}
{synopt:{opt mean:only}}suppress the display; calculate only the mean; programmer's
                  option{p_end}
{synopt:{opt f:ormat}}use variable's display format{p_end}
{synopt:{opt sep:arator(#)}}draw separator line after every {it:#} variables; default
                  is {cmd:separator(5)}{p_end}
{synopt:{opth g:enerate(newvar)}}create variable name {it:newvar}{p_end}
{synoptline}
{p2colreset}{...}
{p 4 6 2}
{cmd:by} is allowed; see {manhelp by D}.{p_end}
{p 4 4 2}
{cmd:fweight}s are allowed; see {help weight}.


{title:Description}

{pstd}
{cmd:whatever} calculates the whatever statistic for the variables in
{varlist} when the data are not stratified.


{title:Options}

{dlgtab:Main}

{phang}
{opt detail} displays detailed output of the calculation.

{phang}
{opt meanonly} restricts the calculation to be based on only the
means.  The default is to use a trimmed mean.

{phang}
{opt format} requests that the summary statistics be displayed using the display formats
associated with the variables, rather than the default {cmd:g} display format; see {bf:[U]
12.5 Formats: controlling how data are displayed}.
```

```
{phang}
{opt separator(#)} specifies how often to insert separation lines
into the output.  The default is {cmd:separator(5)}, meaning that a
line is drawn after every 5 variables.  {cmd:separator(10)} would
draw a line after every 10 variables. {cmd:separator(0)} suppresses
the separation line.
{phang}
{opth generate(newvar)} creates {it:newvar} containing the whatever values.


{title:Remarks}
{pstd}
For detailed information on the whatever statistic, see {bf:[R] intro}.


{title:Examples}
{phang}{cmd:. whatever mpg weight}
{phang}{cmd:. whatever mpg weight, meanonly}


{title:Also see}
{psee}
Manual:  {findalias fradohelp}
{psee}
{space 2}Help:  {manhelp help R}
{p_end}
```
——————————————————————————————————————— end examplehelpfile.sthlp ———————

If you were to select **Help > Stata Command**, and type `examplehelpfile` and click on **OK**, or if you were to type `help examplehelpfile`, this is what you would see:

---

help whatever

Title

> **whatever** — Calculate whatever statistic

Syntax

> **whatever** [*varlist*] [*if*] [*in*] [*weight*] [, *options*]

options	description
Main	
detail	display additional statistics
meanonly	suppress the display; calculate only the mean; programmer's option
format	use variable's display format
separator(*#*)	draw separator line after every # variables; default is **separator(5)**
generate(*newvar*)	create variable name *newvar*

> **by** is allowed; see **[D] by**.
> **fweight**s are allowed; see **weight**.

Description

> **whatever** calculates the whatever statistic for the variables in *varlist* when the data are not stratified.

Options

┌─ Main ─┐

detail displays detailed output of the calculation.

meanonly restricts the calculation to be based on only the means. The default is to use a trimmed mean.

format requests that the summary statistics be displayed using the display formats associated with the variables, rather than the default **g** display format; see **[U] 12.5 Formats: controlling how data are displayed**.

separator(#) specifies how often to insert separation lines into the output. The default is **separator(5)**, meaning that a line is drawn after every 5 variables. **separator(10)** would draw a line after every 10 variables. **separator(0)** suppresses the separation line.

generate(*newvar*) creates *newvar* containing the whatever values.

Remarks

For detailed information on the whatever statistic, see **[R] intro**.

Examples

. **whatever mpg weight**

. **whatever mpg weight, meanonly**

Also see

Manual: **[U] 18.11.6 Writing online help**

Help: **[R] help**

Users will find it easier to understand your programs if you document them the same way that we document ours. We offer the following guidelines:

1. The first line must be

    {smcl}

    This notifies Stata that the help file is in SMCL format.

2. The second line should be

    {* *! version #.#.# *date*}{...}

    The * indicates a comment and the {...} will suppress the blank line. Whenever you edit the help file, update the version number and the date found in the comment line.

3. The third line should contain

    {cmd:help *yourcmd*}
    {hline}

    assuming the help file is named *yourcmd*.sthlp.

4. Include one blank line, and then place the title.

    {title:Title}

    {phang}
    {bf:*yourcmd*} {hline 2} *Your title*

5. Include two blank lines, and place the Syntax title, syntax diagram, and options table:

> {title:Syntax}
>
> {p 8 17 2}
> *syntax line*
>
> {p 8 17 2}
> *second syntax line, if necessary*
>
> {synoptset 20 tabbed}{...}
> {synopthdr}
> {synoptline}
> {syntab:*tab*}
> {synopt:{*option*}}*brief description of option*{p_end}
> {synoptline}
> {p2colreset}{...}
>
> {p 4 6 2}
> *clarifying text, if required*

6. Include two blank lines, and place the Description title and text:

> {title:Description}
>
> {pstd}
> *description text*

Briefly describe what the command does. Do not burden the user with details yet. Assume that the user is at the point of asking whether this is what he or she is looking for.

7. If your command allows options, include two blank lines, and place the Options title and descriptions:

> {title:Options}
>
> {phang}
> {cmd:*optionname*} *option description*
>
> {pmore}
> *continued option description, if necessary*
>
> {phang}
> {cmd:*optionname*} *second option description*

Options should be included in the order in which they appear in the option table. Option paragraphs are reverse indented, with the option name on the far left, where it is easily spotted. If an option requires more than one paragraph, subsequent paragraphs are set using {pmore}. One blank line separates one option from another.

8. Optionally include two blank lines, and place the Remarks title and text:

> {title:Remarks}
>
> {pstd}
> *text*

Include whatever long discussion you feel necessary. Stata's official online help files often omit this because the discussions appear in the manual. Stata's official help files for features added between releases (obtained from the *Stata Journal*, the Stata web site, etc.), however, include this section because the appropriate *Stata Journal* may not be as accessible as the manuals.

9. Optionally include two blank lines, and place the Examples title and text:

   {title:Examples}

   {phang}
   {cmd:. *first example*}

   {phang}
   {cmd:. *second example*}

   Nothing communicates better than providing something beyond theoretical discussion. Examples rarely need much explanation.

10. Optionally include two blank lines, and place the Author title and text:

    {title:Author}

    {pstd}
    Name, affiliation, etc.

    Exercise caution. If you include a telephone number, expect your phone to ring. An email address may be more appropriate.

11. Optionally include two blank lines, and place the References title and text:

    {title:References}

    {pstd}
    Author. year.
    Title. Location: Publisher.

12. Include two blank lines, and place the Also see title and text:

    {title:Also see}

    {psee}
    Manual: {hi:*Manual reference, if any*}

    {psee}
    {space 2}Help: {manhelp *name*}, {manhelp *name*}, ...

We also warn that it is easy to use too much {hi:highlighting}. Use it sparingly. In text, use {cmd:...} to show what would be shown in typewriter typeface it the documentation were printed in this manual.

❑ Technical note

Sometimes it is more convenient to describe two or more related commands in the same .sthlp file. Thus xyz.sthlp might document both the xyz and abc commands. To arrange that typing help abc displays xyz.sthlp, create the file abc.sthlp, containing

```
─────────────────────────────────────────────────────── begin abc.sthlp ──────────
    .h xyz
─────────────────────────────────────────────────────── end abc.sthlp ──────────
```

When a .sthlp file contains one line of the form '.h *refname*', Stata interprets that as an instruction to display help for *refname*.

❑

❏ Technical note

If you write a collection of programs, you need to somehow index the programs so that users (and you) can find the command they want. We do that with our `contents.sthlp` entry. You should create a similar kind of entry. We suggest that you call your private entry `user.sthlp` in your personal ado-directory; see [U] **17.5.2 Where is my personal ado-directory?**. This way, to review what you have added, you can type `help user`.

We suggest that Unix users at large sites also add `site.sthlp` to the SITE directory (typically `/usr/local/ado`, but type `sysdir` to be sure). Then you can type `help site` for a list of the commands available sitewide.

❏

18.11.7 Programming dialog boxes

You cannot only write new Stata commands and help files, but you can also create your own interface, or dialog box, for a command you have written. Stata provides a dialog box programming language to allow you to create your own dialog boxes. In fact, most of the dialog boxes you see in Stata's interface have been created using this language.

This is not for the faint of heart, but if you want to create your own dialog box for a command, type

```
. help dialog programming
```

The help file contains all the details on creating and programming dialog boxes.

18.12   A compendium of useful commands for programmers

You can use any Stata command in your programs and ado-files. Also, some commands are intended solely for use by Stata programmers. You should see the section under the *Programming* heading in the subject table of contents at the beginning of the *Quick Reference and Index*.

18.13   References

Baum, C. F. 2009. *An Introduction to Stata Programming*. College Station, TX: Stata Press.

Belsley, D. A., E. Kuh, and R. E. Welsch. 1980. *Regression Diagnostics: Identifying Influential Data and Sources of Collinearity*. New York: Wiley.

Gould, W. W. 2001. Statistical software certification. *Stata Journal* 1: 29–50.

19 Immediate commands

Contents

19.1   Overview

An *immediate* command is a command that obtains data not from the data stored in memory but from numbers typed as arguments. Immediate commands, in effect, turn Stata into a glorified hand calculator.

There are many instances when you may not have the data, but you do know something about the data, and what you know is adequate to perform statistical tests. For instance, you do not have to have individual-level data to obtain the standard error of the mean, and thereby a confidence interval, if you know the mean, standard deviation, and number of observations. In other instances, you may actually have the data, and you could enter the data and perform the test, but it would be easier if you could just ask for the statistic based on a summary. For instance, you flip a coin 10 times, and it comes up heads twice. You could enter a 10-observation dataset with two ones (standing for heads) and eight zeros (meaning tails).

Immediate commands are meant to solve those problems. Immediate commands have the following properties:

1. They never disturb the data in memory. You can perform an immediate calculation as an aside without changing your data.

2. The syntax for these commands is the same, the command name followed by numbers, which are the summary statistics from which the statistic is calculated. The numbers are almost always summary statistics, and the order in which they are specified is in some sense "natural".

3. Immediate commands all end in the letter i, although the converse is not true. Usually, if there is an immediate command, there is a nonimmediate form also, that is, a form that works on the data in memory. For every statistical command in Stata, we have included an immediate form if it is reasonable to assume that you might know the requisite summary statistics without having the underlying data and if typing those statistics is not absurdly burdensome.

4. Immediate commands are documented along with their nonimmediate counterparts. Thus, if you want to obtain a confidence interval, whether it be from summary data with an immediate command or using the data in memory, use the table of contents or index to discover that [R] **ci** discusses confidence intervals. There, you learn that ci calculates confidence intervals by using the data in memory and that cii does the same with the data specified immediately following the command.

19.1.1 Examples

▷ Example 1

Let's take the example of confidence intervals. Professional papers often publish the mean, standard deviation, and number of observations for variables used in the analysis. Those statistics are sufficient for calculating a confidence interval. If we know that the mean mileage rating of cars in some sample is 24, that the standard deviation is 6, and that there are 97 cars in the sample, we can calculate

```
. cii 97 24 6
    Variable │     Obs        Mean    Std. Err.      [95% Conf. Interval]
─────────────┼───────────────────────────────────────────────────────────
             │      97          24    .6092077       22.79073     25.20927
```

We learn that the mean's standard error is 0.61 and its 95% confidence interval is $[22.8, 25.2]$. To obtain this, we typed cii (the immediate form of the ci command) followed by the number of observations, the mean, and the standard deviation. We knew the order in which to specify the numbers because we had read [R] **ci**.

We could use the immediate form of the ttest command to test the hypothesis that the true mean is 22:

```
. ttesti 97 24 6 22
One-sample t test
─────────────────────────────────────────────────────────────────────────────────
             │     Obs       Mean   Std. Err.   Std. Dev.    [95% Conf. Interval]
─────────────┼─────────────────────────────────────────────────────────────────────
          x  │      97         24   .6092077           6    22.79073     25.20927
─────────────┴─────────────────────────────────────────────────────────────────────
    mean = mean(x)                                               t =     3.2830
Ho: mean = 22                                   degrees of freedom =         96

   Ha: mean < 22              Ha: mean != 22                  Ha: mean > 22
Pr(T < t) = 0.9993       Pr(|T| > |t|) = 0.0014           Pr(T > t) = 0.0007
```

The first three numbers were as we specified in the cii command. ttesti requires a fourth number, which is the constant against which the mean is being tested; see [R] **ttest**.

◁

▷ Example 2

We mentioned flipping a coin 10 times and having it come up heads twice. The 99% confidence interval can also be obtained from ci:

```
. cii 10 2, level(99)
                                                  — Binomial Exact —
    Variable │     Obs        Mean    Std. Err.      [99% Conf. Interval]
─────────────┼───────────────────────────────────────────────────────────
             │      10          .2    .1264911       .0108505     .6482012
```

In the previous example, we specified cii with three numbers following it; in this example, we specify 2. Immediate commands often determine what to do by the number of arguments following the command. With two arguments, ci assumes that we are specifying the number of trials and successes from a binomial experiment; see [R] **ci**.

The immediate form of the `bitest` command performs exact hypothesis testing:

```
. bitesti 10 2 .5
         N    Observed k    Expected k    Assumed p    Observed p

        10            2             5      0.50000      0.20000
Pr(k >= 2)                = 0.989258  (one-sided test)
Pr(k <= 2)                = 0.054688  (one-sided test)
Pr(k <= 2 or k >= 8) = 0.109375  (two-sided test)
```

For a full explanation of this output, see [R] **bitest**.

◁

▷ Example 3

Stata's `tabulate` command makes tables and calculates various measures of association. The immediate form, `tabi`, does the same, but we specify the contents of the table following the command:

```
. tabi 5 10 \ 2 14
            |        col
        row |        1          2 |     Total

          1 |        5         10 |        15
          2 |        2         14 |        16

      Total |        7         24 |        31
            Fisher's exact =                0.220
    1-sided Fisher's exact =                0.170
```

The `tabi` command is slightly different from most immediate commands because it uses '\' to indicate where one row ends and another begins.

◁

(Continued on next page)

19.1.2   A list of the immediate commands

Command	Reference	Description
bitesti	[R] **bitest**	Binomial probability test
cci	[ST] **epitab**	Tables for epidemiologists
csi		
iri		
mcci		
cii	[R] **ci**	Confidence intervals for means, proportions, and counts
prtesti	[R] **prtest**	One- and two-sample tests of proportions
sampsi	[R] **sampsi**	Sample size and power determination
sdtesti	[R] **sdtest**	Variance comparison tests
symmi	[R] **symmetry**	Symmetry and marginal homogeneity tests
tabi	[R] **tabulate twoway**	Two-way tables of frequencies
ttesti	[R] **ttest**	Mean comparison tests
twoway pci	[G] **graph twoway pci**	Paired-coordinate plot with spikes or lines
twoway pcarrowi	[G] **graph twoway pcarrowi**	Paired-coordinate plot with arrows
twoway scatteri	[G] **graph twoway scatteri**	Twoway scatterplot

19.2   The display command

display is not really an immediate command, but it can be used as a hand calculator.

```
. display 2+5
7
. display sqrt(2+sqrt(3^2-4*2*-2))/(2*3)
.44095855
```

See [R] **display**.

20 Estimation and postestimation commands

Contents

20.1   All estimation commands work the same way

All Stata commands that fit statistical models—commands such as regress, logit, sureg, and so on—work the same way. Most single-equation estimation commands have the syntax

$$command\ varlist\ \left[\,if\,\right]\ \left[\,in\,\right]\ \left[\,weight\,\right]\ \left[\,,\ options\right]$$

259

and most multiple-equation estimation commands have the syntax

$$command \ (varlist) \ (varlist) \ \ldots \ (varlist) \ \big[\, if \,\big] \ \big[\, in \,\big] \ \big[\, weight \,\big] \ \big[\, , \ options \,\big]$$

Adopt a loose definition of single and multiple equation in interpreting this. For instance, heckman is a two-equation system, mathematically speaking, yet we categorize it, syntactically, with single-equation commands because most researchers think of it as a linear regression with an adjustment for the censoring. The important thing is that most estimation commands have one or the other of these two syntaxes.

In single-equation commands, the first variable in the *varlist* is the dependent variable, and the remaining variables are the independent variables, with some exceptions. For instance, xtmixed allows special variable prefixes to identify random factors.

Prefix commands may be specified in front of an estimation command to modify what it does. The syntax is

$$prefix: \ command \ \ldots$$

where the prefix commands are

prefix command	description	manual entry
by	repeat command on subsets of data	[D] **by**
statsby	collect results across subsets of data	[D] **statsby**
rolling	time-series rolling estimation	[TS] **rolling**
*svy	estimation for complex survey data	[SVY] **svy**
*mi estimate	multiply imputed data and multiple imputation	[MI] **mi estimate**
*nestreg	nested model statistics	[R] **nestreg**
*stepwise	stepwise estimation	[R] **stepwise**
*xi	interaction expansion	[R] **xi**
*fracpoly	fractional polynomials	[R] **fracpoly**
*mfp	multiple fractional polynomials	[R] **mfp**

*Available for some but not all estimation commands

Two other prefix commands—bootstrap and jackknife—also work with estimation commands— see [R] **bootstrap** and [R] **jackknife**—but usually it is easier to specify the estimation-command option vce(bootstrap) or vce(jackknife).

Also, all estimation commands—whether single or multiple equation—share the following features:

1. You can use the standard features of Stata's syntax—if *exp* and in *range*—to specify the estimation subsample; you do not have to make a special dataset.

2. You can retype the estimation command without arguments to redisplay the most recent estimation results. For instance, after fitting a model with regress, you can see the estimates again by typing regress by itself. You do not have to do this immediately—any number of commands can occur between the estimation and the replaying, and, in fact, you can even replay the last estimates after the data have changed or you have dropped the data altogether. Stata never forgets (unless you type discard; see [P] **discard**).

3. You can specify the level() option at the time of estimation, or when you redisplay results if that makes sense, to specify the width of the confidence intervals for the coefficients. The default is level(95), meaning 95% confidence intervals. You can reset the default with set level; see [R] **level**.

4. You can use the postestimation command `margins` to display model results in terms of marginal effects (dy/dx or even $df(y)/dx$), which can be displayed as either derivatives or elasticities; see [R] **margins**.

5. You can use the postestimation command `margins` to obtain tables of estimated marginal means, adjusted predictions, and predictive margins; see [R] **margins**.

6. You can use the postestimation command `estat` to obtain common statistics associated with the model. What statistics are available are documented in the postestimation section following the documentation of the estimation command, for instance, in [R] **regress postestimation** following [R] **regress**.

   You can always use the postestimation command `estat vce` to obtain the variance–covariance matrix of the estimators (VCE), presented as either a correlation matrix or a covariance matrix. (You can also obtain the estimated coefficients and covariance matrix as vectors and matrices and manipulate them with Stata's matrix capabilities; see [U] **14.5 Accessing matrices created by Stata commands**.)

7. You can use the postestimation command `predict` to obtain predictions, residuals, influence statistics, and the like, either for the data on which you just estimated or for some other data. You can use postestimation command `predictnl` to obtain point estimates, standard errors, etc., for customized predictions.

8. You can refer to the values of coefficients and standard errors in expressions (such as with `generate`) by using standard notation; see [U] **13.5 Accessing coefficients and standard errors**. You can refer in expressions to the values of other estimation-related statistics by using `e(`*resultname*`)`. For instance, all commands define `e(N)` recording the number of observations in the estimation subsample. After estimation, type `ereturn list` to see a list of all that is available. See the *Saved results* section in the estimation command's documentation for their definition.

   An especially useful `e()` result is `e(sample)`: it returns 1 if an observation was used in the estimation and 0 otherwise, so you can add `if e(sample)` to the end of other commands to restrict them to the estimation subsample. You could type, for instance, `summarize if e(sample)`.

9. You can use the postestimation command `test` to perform tests on the estimated parameters (Wald tests of linear hypotheses), `testnl` to perform Wald tests of nonlinear hypotheses, and `lrtest` to perform likelihood-ratio tests. You can use the postestimation command `lincom` to obtain point estimates and confidence intervals for linear combinations of the estimated parameters and the postestimation command `nlcom` to obtain nonlinear combinations.

10. You can specify the `coeflegend` option at the time of estimation or when you redisplay results to see how to type your coefficients in postestimation commands such as `test` and `lincom` (see [R] **test** and [R] **lincom**) and in expressions.

11. You can use the `statsby` prefix command (see [D] **statsby**) to fit models over each category in a categorical variable and collect the results in a Stata dataset.

12. You can use the postestimation command `estimates` to store estimation results by name for later retrieval or for displaying/comparing multiple models by using `estimates`, or for saving them in a file; see [R] **estimates**.

13. You can use the postestimation command `_estimates` to hold estimates, perform other estimation commands, and then restore the prior estimates. This is of particular interest to programmers.

14. You can use the postestimation command suest to obtain the joint parameter vector and variance–covariance matrix for coefficients from two different models by using seemingly unrelated estimation. This is especially useful for testing the equality, say, of coefficients across models; see [R] **suest**.

15. You can use the postestimation command hausman to perform Hausman model-specification tests by using hausman; see [R] **hausman**.

16. With some exceptions, you can specify the vce(robust) option at the time of estimation to obtain the Huber/White/robust alternate estimate of variance, or you can specify the vce(cluster *clustvar*) option to relax the assumption of independence of the observations.

    Most estimation commands also allow a vce(*vcetype*) option to specify other alternative variance estimators—which ones are allowed are documented with the estimator—and usually vce(opg), vce(bootstrap), and vce(jackknife) are available.

20.2 Standard syntax

You can combine Stata's if *exp* and in *range* with any estimation command. Estimation commands also allow by *varlist*:, where it would be sensible.

▷ Example 1

We have data on 74 automobiles that record the mileage rating (mpg), weight (weight), and whether the car is domestic or foreign produced (foreign). We can fit a linear regression model of mpg on weight and the square of weight, using just the foreign-made automobiles, by typing

```
. use http://www.stata-press.com/data/r11/auto
(1978 Automobile Data)

. regress mpg weight c.weight#c.weight if foreign
```

Source	SS	df	MS		Number of obs =	22
					F(2, 19) =	8.31
Model	428.256889	2	214.128444		Prob > F =	0.0026
Residual	489.606747	19	25.7687762		R-squared =	0.4666
					Adj R-squared =	0.4104
Total	917.863636	21	43.7077922		Root MSE =	5.0763

mpg	Coef.	Std. Err.	t	P>|t|	[95% Conf. Interval]	
weight	-.0132182	.0275711	-0.48	0.637	-.0709252	.0444888
c.weight#c.weight	5.50e-07	5.41e-06	0.10	0.920	-.0000108	.0000119
_cons	52.33775	34.1539	1.53	0.142	-19.14719	123.8227

We use the factor-variable notation c.weight#c.weight to add the square of weight to our regression; see [U] **11.4.3 Factor variables**.

We can run separate regressions for the domestic and foreign-produced automobiles with the by *varlist*: prefix:

```
. use http://www.stata-press.com/data/r11/auto
(1978 Automobile Data)
. by foreign: regress mpg weight c.weight#c.weight
```

```
-> foreign = Domestic
```

Source	SS	df	MS		Number of obs	=	52
					F(2, 49)	=	91.64
Model	905.395466	2	452.697733		Prob > F	=	0.0000
Residual	242.046842	49	4.93973146		R-squared	=	0.7891
					Adj R-squared	=	0.7804
Total	1147.44231	51	22.4988688		Root MSE	=	2.2226

mpg	Coef.	Std. Err.	t	P>|t|	[95% Conf. Interval]	
weight	-.0131718	.0032307	-4.08	0.000	-.0196642	-.0066794
c.weight# c.weight	1.11e-06	4.95e-07	2.25	0.029	1.19e-07	2.11e-06
_cons	50.74551	5.162014	9.83	0.000	40.37205	61.11896

```
-> foreign = Foreign
```

Source	SS	df	MS		Number of obs	=	22
					F(2, 19)	=	8.31
Model	428.256889	2	214.128444		Prob > F	=	0.0026
Residual	489.606747	19	25.7687762		R-squared	=	0.4666
					Adj R-squared	=	0.4104
Total	917.863636	21	43.7077922		Root MSE	=	5.0763

mpg	Coef.	Std. Err.	t	P>|t|	[95% Conf. Interval]	
weight	-.0132182	.0275711	-0.48	0.637	-.0709252	.0444888
c.weight# c.weight	5.50e-07	5.41e-06	0.10	0.920	-.0000108	.0000119
_cons	52.33775	34.1539	1.53	0.142	-19.14719	123.8227

Although all estimation commands allow if *exp* and in *range*, only some allow the by *varlist*: prefix. For by(), the duration of Stata's memory is limited: it remembers the *last* set of estimates only. This means that, if we were to use any of the other features described below, they would use the last regression estimated, which right now is mpg on weight and square of weight for the Foreign subsample.

We can instead collect the statistics from each of the by-groups using the [D] **statsby** prefix.

```
. statsby, by(foreign): regress mpg weight c.weight#c.weight
(running regress on estimation sample)
      command:  regress mpg weight c.weight#c.weight
           by:  foreign
Statsby groups
 ───────┼──── 1 ───┼──── 2 ───┼──── 3 ───┼──── 4 ───┼──── 5
 ..
```

statsby runs the regression first on Domestic cars then on Foreign cars and saves the coefficients by overwriting our dataset. Do not worry; if the dataset has not been previously saved, statsby will refuse to run unless we also specify the clear option.

Here is what we now have in memory.

. list

	foreign	_b_weight	_stat_2	_b_cons
1.	Domestic	-.0131718	1.11e-06	50.74551
2.	Foreign	-.0132182	5.50e-07	52.33775

These are the coefficients from the two regressions above. statsby does not know how to name the coefficient for c.weight#c.weight so it labels the coefficient with the generic name _stat_2. We can also save the standard errors and other statistics from the regressions; see [D] **statsby**.

◁

20.3   Replaying prior results

When you type an estimation command without arguments, it redisplays prior results.

▷ Example 2

To perform a regression of mpg on the variables weight and displacement, we could type

. regress mpg weight displacement

Source	SS	df	MS
Model	1595.40969	2	797.704846
Residual	848.049768	71	11.9443629
Total	2443.45946	73	33.4720474

Number of obs = 74
F(2, 71) = 66.79
Prob > F = 0.0000
R-squared = 0.6529
Adj R-squared = 0.6432
Root MSE = 3.4561

mpg	Coef.	Std. Err.	t	P>|t|	[95% Conf. Interval]	
weight	-.0065671	.0011662	-5.63	0.000	-.0088925	-.0042417
displacement	.0052808	.0098696	0.54	0.594	-.0143986	.0249602
_cons	40.08452	2.02011	19.84	0.000	36.05654	44.11251

We now go on to do other things, summarizing data, listing observations, performing hypothesis tests, or anything else. If we decide that we want to see the last set of estimates again, we type the estimation command without arguments.

. regress

Source	SS	df	MS
Model	1595.40969	2	797.704846
Residual	848.049768	71	11.9443629
Total	2443.45946	73	33.4720474

Number of obs = 74
F(2, 71) = 66.79
Prob > F = 0.0000
R-squared = 0.6529
Adj R-squared = 0.6432
Root MSE = 3.4561

mpg	Coef.	Std. Err.	t	P>|t|	[95% Conf. Interval]	
weight	-.0065671	.0011662	-5.63	0.000	-.0088925	-.0042417
displacement	.0052808	.0098696	0.54	0.594	-.0143986	.0249602
_cons	40.08452	2.02011	19.84	0.000	36.05654	44.11251

This feature works with *every* estimation command, so we could just as well have done it with, say, stcox or logit.   ◁

20.4   Cataloging estimation results

Stata keeps only the results of the most recently fitted model in active memory. You can use Stata's estimates command, however, to temporarily store estimation results for displaying, comparing, cross-model testing, etc., during the same session. You can also save estimation results to disk, but that will be the subject of the next section. You may temporarily store up to 300 sets of estimation results.

▷ Example 3

Continuing with our automobile data, we fit four models and estimates store them. We fit the models quietly to keep the output to a minimum.

```
. quietly regress mpg weight displ
. estimates store r_base
. quietly regress mpg weight displ foreign
. estimates store r_alt
. quietly qreg mpg weight displ
. estimates store q_base
. quietly qreg mpg weight displ foreign
. estimates store q_alt
```

We saved the four models under the names r_base, r_alt, q_base, and q_alt but, if we forget, we can ask to see a directory of what is stored:

```
. estimates dir
```

model	command	depvar	npar	title
r_base	regress	mpg	3	
r_alt	regress	mpg	4	
q_base	qreg	mpg	3	
q_alt	qreg	mpg	4	

We can ask that any of the previous models be replayed:

```
. estimates replay r_base
```

Model **r_base**

Source	SS	df	MS		
Model	1595.40969	2	797.704846		
Residual	848.049768	71	11.9443629		
Total	2443.45946	73	33.4720474		

Number of obs =   74
F(2,   71) =   66.79
Prob > F   = 0.0000
R-squared   = 0.6529
Adj R-squared = 0.6432
Root MSE   = 3.4561

mpg	Coef.	Std. Err.	t	P>|t|	[95% Conf. Interval]	
weight	-.0065671	.0011662	-5.63	0.000	-.0088925	-.0042417
displacement	.0052808	.0098696	0.54	0.594	-.0143986	.0249602
_cons	40.08452	2.02011	19.84	0.000	36.05654	44.11251

Or we can ask to see all the models in a combined table:

```
. estimates table _all
```

Variable	r_base	r_alt	q_base	q_alt
weight	-.00656711	-.00677449	-.00581173	-.00595056
displacement	.00528078	.00192865	.00428411	.00018552
foreign		-1.6006312		-2.1326004
_cons	40.084522	41.847949	37.559865	39.213348

estimates displayed just the coefficients, but we could ask for other statistics. Finally, we can also select one of the stored estimates to be made active, meaning things are just as if we had just fit the model:

```
. estimates restore r_alt
(results r_alt are active now)

. regress
```

Source	SS	df	MS
Model	1619.71935	3	539.906448
Residual	823.740114	70	11.7677159
Total	2443.45946	73	33.4720474

Number of obs =   74
F(3,   70) =   45.88
Prob > F   = 0.0000
R-squared   = 0.6629
Adj R-squared = 0.6484
Root MSE   = 3.4304

mpg	Coef.	Std. Err.	t	P>|t|	[95% Conf. Interval]
weight	-.0067745	.0011665	-5.81	0.000	-.0091011 -.0044479
displacement	.0019286	.0100701	0.19	0.849	-.0181556 .0220129
foreign	-1.600631	1.113648	-1.44	0.155	-3.821732 .6204699
_cons	41.84795	2.350704	17.80	0.000	37.15962 46.53628

◁

You can do a lot more with estimates; see [R] **estimates**. In particular, estimates makes it easy to perform cross-model tests, such as the Hausman specification test.

20.5   Saving estimation results

estimates can also save estimation results into a file.

```
. estimates save alt
    file alt.ster saved
```

That saved the active estimation results, the ones we just estimated or, in our case, the ones we just restored. Later, even in another Stata session, we could reload our estimates:

```
. estimates use alt
. regress
```

Source	SS	df	MS
Model	1619.71935	3	539.906448
Residual	823.740114	70	11.7677159
Total	2443.45946	73	33.4720474

```
Number of obs =      74
F(  3,    70) =   45.88
Prob > F      =  0.0000
R-squared     =  0.6629
Adj R-squared =  0.6484
Root MSE      =  3.4304
```

mpg	Coef.	Std. Err.	t	P>|t|	[95% Conf.	Interval]
weight	-.0067745	.0011665	-5.81	0.000	-.0091011	-.0044479
displacement	.0019286	.0100701	0.19	0.849	-.0181556	.0220129
foreign	-1.600631	1.113648	-1.44	0.155	-3.821732	.6204699
_cons	41.84795	2.350704	17.80	0.000	37.15962	46.53628

There is one important difference between storing results in memory and saving them in a file: e(sample) is lost. We have not discussed e(sample) yet, but it allows us to identify the observations among those currently in memory that were used in the estimation. For instance, after estimation, we could type

```
. summarize mpg weight displ foreign if e(sample)
  (output omitted)
```

and see the summary statistics of the relevant data. We could do that after an estimates restore, too. But we cannot do it after an estimates use. Part of the reason is that we might not even have the relevant data in memory. Even if we do, however, here is what will happen:

```
. summarize mpg weight displ foreign if e(sample)
```

Variable	Obs	Mean	Std. Dev.	Min	Max
mpg	0				
weight	0				
displacement	0				
foreign	0				

Stata will just assume that none of the data in memory played a role in obtaining the estimation results.

There is more worth knowing. You could, for instance, type estimates describe to see the command line that produced the estimates. See [R] **estimates**.

20.6   Specifying the estimation subsample

You specify the estimation subsample—the sample to be used in estimation—by specifying the if *exp* and/or in *range* modifiers with the estimation command.

Once an estimation command has been run or previous estimates restored, Stata remembers the estimation subsample, and you can use the modifier if e(sample) on the end of other Stata commands. The term *estimation subsample* refers to the set of observations used to produce the active estimation results. That might turn out to be all the observations (as it was in the above example) or some of the observations:

```
. regress mpg weight 5.rep78 if foreign
```

Source	SS	df	MS
Model	423.317154	2	211.658577
Residual	372.96856	18	20.7204756
Total	796.285714	20	39.8142857

Number of obs =	21
F(2, 18) =	10.21
Prob > F =	0.0011
R-squared =	0.5316
Adj R-squared =	0.4796
Root MSE =	4.552

mpg	Coef.	Std. Err.	t	P>|t|	[95% Conf. Interval]	
weight	-.0131402	.0029684	-4.43	0.000	-.0193765	-.0069038
5.rep78	5.052676	2.13492	2.37	0.029	.5673764	9.537977
_cons	52.86088	6.540147	8.08	0.000	39.12054	66.60122

```
. summarize mpg weight 5.rep78 if e(sample)
```

Variable	Obs	Mean	Std. Dev.	Min	Max
mpg	21	25.28571	6.309856	17	41
weight	21	2263.333	364.7099	1760	3170
5.rep78	21	.4285714	.5070926	0	1

Twenty-one observations were used in the above regression and we subsequently obtained the means for those same 21 observations by typing summarize ... if e(sample). There are two reasons observations were dropped: we specified if foreign when we ran the regression, and there were observations for which 5.rep78 was missing. The reason does not matter; e(sample) is true if the observation was used and false otherwise.

You can use if e(sample) on the end of any Stata command that allows an if *exp*.

Here Stata has a shorthand command that produces the same results as summarize ... if e(sample):

```
. estat summarize, label
```

Estimation sample regress   Number of obs =   21

Variable	Mean	Std. Dev.	Min	Max	Label
mpg	25.28571	6.309856	17	41	Mileage (mpg)
weight	2263.333	364.7099	1760	3170	Weight (lbs.)
5.rep78	.4285714	.5070926	0	1	Repair Record 1978

See [R] **estat**.

20.7   Specifying the width of confidence intervals

You can specify the width of the confidence intervals for the coefficients using the level() option at estimation or when you play back the results.

▷ Example 4

To obtain narrower, 90% confidence intervals when we fit the model, we type

```
. regress mpg weight displ, level(90)
```

Source	SS	df	MS	
Model	1595.40969	2	797.704846	
Residual	848.049768	71	11.9443629	
Total	2443.45946	73	33.4720474	

```
Number of obs =      74
F(  2,    71) =   66.79
Prob > F      =  0.0000
R-squared     =  0.6529
Adj R-squared =  0.6432
Root MSE      =  3.4561
```

mpg	Coef.	Std. Err.	t	P>|t|	[90% Conf. Interval]	
weight	-.0065671	.0011662	-5.63	0.000	-.0085108	-.0046234
displacement	.0052808	.0098696	0.54	0.594	-.0111679	.0217294
_cons	40.08452	2.02011	19.84	0.000	36.71781	43.45124

If we subsequently typed regress, without arguments, 95% confidence intervals would be reported. If we initially fit the model with 95% confidence intervals, we could later type regress, level(90) to redisplay results with 90% confidence intervals.

Also, we could type set level 90 to make 90% intervals our default; see [R] **level**.

Stata allows noninteger confidence intervals between 10.00 and 99.99, with a maximum of two digits following the decimal point. For instance, we could type

```
. regress mpg weight displ, level(92.5)
```

Source	SS	df	MS	
Model	1595.40969	2	797.704846	
Residual	848.049768	71	11.9443629	
Total	2443.45946	73	33.4720474	

```
Number of obs =      74
F(  2,    71) =   66.79
Prob > F      =  0.0000
R-squared     =  0.6529
Adj R-squared =  0.6432
Root MSE      =  3.4561
```

mpg	Coef.	Std. Err.	t	P>|t|	[92.5% Conf. Interval]	
weight	-.0065671	.0011662	-5.63	0.000	-.0086745	-.0044597
displacement	.0052808	.0098696	0.54	0.594	-.0125535	.023115
_cons	40.08452	2.02011	19.84	0.000	36.43419	43.73485

◁

20.8   Obtaining the variance–covariance matrix

Typing estat vce displays the variance–covariance matrix of the estimators in active memory.

▷ Example 5

In example 2, we typed regress mpg weight displacement. The full variance–covariance matrix of the estimators can be displayed at any time after estimation:

```
. estat vce
Covariance matrix of coefficients of regress model
        e(V) |     weight  displace~t        _cons
-------------+------------------------------------
      weight |   1.360e-06
displacement |  -.0000103    .00009741
       _cons |  -.00207455   .01188356    4.0808455
```

Typing `estat vce` with the `corr` option presents this matrix as a correlation matrix:

```
. estat vce, corr
Correlation matrix of coefficients of regress model
        e(V) |    weight   displa~t      _cons
-------------+---------------------------------
      weight |   1.0000
displacement |  -0.8949     1.0000
       _cons |  -0.8806     0.5960     1.0000
```

See [R] **estat**.

Also, Stata's matrix commands understand that `e(V)` refers to the matrix:

```
. matrix list e(V)
symmetric e(V)[3,3]
                   weight  displacement        _cons
      weight     1.360e-06
displacement     -.0000103    .00009741
       _cons    -.00207455    .01188356    4.0808455
. mat Vinv = invsym(e(V))
. mat list Vinv
symmetric Vinv[3,3]
                   weight  displacement        _cons
      weight      60175851
displacement     4081161.2     292709.46
       _cons     18706.732     1222.3339    6.1953911
```

See [U] **14.5 Accessing matrices created by Stata commands**.

◁

20.9   Obtaining predicted values

Our discussion below, although cast in terms of predicted values, applies equally to the other statistics generated by `predict`; see [R] **predict**.

When Stata fits a model, whether it is regression or anything else, it internally saves the results, including the estimated coefficients and the variable names. The `predict` command allows you to use that information.

▷ Example 6

Let's perform a linear regression of mpg on weight and the square of weight:

```
. regress mpg weight c.weight#c.weight
```

Source	SS	df	MS
Model	1642.52197	2	821.260986
Residual	800.937487	71	11.2808097
Total	2443.45946	73	33.4720474

```
Number of obs =      74
F(  2,    71) =   72.80
Prob > F      =  0.0000
R-squared     =  0.6722
Adj R-squared =  0.6630
Root MSE      =  3.3587
```

mpg	Coef.	Std. Err.	t	P>|t|	[95% Conf. Interval]	
weight	-.0141581	.0038835	-3.65	0.001	-.0219016	-.0064145
c.weight# c.weight	1.32e-06	6.26e-07	2.12	0.038	7.67e-08	2.57e-06
_cons	51.18308	5.767884	8.87	0.000	39.68225	62.68392

After the regression, predict is defined to be

$$-.0141581\text{weight} + 1.32 \cdot 10^{-6}\text{weight}^2 + 51.18308$$

(Actually, it is more precise because the coefficients are internally stored at much higher precision than shown in the output.) Thus we can create a new variable—call it fitted—equal to the prediction by typing predict fitted and then use scatter to display the fitted and actual values separately for domestic and foreign automobiles:

```
. predict fitted
(option xb assumed; fitted values)
. scatter mpg fitted weight, by(foreign, total) c(. l) m(o i) sort
```

predict can calculate much more than just predicted values. For predict after linear regression, predict can calculate residuals, standardized residuals, studentized residuals, influence statistics, etc. In any case, we specify what is to be calculated via an option, so if we wanted the residuals stored in new variable r, we would type

```
. predict r, resid
```

The options that may be specified following `predict` vary according to the estimation command previously used; the `predict` options are documented along with the estimation command. For instance, to discover all the things `predict` can do following `regress`, see [R] **regress**.

◁

20.9.1 Using predict

The use of `predict` is not limited to linear regression. `predict` can be used after any estimation command.

▷ Example 7

You fit a logistic regression model of whether a car is manufactured outside the United States on the basis of its weight and mileage rating using either the `logistic` or the `logit` command; see [R] **logistic** and [R] **logit**. We will use `logit`.

```
. use http://www.stata-press.com/data/r11/auto
. logit foreign weight mpg
Iteration 0:    log likelihood =  -45.03321
Iteration 1:    log likelihood = -29.898968
Iteration 2:    log likelihood = -27.495771
Iteration 3:    log likelihood = -27.184006
Iteration 4:    log likelihood = -27.175166
Iteration 5:    log likelihood = -27.175156
```

Logistic regression				Number of obs	=	74
				LR chi2(2)	=	35.72
				Prob > chi2	=	0.0000
Log likelihood = -27.175156				Pseudo R2	=	0.3966

foreign	Coef.	Std. Err.	z	P>|z|	[95% Conf. Interval]	
weight	-.0039067	.0010116	-3.86	0.000	-.0058894	-.001924
mpg	-.1685869	.0919174	-1.83	0.067	-.3487418	.011568
_cons	13.70837	4.518707	3.03	0.002	4.851864	22.56487

After `logit`, `predict` without options calculates the probability of a positive outcome (we learned that by looking at [R] **logit**). To obtain the predicted probabilities that each car is manufactured outside the United States, we type

```
. predict probhat
(option pr assumed; Pr(foreign))
. summarize probhat
```

Variable	Obs	Mean	Std. Dev.	Min	Max
probhat	74	.2972973	.3052979	.000729	.8980594

```
. list make mpg weight foreign probhat in 1/5
```

	make	mpg	weight	foreign	probhat
1.	AMC Concord	22	2,930	Domestic	.1904363
2.	AMC Pacer	17	3,350	Domestic	.0957767
3.	AMC Spirit	22	2,640	Domestic	.4220815
4.	Buick Century	20	3,250	Domestic	.0862625
5.	Buick Electra	15	4,080	Domestic	.0084948

◁

20.9.2   Making in-sample predictions

`predict` does not retrieve a vector of prerecorded values—it calculates the predictions on the basis of the recorded coefficients and the data currently in memory. In the above examples, when we typed things like

        . predict probhat

predict filled in the prediction everywhere that it could be calculated.

Sometimes we have more data in memory than were used by the estimation command, either because we explicitly ignored some of the observations by specifying an if *exp* with the estimation command or because there are missing values. In such cases, if we want to restrict the calculation to the estimation subsample, we would do that in the usual way by adding if e(sample) to the end of the command:

        . predict probhat if e(sample)

20.9.3   Making out-of-sample predictions

Because `predict` makes its calculations on the basis of the recorded coefficients and the data in memory, `predict` can do more than calculate predicted values for the data on which the estimation took place—it can make out-of-sample predictions, as well.

If you fit your model on a subset of the observations, you could then predict the outcome for all the observations:

        . logit foreign weight mpg if rep78 > 3
        . predict pall

If you do not specify if e(sample) at the end of the `predict` command, `predict` calculates the predictions for all observations possible.

In fact, because `predict` works from the active estimation results, you can use `predict` with *any* dataset that contains the necessary variables.

▷ Example 8

Continuing with our previous `logit` example, assume that we have a second dataset containing the mpg and weight of a different sample of cars. We have just fit your model and now continue:

        . use otherdat, clear
        (Different cars)

        . predict probhat   *Stata remembers the previous model*
        (option pr assumed; Pr(foreign))

        . summarize probhat foreign

Variable	Obs	Mean	Std. Dev.	Min	Max
probhat	12	.2505068	.3187104	.0084948	.8920776
foreign	12	.1666667	.3892495	0	1

◁

▷ Example 9

There are many ways to obtain out-of-sample predictions. Above, we estimated on one dataset and then used another. If our first dataset had contained both sets of cars, marked, say, by the variable difcars being 0 if from the first sample and 1 if from the second, we could type

```
. logit foreign weight mpg if difcars==0
same output as above appears
. predict probhat
(option pr assumed; Pr(foreign))
. summarize probhat foreign if difcars==1
same output as directly above appears
```

If we just had a few additional cars, we could even input them after estimation. Assume that our data once again contain only the first sample of cars, and assume that we are interested in an additional sample of only two rather than 12 cars; we could type

```
. use http://www.stata-press.com/data/r11/auto
. keep make mpg weight foreign
. logit foreign weight mpg
same output as above appears
. input
                        make        mpg     weight    foreign
 75. "Merc. Zephyr" 20 2830 0                   we type in our new data
 76. "VW Dasher" 23 2160 1
 77. end
. predict probhat                      obtain all the predictions
(option pr assumed; Pr(foreign))
. list in -2/1
```

	make	mpg	weight	foreign	probhat
75.	Merc. Zephyr	20	2830	Domestic	.3275397
76.	VW Dasher	23	2160	Foreign	.8009743

◁

20.9.4 Obtaining standard errors, tests, and confidence intervals for predictions

When you use predict, you create, for each observation in the prediction sample, a statistic that is a function of the data and the estimated model parameters. You also could have generated your own customized predictions by using generate. In either case, to get standard errors, Wald tests, and confidence intervals for your predictions, use predictnl. For example, if we wanted the standard errors for our predicted probabilities, we could type

```
. drop probhat
. predictnl probhat = predict(), se(phat_se)
. list in 1/5
```

	make	mpg	weight	foreign	probhat	phat_se
1.	AMC Concord	22	2,930	Domestic	.1904363	.0658386
2.	AMC Pacer	17	3,350	Domestic	.0957767	.0536296
3.	AMC Spirit	22	2,640	Domestic	.4220815	.0892845
4.	Buick Century	20	3,250	Domestic	.0862625	.0461927
5.	Buick Electra	15	4,080	Domestic	.0084948	.0093079

Comparing this output to our previous listing of the first five predicted probabilities, you will notice that the output is identical, except that we now have an additional variable, phat_se, which contains the estimated standard error for each predicted probability.

We first had to drop probhat because predictnl will regenerate it. Note also the use of predict() within predictnl—it specified that we wanted to generate a point estimate (and standard error) for the default prediction after logit; see [R] **predictnl** for more details.

20.10 Accessing estimated coefficients

You can access coefficients and standard errors after estimation by referring to _b[*name*] and _se[*name*]; see [U] **13.5 Accessing coefficients and standard errors**.

▷ Example 10

Let's return to linear regression. We are doing a study of earnings of men and women at a particular company. In addition to each person's earnings, we have information on their educational attainment and tenure with the company. We type the following:

```
. regress lnearn ed tenure i.female female#(c.ed c.tenure)
(output omitted )
```

If you are not familiar with the # notation, see [U] **11.4.3 Factor variables**.

We now wish to predict everyone's income as if they were male and then compare these as-if earnings with the actual earnings:

```
. generate asif = _b[_cons] + _b[ed]*ed + _b[tenure]*tenure
```

◁

▷ Example 11

We are analyzing the mileage of automobiles and are using a slightly more sophisticated model than any we have used so far. As we have previously, we will fit a linear regression model of mpg on weight and the square of weight, but we also add the interaction of foreign with weight, the car's gear ratio (gear_ratio), and foreign interacted with gear_ratio. We will use factor-variable notation to create the squared term and the interactions; see [U] **11.4.3 Factor variables**.

(Continued on next page)

```
. use http://www.stata-press.com/data/r11/auto, clear
(1978 Automobile Data)

. regress mpg weight c.weight#c.weight i.foreign#c.weight gear_ratio
> i.foreign#c.gear_ratio
```

Source	SS	df	MS
Model	1737.05293	5	347.410585
Residual	706.406534	68	10.3883314
Total	2443.45946	73	33.4720474

```
Number of obs =      74
F(  5,    68) =   33.44
Prob > F      =  0.0000
R-squared     =  0.7109
Adj R-squared =  0.6896
Root MSE      =  3.2231
```

mpg	Coef.	Std. Err.	t	P>|t|	[95% Conf. Interval]
weight	-.0118517	.0045136	-2.63	0.011	-.0208584 -.002845
c.weight# c.weight	9.81e-07	7.04e-07	1.39	0.168	-4.25e-07 2.39e-06
foreign# c.weight 1	-.0032241	.0015577	-2.07	0.042	-.0063326 -.0001157
gear_ratio	1.159741	1.553418	0.75	0.458	-1.940057 4.259539
foreign# c.gear_ratio 1	1.597462	1.205313	1.33	0.189	-.8077036 4.002627
_cons	44.61644	8.387943	5.32	0.000	27.87856 61.35432

If you are not experienced in both regression technology and automobile technology, you may find it difficult to interpret this regression. Putting aside issues of statistical significance, we find that mileage decreases with a car's weight but increases with the square of weight; decreases even more rapidly with weight for foreign cars; increases with higher gear ratio; and increases even more rapidly with higher gear ratio in foreign cars.

Thus do foreign cars yield better or worse gas mileage? Results are mixed. As the foreign cars' weight increases, they do more poorly in relation to domestic cars, but they do better at higher gear ratios. One way to compare the results is to predict what mileage foreign cars would have *if they were manufactured domestically*. The regression provides all the information necessary for making that calculation; mileage for domestic cars is estimated to be

$$-.012\,\texttt{weight} + 9.81 \cdot 10^{-7}\,\texttt{weight}^2 + 1.160\,\texttt{gear\_ratio} + 44.6$$

We can use that equation to predict the mileage of foreign cars and then compare it with the true outcome. The _b[] function simplifies reference to the estimated coefficients. We can type

```
. gen asif=_b[weight]*weight + _b[c.weight#c.weight]*c.weight#c.weight +
    _b[gear_ratio]*gear_ratio + _b[_cons]
```

_b[weight] refers to the estimated coefficient on weight, _b[c.weight#c.weight] to the estimated coefficient on c.weight#c.weight, and so on.

We might now ask how the actual mileage of a Honda compares with the `asif` prediction:

```
. list make asif mpg if strpos(make,"Honda")
```

	make	asif	mpg
61.	Honda Accord	26.52597	25
62.	Honda Civic	30.62202	28

Notice the way we constructed our `if` clause to select Hondas. `strpos()` is the string function that returns the location in the first string where the second string is found or, if the second string does not occur in the first, zero. Thus any recorded `make` that contains the string "Honda" anywhere in it would be listed; see [D] **functions**.

We find that both Honda models yield slightly lower gas mileage than the `asif` domestic car–based prediction. (We do not endorse this model as a complete model of the determinants of mileage, nor do we single out the Honda for any special scorn. In fact, please note that the observed values are within the root mean squared error of the average prediction.)

We might wish to compare the overall average `mpg` and the `asif` prediction over all foreign cars in the data:

```
. summarize mpg asif if foreign
```

Variable	Obs	Mean	Std. Dev.	Min	Max
mpg	22	24.77273	6.611187	14	41
asif	22	26.67124	3.142912	19.70466	30.62202

We find that, on average, foreign cars yield slightly lower mileage than our `asif` prediction. This might lead us to ask if any foreign cars do better than the `asif` prediction:

```
. list make asif mpg if foreign & mpg>asif, sep(0)
```

	make	asif	mpg
55.	BMW 320i	24.31697	25
57.	Datsun 210	28.96818	35
63.	Mazda GLC	29.32015	30
66.	Subaru	28.85993	35
68.	Toyota Corolla	27.01144	31
71.	VW Diesel	28.90355	41

We find six such automobiles.

◁

(Continued on next page)

20.11   Performing hypothesis tests on the coefficients

20.11.1   Linear tests

After estimation, `test` is used to perform tests of linear hypotheses on the basis of the variance–covariance matrix of the estimators (Wald tests).

▷ Example 12

(`test` has many syntaxes and features, so do not use this example as an excuse for not reading [R] **test**.) Using the automobile data, we perform the following regression:

```
. use http://www.stata-press.com/data/r11/auto, clear
(1978 Automobile Data)

. generate weightsq=weight^2

. regress mpg weight weightsq foreign
```

Source	SS	df	MS		Number of obs =	74
					F(3, 70) =	52.25
Model	1689.15372	3	563.05124		Prob > F =	0.0000
Residual	754.30574	70	10.7757963		R-squared =	0.6913
					Adj R-squared =	0.6781
Total	2443.45946	73	33.4720474		Root MSE =	3.2827

mpg	Coef.	Std. Err.	t	P>|t|	[95% Conf. Interval]	
weight	-.0165729	.0039692	-4.18	0.000	-.0244892	-.0086567
weightsq	1.59e-06	6.25e-07	2.55	0.013	3.45e-07	2.84e-06
foreign	-2.2035	1.059246	-2.08	0.041	-4.3161	-.0909002
_cons	56.53884	6.197383	9.12	0.000	44.17855	68.89913

We can use the `test` command to calculate the joint significance of `weight` and `weightsq`:

```
. test weight weightsq
 ( 1)   weight = 0
 ( 2)   weightsq = 0
       F( 2,    70) =   60.83
            Prob > F =    0.0000
```

We are not limited to testing whether the coefficients are zero. We can test whether the coefficient on `foreign` is -2 by typing

```
. test foreign = -2
 ( 1)   foreign = -2
       F( 1,    70) =    0.04
            Prob > F =    0.8482
```

We can even test more complicated hypotheses because `test` can perform basic algebra. Here is an absurd hypothesis:

```
. test 2*(weight+weightsq)=-3*(foreign-(weight-weightsq))
 ( 1) - weight + 5.0 weightsq + 3.0 foreign = 0
       F( 1,    70) =    4.31
            Prob > F =    0.0416
```

test simplified the algebra of our hypothesis and then presented the test results. We discover that the hypothesis may be absurd but we cannot reject it at the 1% or even 4% level. We can also use test's `accumulate` option to combine this test with another test:

```
. test foreign+weight=0, accum
 ( 1) - weight + 5.0 weightsq + 3.0 foreign = 0
 ( 2)   weight + foreign = 0
       F(  2,    70) =    9.12
            Prob > F =    0.0003
```

There are limitations. test can test only linear hypotheses. If we attempt to test a nonlinear hypothesis, test will tell us that it is not possible:

```
. test weight/foreign=0
not possible with test
r(131);
```

Testing nonlinear hypotheses is discussed in [U] **20.11.4 Nonlinear Wald tests** below.

◁

20.11.2   Using test

test bases its results on the estimated variance–covariance matrix of the estimators (i.e., performs a Wald test), so it can be used after any estimation command. For maximum likelihood estimation, you will have to decide whether you want to perform tests on the basis of the information matrix instead of constraining the equation, reestimating it, and then calculating the likelihood-ratio test (see [U] **20.11.3 Likelihood-ratio tests**). Because test bases its results on the information matrix, its results have the same standing as the asymptotic z statistic presented in the coefficient table.

▷ Example 13

Let's examine the repair records of the cars in our automobile data as rated by *Consumer Reports*:

```
. tabulate rep78 foreign
```

Repair Record 1978	Car type Domestic	Foreign	Total
1	2	0	2
2	8	0	8
3	27	3	30
4	9	9	18
5	2	9	11
Total	48	21	69

The values are coded 1–5, corresponding to well below average to well above average. We will fit this variable by using a maximum-likelihood ordered logit model (the `nolog` option suppresses the iteration log, saving us some paper):

```
. ologit rep78 price foreign weight weightsq displ, nolog
Ordered logistic regression                      Number of obs   =          69
                                                 LR chi2(5)      =       33.12
                                                 Prob > chi2     =      0.0000
Log likelihood = -77.133082                      Pseudo R2       =      0.1767
```

rep78	Coef.	Std. Err.	z	P>|z|	[95% Conf. Interval]	
price	-.000034	.0001188	-0.29	0.775	-.0002669	.000199
foreign	2.685648	.9320398	2.88	0.004	.8588833	4.512412
weight	-.0037447	.0025609	-1.46	0.144	-.0087639	.0012745
weightsq	7.87e-07	4.50e-07	1.75	0.080	-9.43e-08	1.67e-06
displacement	-.0108919	.0076805	-1.42	0.156	-.0259455	.0041617
/cut1	-9.417196	4.298201			-17.84151	-.9928766
/cut2	-7.581864	4.23409			-15.88053	.7168002
/cut3	-4.82209	4.147679			-12.95139	3.307212
/cut4	-2.79344	4.156219			-10.93948	5.352599

We now wonder whether all our variables other than `foreign` are jointly significant. We test the hypothesis just as we would after linear regression:

```
. test weight weightsq displ price
( 1)  [rep78]weight = 0
( 2)  [rep78]weightsq = 0
( 3)  [rep78]displacement = 0
( 4)  [rep78]price = 0
          chi2(  4) =     3.63
        Prob > chi2 =   0.4590
```

To compare this with the results performed by a likelihood-ratio test, see [U] **20.11.3 Likelihood-ratio tests**. Here results differ little.

◁

20.11.3   Likelihood-ratio tests

After maximum likelihood estimation, you can obtain likelihood-ratio tests by fitting both the unconstrained and constrained models, storing the results using `estimates store`, and then running `lrtest`. See [R] **lrtest** for the full details.

▷ Example 14

In [U] **20.11.2 Using test** above, we fit an ordered logit on `rep78` and then tested the significance of all the explanatory variables except `foreign`.

To obtain the likelihood-ratio test, sometime after fitting the full model, we type `estimates store` *full_model_name*, where *full_model_name* is just a label that we assign to these results.

```
. ologit rep78 price foreign weight weightsq displ
(output omitted )
. estimates store myfullmodel
```

This command saves the current model results with the name `myfullmodel`.

Next we fit the constrained model. After that, typing 'lrtest myfullmodel .' compares the current model with the model we saved:

```
. ologit rep78 foreign
Iteration 0:   log likelihood = -93.692061
Iteration 1:   log likelihood = -79.696089
Iteration 2:   log likelihood = -79.044933
Iteration 3:   log likelihood = -79.029267
Iteration 4:   log likelihood = -79.029243
Ordered logistic regression                    Number of obs   =        69
                                               LR chi2(1)      =     29.33
                                               Prob > chi2     =    0.0000
Log likelihood = -79.029243                    Pseudo R2       =    0.1565
```

rep78	Coef.	Std. Err.	z	P>|z|	[95% Conf. Interval]	
foreign	2.98155	.6203637	4.81	0.000	1.76566	4.197441
/cut1	-3.158382	.7224269			-4.574313	-1.742452
/cut2	-1.362642	.3557343			-2.059868	-.6654154
/cut3	1.232161	.3431227			.5596533	1.90467
/cut4	3.246209	.5556646			2.157127	4.335292

```
. lrtest myfullmodel .
Likelihood-ratio test                          LR chi2(4)  =      3.79
(Assumption: . nested in myfullmodel)          Prob > chi2 =    0.4348
```

When we tested the same constraint with test (which performed a Wald test), we obtained a χ^2 of 3.63 and a significance level of 0.4590. We used . (the dot) to specify the results in active memory, although we also could have stored them with estimates store and referred to them by name instead. Also, the order in which you specify the two models to lrtest doesn't matter; lrtest is smart enough to know the full model from the constrained model.

◁

Two other postestimation commands work in the same way as lrtest, meaning that they accept names of stored estimation results as their input: hausman for performing Hausman specification tests and suest for seemingly unrelated estimation. We do not cover these commands here; see [R] **hausman** and [R] **suest** for more details.

20.11.4 Nonlinear Wald tests

testnl can be used to test nonlinear hypotheses about the parameters of the active estimation results. testnl, like test, bases its results on the variance–covariance matrix of the estimators (i.e., performs a Wald test), so it can be used after any estimation command; see [R] **testnl**.

▷ Example 15

We fit the model

```
. regress price mpg weight foreign
  (output omitted )
```

and then type

```
. testnl (38*_b[mpg]^2 = _b[foreign]) (_b[mpg]/_b[weight]=4)
 (1)  38*_b[mpg]^2 = _b[foreign]
 (2)  _b[mpg]/_b[weight]=4
              F(2, 70) =        0.02
              Prob > F =      0.9806
```

We performed this test on linear regression estimates, but tests of this type could be performed after any estimation command.

◁

20.12   Obtaining linear combinations of coefficients

lincom computes point estimates, standard errors, t or z statistics, p-values, and confidence intervals for a linear combination of coefficients after any estimation command. Results can optionally be displayed as odds ratios, incidence-rate ratios, or relative-risk ratios.

▷ Example 16

We fit a linear regression:

```
. use http://www.stata-press.com/data/r11/regress, clear
. regress y x1 x2 x3
```

Source	SS	df	MS		Number of obs =	148
					F(3, 144) =	96.12
Model	3259.3561	3	1086.45203		Prob > F =	0.0000
Residual	1627.56282	144	11.3025196		R-squared =	0.6670
					Adj R-squared =	0.6600
Total	4886.91892	147	33.2443464		Root MSE =	3.3619

y	Coef.	Std. Err.	t	P>|t|	[95% Conf. Interval]	
x1	1.457113	1.07461	1.36	0.177	-.6669339	3.581161
x2	2.221682	.8610358	2.58	0.011	.5197797	3.923583
x3	-.006139	.0005543	-11.08	0.000	-.0072345	-.0050435
_cons	36.10135	4.382693	8.24	0.000	27.43863	44.76407

Suppose that we want to see the difference of the coefficients of x2 and x1. We type

```
. lincom x2 - x1
 ( 1)  - x1 + x2 = 0
```

y	Coef.	Std. Err.	t	P>|t|	[95% Conf. Interval]	
(1)	.7645682	.9950282	0.77	0.444	-1.20218	2.731316

◁

lincom is handy for computing the odds ratio of one covariate group relative to another.

▷ Example 17

We estimate the parameters of a logistic model of low birthweight:

```
. use http://www.stata-press.com/data/r11/lbw3
(Hosmer & Lemeshow data)

. logit low age lwd i.race smoke ptd ht ui

Iteration 0:   log likelihood =   -117.336
Iteration 1:   log likelihood =  -99.3982
Iteration 2:   log likelihood = -98.780418
Iteration 3:   log likelihood = -98.777998
Iteration 4:   log likelihood = -98.777998
```

```
Logistic regression                               Number of obs   =        189
                                                  LR chi2(8)      =      37.12
                                                  Prob > chi2     =     0.0000
Log likelihood = -98.777998                       Pseudo R2       =     0.1582
```

low	Coef.	Std. Err.	z	P>|z|	[95% Conf. Interval]	
age	-.0464796	.0373888	-1.24	0.214	-.1197603	.0268011
lwd	.8420615	.4055338	2.08	0.038	.0472299	1.636893
race						
2	1.073456	.5150753	2.08	0.037	.0639273	2.082985
3	.815367	.4452979	1.83	0.067	-.0574008	1.688135
smoke	.8071996	.404446	2.00	0.046	.0145001	1.599899
ptd	1.281678	.4621157	2.77	0.006	.3759478	2.187408
ht	1.435227	.6482699	2.21	0.027	.1646414	2.705813
ui	.6576256	.4666192	1.41	0.159	-.2569313	1.572182
_cons	-1.216781	.9556797	-1.27	0.203	-3.089878	.656317

Level 1 of race designates white, level 2 designates black, and level 3 designates other.

If we want to obtain the odds ratio for black smokers relative to white nonsmokers (the reference group), we type

```
. lincom 2.race + smoke, or
 ( 1)  [low]2.race + [low]smoke = 0
```

low	Odds Ratio	Std. Err.	z	P>|z|	[95% Conf. Interval]	
(1)	6.557805	4.744692	2.60	0.009	1.588176	27.07811

lincom computed $\exp(\beta_{\mathrm{race}==2} + \beta_{\mathrm{smoke}}) = 6.56$.

◁

20.13   Obtaining nonlinear combinations of coefficients

lincom is limited to estimating linear combinations of coefficients, e.g., 2.race + smoke, or exponentiated linear combinations, as in the above. For general nonlinear combinations, use nlcom.

▷ Example 18

Continuing our previous example: suppose that we wanted the ratio of the coefficients (and standard errors, Wald test, confidence interval, etc.) of blacks and races other than white and black:

```
. nlcom _b[2.race]/_b[3.race]
      _nl_1:  _b[2.race]/_b[3.race]
```

low	Coef.	Std. Err.	z	P>|z|	[95% Conf. Interval]	
_nl_1	1.316531	.7359262	1.79	0.074	-.1258574	2.75892

The Wald test given is that of the null hypothesis that the nonlinear combination is zero versus the two-sided alternative—this is probably not informative for a ratio. If we would instead like to test whether this ratio is one, we can rerun `nlcom`, this time subtracting one from our ratio estimate.

```
. nlcom _b[2.race]/_b[3.race] - 1
      _nl_1:  _b[2.race]/_b[3.race] - 1
```

low	Coef.	Std. Err.	z	P>|z|	[95% Conf. Interval]	
_nl_1	.3165314	.7359262	0.43	0.667	-1.125857	1.75892

We can interpret this as not much evidence that the "ratio minus 1" is different from zero, meaning that we cannot reject the null hypothesis that the ratio equals one.

When using `nlcom`, we needed to refer to the model coefficients by their "proper" names, e.g., `_b[2.race]`, and not by the shorthand `2.race`, such as when using `lincom`. If we had typed

```
. nlcom 2.race/3.race
```

Stata would have reported an error.

If you have difficulty determining what to type for a coefficient when using `lincom` or `nlcom` replay your results using the `coeflegend` option. Here are the results for our current estimates,

```
. logit, coeflegend
Logistic regression
```

Number of obs =	189
LR chi2(8) =	37.12
Prob > chi2 =	0.0000
Pseudo R2 =	0.1582

Log likelihood = -98.777998

low	Coef.	Legend
age	-.0464796	_b[low:age]
lwd	.8420615	_b[low:lwd]
race		
2	1.073456	_b[low:2.race]
3	.815367	_b[low:3.race]
smoke	.8071996	_b[low:smoke]
ptd	1.281678	_b[low:ptd]
ht	1.435227	_b[low:ht]
ui	.6576256	_b[low:ui]
_cons	-1.216781	_b[low:_cons]

◁

20.14   Obtaining marginal means, adjusted predictions, and predictive margins

predict uses the current estimation results (the coefficients and the VCE) to estimate the value of statistics for observations in the data. lincom and nlcom use the current estimation results to estimate a specific linear or nonlinear expression of the coefficients. The margins command combines aspects of both and estimates margins of responses.

margins answers the question "What does my model have to say about such-and-such a group or such-and-such a person", where such-and-such might be

- my estimation sample or another sample

- a sample with the values of some covariates fixed

- a sample evaluated at each level of a treatment

- a population represented by a complex survey sample

- someone who looks like the fifth person in my sample

- someone who looks like the mean of the covariates in my sample

- someone who looks like the median of the covariates in my sample

- someone who looks like the 25th percentile of the covariates in my sample

- someone who looks like some other statistics of the covariates in my sample

- a standardized population

- a balanced experimental design

- any combination of the above

- any comparison of the above

It answers these questions either conditionally, based on fixed values of all covariates, or averaged over the observations in a sample. It answers these questions about almost any predictions or any other response that you can calculate as a function of your estimated parameters—linear responses, probabilities, hazards, survival times, odds ratios, risk differences, etc. It answers these questions in terms of the response given covariate levels, or in terms of the change in the response for a change in levels (also known as marginal effects). It answers these questions providing standard errors, test statistics, and confidence intervals; and those statistics can take the covariates as given or adjust for sampling, also known as predictive margins and survey statistics.

A margin is a statistic based on a response for a fitted model calculated over a dataset in which some of or all the covariates are fixed at values different from what they really are.

Margins go by different names in different fields, and they can estimate many interesting statistics related to a fitted model. We discuss some common uses below; see [R] **margins** for more applications.

20.14.1   Obtaining expected marginal means

A classic application of margins is to estimate the expected marginal means from a linear estimator as though the design for the covariates were balanced—assuming an equal number of observations for each unique combination of levels for the factor-variable covariates. These means have a long history in the study of ANOVA and MANOVA but are of limited use with nonexperimental data. For a discussion, see *Obtaining margins as though the data were balanced* in [R] **margins** and example 4 in [R] **anova**.

Estimated marginal means are also called "least-squares means".

Consider an analysis of variance of the change in systolic blood pressure as determined by one of four drug treatments and adjusting for the patient's disease (Afifi and Azen 1979).

```
. use http://www.stata-press.com/data/r11/systolic
(Systolic Blood Pressure Data)

. tabulate drug disease
```

		Patient's Disease		
Drug Used	1	2	3	Total
1	6	4	5	15
2	5	4	6	15
3	3	5	4	12
4	5	6	5	16
Total	19	19	20	58

```
. anova systolic drug##disease
```

| | | Number of obs = | 58 | R-squared | = 0.4560 |
| | | Root MSE | = 10.5096 | Adj R-squared = | 0.3259 |

Source	Partial SS	df	MS	F	Prob > F
Model	4259.33851	11	387.212591	3.51	0.0013
drug	2997.47186	3	999.157287	9.05	0.0001
disease	415.873046	2	207.936523	1.88	0.1637
drug#disease	707.266259	6	117.87771	1.07	0.3958
Residual	5080.81667	46	110.452536		
Total	9340.15517	57	163.862371		

Despite having randomized on drug, we see in the tabulation that our data are not balanced—for example, 12 patients were administered drug 3, whereas 16 were administered drug 4. The diseases are also not balanced across drugs. To estimate the marginal mean for each level of drug while treating the design as though it were balanced, we type

```
. margins drug, asbalanced
Adjusted predictions                              Number of obs    =         58
Expression    : Linear prediction, predict()
at            : drug             (asbalanced)
                disease          (asbalanced)
```

		Delta-method				
	Margin	Std. Err.	z	P>|z|	[95% Conf. Interval]	
drug						
1	25.99444	2.751008	9.45	0.000	20.60257	31.38632
2	26.55556	2.751008	9.65	0.000	21.16368	31.94743
3	9.744444	3.100558	3.14	0.002	3.667462	15.82143
4	13.54444	2.637123	5.14	0.000	8.375778	18.71311

Assuming everyone in the sample were treated with drug 4 and that the diseases were equally distributed across the drug treatments, the expected mean change in pressure resulting from treatment with drug 4 is 13.54. Because we are treating the data as balanced, we could also say that 13.54 is the expected mean change resulting from drug 4 for any sample where an equal number of patients has each of the three diseases.

If we want an estimate of the mean that uses the distribution of diseases observed in the sample, we would remove the asbalanced option:

```
. margins drug

Predictive margins                                Number of obs    =        58
Expression    : Linear prediction, predict()
```

	Margin	Delta-method Std. Err.	z	P>|z|	[95% Conf. Interval]
drug					
1	25.89799	2.750533	9.42	0.000	20.50704 31.28893
2	26.41092	2.742762	9.63	0.000	21.0352 31.78664
3	9.722989	3.099185	3.14	0.002	3.648697 15.79728
4	13.55575	2.640602	5.13	0.000	8.380261 18.73123

We can now say that a pressure change of 13.56 is expected if everyone in the sample is given drug 4 and the distribution of diseases is as observed in the sample.

The second set of margins are not usually called estimated marginal means because they do not impose a balanced design when estimating the mean. They are adjusted predictions that just happen to be means because the response is linear.

Neither of these values is the average pressure change for those taking drug 4 in our sample because margins treats everyone in the sample as having taken drug 4. Treating everyone as though they have taken each drug is what makes the means comparable. We are essentially standardizing on the values of all the other covariates in our model (in this example, just disease).

To obtain the observed mean for those taking drug 4, we must tell margins to treat drug 4 as its sample, which we do with the over() option.

```
. summarize systolic if drug==4
    Variable |      Obs       Mean    Std. Dev.       Min        Max
    systolic |       16       13.5    9.323805         -5         27
. margins, over(drug)

Predictive margins                                Number of obs    =        58
Expression    : Linear prediction, predict()
over          : drug
```

	Margin	Delta-method Std. Err.	z	P>|z|	[95% Conf. Interval]
drug					
1	26.06667	2.713577	9.61	0.000	20.74815 31.38518
2	25.53333	2.713577	9.41	0.000	20.21482 30.85185
3	8.75	3.033872	2.88	0.004	2.803721 14.69628
4	13.5	2.62741	5.14	0.000	8.350371 18.64963

The margin in the last line of the table matches the mean from summarize.

For many questions, we prefer one of the first two estimates of margins to the last one. If we compare drugs 3 and 4 from the last results, the 8.75 and 13.5 include both the effect from the drug and the differing distribution of diseases among patients taking drug 3 and drug 4 in our sample. Our first set of margins, those from margins drug, asbalanced, assumed that for both drug 3 and drug 4, we had an equal number of patients with each disease. Our second set of margins, those from margins drug, assumed that for both drug 3 and drug 4, we wanted the observed distribution of patients from the whole sample. By assuming a common distribution of diseases across the drugs, our first two sets of margins remove the effect of disease when we compare across drugs.

20.14.2 Obtaining adjusted predictions

We will use the term adjusted predictions to refer to margins that are evaluated at fixed values for all covariates. The `margins` command has a great deal of flexibility in letting you choose what those fixed values are. Consider a model of high blood pressure as a function of sex, age group, and body mass index (BMI, a common measure of weight relative to height; variable `bmi`). We will allow the effect of age to differ for males and females by interacting the age group and sex variables. We will also allow the effect of BMI to differ across all combinations of age group and sex by specifying a full factorial model.

```
. use http://www.stata-press.com/data/r11/nhanes2

. generate bmi = weight/(height/100)^2

. logistic highbp sex##agegrp##c.bmi
```

Logistic regression				Number of obs	=	10351
				LR chi2(23)	=	1151.80
				Prob > chi2	=	0.0000
Log likelihood = -3403.3345				Pseudo R2	=	0.1447

highbp	Odds Ratio	Std. Err.	z	P>|z|	[95% Conf. Interval]	
2.sex	.8875349	1.134604	-0.09	0.926	.0724484	10.87281
agegrp						
2	1.096495	1.407414	0.07	0.943	.0886015	13.56978
3	11.85822	13.86645	2.11	0.034	1.198572	117.3208
4	54.32365	58.08088	3.74	0.000	6.682134	441.6343
5	36.58197	35.67608	3.69	0.000	5.409339	247.3945
6	412.8948	484.3409	5.13	0.000	41.43321	4114.626
sex#agegrp						
2 2	2.13253	3.817311	0.42	0.672	.0638574	71.21623
2 3	2.877815	4.650595	0.65	0.513	.1212014	68.33104
2 4	1.929862	2.926537	0.43	0.665	.0987923	37.69897
2 5	2.361945	3.33027	0.61	0.542	.1489711	37.44879
2 6	.2006528	.3252387	-0.99	0.322	.0083701	4.81017
bmi	1.244033	.0370629	7.33	0.000	1.173471	1.318838
sex#c.bmi						
2	.9582013	.0407832	-1.00	0.316	.881511	1.041563
agegrp#c.bmi						
2	1.007464	.0451481	0.17	0.868	.9227504	1.099955
3	.9501658	.039221	-1.24	0.216	.8763215	1.030233
4	.9181214	.0349998	-2.24	0.025	.8520232	.9893474
5	.9314019	.0324088	-2.04	0.041	.8699994	.9971381
6	.8421064	.0362688	-3.99	0.000	.7739384	.9162785
sex#agegrp# c.bmi						
2 2	.9895392	.0588217	-0.18	0.860	.8807134	1.111812
2 3	.9976554	.0546945	-0.04	0.966	.8960147	1.110826
2 4	1.006481	.0518212	0.13	0.900	.9098702	1.113351
2 5	1.003616	.0478563	0.08	0.940	.9140686	1.101935
2 6	1.116955	.0630488	1.96	0.050	.9999723	1.247624

There are six levels for `agegrp` and two levels for `sex`. This dataset has value labels attached to those levels, so the easiest way to see what those levels mean is to let Stata tell us:

```
. table sex agegrp
```

1=male, 2=female	Age groups 1-6					
	age20-29	age30-39	age40-49	age50-59	age60-69	age 70+
Male	1,116	770	610	602	1,369	448
Female	1,204	852	662	689	1,491	538

We can evaluate the probability of having high blood pressure for each age group while holding the proportion of males and females and the value of bmi to its average by specifying the covariate agegrp to margins and including the option atmeans:

```
. margins agegrp, atmeans
Adjusted predictions                          Number of obs   =        10351
Model VCE     : OIM

Expression    : Pr(highbp), predict()
at            : 1.sex          =     .4748333 (mean)
                2.sex          =     .5251667 (mean)
                1.agegrp       =     .2241329 (mean)
                2.agegrp       =     .1566998 (mean)
                3.agegrp       =     .1228867 (mean)
                4.agegrp       =     .1247222 (mean)
                5.agegrp       =     .2763018 (mean)
                6.agegrp       =     .0952565 (mean)
                bmi            =      25.5376 (mean)
```

	Margin	Delta-method Std. Err.	z	P>|z|	[95% Conf. Interval]	
agegrp						
1	.0209216	.0035683	5.86	0.000	.0139278	.0279153
2	.0353277	.0051429	6.87	0.000	.0252477	.0454077
3	.1038999	.0091758	11.32	0.000	.0859157	.1218842
4	.1679085	.0111415	15.07	0.000	.1460715	.1897454
5	.1734584	.00754	23.01	0.000	.1586803	.1882365
6	.1720227	.0124465	13.82	0.000	.1476281	.1964173

The header of the table showed us the mean values of each covariate. These are the values at which the probabilities were evaluated. The mean values for the levels of agegrp appear in the header even though they were not used. agegrp assumed the values 1, 2, 3, 4, 5, and 6, as shown in the table. The means of the levels of agegrp are shown because we might have asked for more margins in the table, for example, margins sex agegrp.

The modeled probability remains below 4% for those under 40 years of age, and then increases fairly rapidly to just over 16.8% in the 50–59 age group. Above age 59, the probability almost flattens, remaining under 17.5% in the last two age groups. It is often easier for nonstatisticians to interpret the statistics computed by margins than the coefficients of a fitted model.

20.14.3   Obtaining predictive margins

Rather than evaluate the probability of having high blood pressure at one fixed point (the means), as we did above, we can evaluate the probability at the covariate values for each observation in our data and average those probabilities. Here is the modeled probability averaged over our sample:

```
. margins
Predictive margins                                  Number of obs    =      10351
Model VCE     : OIM
Expression    : Pr(highbp), predict()
```

	Margin	Delta-method Std. Err.	z	P>|z|	[95% Conf. Interval]	
_cons	.128973	.0031014	41.59	0.000	.1228945	.1350516

If we fix the level of `agegrp` to 1, compute the probability for each observation, and then average those probabilities, the result is the predictive margin for level 1 of `agegrp`. `margins`, by default, computes these margins for each level of each variable specified on the command line. Let's compute the predictive margins for `agegrp`:

```
. margins agegrp
Predictive margins                                  Number of obs    =      10351
Model VCE     : OIM
Expression    : Pr(highbp), predict()
```

	Margin	Delta-method Std. Err.	z	P>|z|	[95% Conf. Interval]	
agegrp						
1	.0375314	.004423	8.49	0.000	.0288624	.0462003
2	.0557658	.0053934	10.34	0.000	.0451949	.0663367
3	.1214814	.0086634	14.02	0.000	.1045015	.1384612
4	.181929	.0102836	17.69	0.000	.1617736	.2020844
5	.1892586	.0069432	27.26	0.000	.1756501	.202867
6	.1818377	.0118687	15.32	0.000	.1585755	.2051

One way of looking at predictive margins is that they answer the question "What would the average response (probability) be in my sample if everyone were in one age group?" Another way of looking at predictive margins is that they standardize the effect of being in an age group with the distribution of other covariate values in our sample. The margins above are comparable because only the level of `agegrp` is changing across the margins. They represent our sample because all the other covariates take on their values in the sample when the margins are evaluated.

The predictive margins in this table differ from the adjusted predictions we estimated in [U] **20.14.2 Obtaining adjusted predictions** because the probability is a nonlinear function of the coefficients in a logistic model; see *Example 3: Average response versus response at average* in [R] **margins** for details.

Our analysis so far has been a bit naïve. The dataset we are using is from the Second National Health and Nutrition Examination Survey (NHANES II). It has weights to make it representative of the population from which it was drawn as well as other survey characteristics—strata and primary sampling units. The data have already been `svyset`; see [SVY] **svyset**. We should take note of these characteristics and use the `svy` prefix when fitting our model.

```
. svy: logistic highbp sex##agegrp##c.bmi
  (output omitted )
```

If we were to repeat the command `margins agegrp`, we would see that our point estimates differ only a little, but our standard errors are generally larger.

We are not restricted to margining over a single factor variable. Let's see if the pattern of high blood pressure over age groups differs for men and women. We do that by specifying the interaction of sex and agegrp to margins.

```
. margins sex#agegrp
Predictive margins                              Number of obs    =      10351
Model VCE     : Linearized
Expression    : Pr(highbp), predict()
```

	Margin	Delta-method Std. Err.	z	P>|z|	[95% Conf. Interval]	
sex#agegrp						
1 1	.0597492	.0102037	5.86	0.000	.0397502	.0797482
1 2	.0743686	.0090047	8.26	0.000	.0567197	.0920175
1 3	.139588	.0127725	10.93	0.000	.1145543	.1646218
1 4	.2027485	.0181733	11.16	0.000	.1671295	.2383675
1 5	.2154491	.0127246	16.93	0.000	.1905093	.2403888
1 6	.1562754	.0203574	7.68	0.000	.1163757	.1961752
2 1	.0178699	.0048167	3.71	0.000	.0084293	.0273104
2 2	.0324522	.0060014	5.41	0.000	.0206897	.0442146
2 3	.08906	.0129904	6.86	0.000	.0635994	.1145207
2 4	.1452838	.017242	8.43	0.000	.1114901	.1790775
2 5	.1657727	.0123653	13.41	0.000	.1415372	.1900081
2 6	.1833488	.0210316	8.72	0.000	.1421277	.22457

Each line in the table corresponds to holding both sex and agegrp to fixed values while using the observed level of bmi to evaluate the probability and then averaging over the observations in the sample. To calculate the results in the first line of the table, margins fixed sex = 1 and agegrp = 1, evaluated the probability for each observation, and then averaged the probabilities. All these margins reflect the observed distribution of bmi in the sample.

The first six lines represent males, and the second six lines represent females. Comparing males with females for the same age groups, males are over three times as likely to have high blood pressure in the first age group $(0.060/0.018 = 3.3)$, they are over twice as likely in the second age group, and while the relative gap narrows, it is not until above age 70 that the probability for males drops below the probability for females.

Can the pattern of probabilities be affected by controlling one's bmi? Let's reevaluate the probabilities while holding bmi to two levels—20 (which is well within the normal range) and 30 (which is at the boundary between overweight and obese). We add the option at(bmi=(20 30)) to set bmi first to 20 and then to 30.

(Continued on next page)

```
. margins sex#agegrp, at(bmi=(20 30))
```

Adjusted predictions   Number of obs   =   10351

Model VCE   : Linearized

Expression   : Pr(highbp), predict()

1._at   : bmi   =   20

2._at   : bmi   =   30

	Margin	Delta-method Std. Err.	z	P>|z|	[95% Conf. Interval]	
_at#sex# agegrp						
1 1 1	.0109371	.0032537	3.36	0.001	.00456	.0173142
1 1 2	.0156812	.0047009	3.34	0.001	.0064677	.0248947
1 1 3	.0482213	.0122271	3.94	0.000	.0242566	.072186
1 1 4	.0949467	.0173769	5.46	0.000	.0608887	.1290048
1 1 5	.101735	.0142451	7.14	0.000	.0738152	.1296548
1 1 6	.108137	.0203938	5.30	0.000	.0681659	.1481082
1 2 1	.0053248	.0022848	2.33	0.020	.0008466	.0098029
1 2 2	.0101007	.0036738	2.75	0.006	.0029001	.0173012
1 2 3	.0422142	.0118314	3.57	0.000	.0190251	.0654033
1 2 4	.0912119	.0201067	4.54	0.000	.0518035	.1306203
1 2 5	.0927126	.011551	8.03	0.000	.070073	.1153521
1 2 6	.1035166	.0235733	4.39	0.000	.0573138	.1497194
2 1 1	.095307	.018967	5.02	0.000	.0581324	.1324815
2 1 2	.1218371	.0174947	6.96	0.000	.0875481	.1561261
2 1 3	.2275182	.027168	8.37	0.000	.17427	.2807665
2 1 4	.3084116	.0306717	10.06	0.000	.248296	.3685271
2 1 5	.3276512	.0235645	13.90	0.000	.2814657	.3738367
2 1 6	.2001169	.0352892	5.67	0.000	.1309514	.2692825
2 2 1	.0258852	.007303	3.54	0.000	.0115715	.0401989
2 2 2	.0483494	.0092976	5.20	0.000	.0301264	.0665723
2 2 3	.1303522	.0198102	6.58	0.000	.0915249	.1691795
2 2 4	.1946575	.0192303	10.12	0.000	.1569668	.2323482
2 2 5	.2338165	.0167405	13.97	0.000	.2010058	.2666272
2 2 6	.2582884	.0256129	10.08	0.000	.2080881	.3084887

That is a lot of margins, but they are in sets of six age groups. The first six margins are men with a BMI of 20, the second six are women with a BMI of 20, the third six are men with a BMI of 30, and the last six are women with a BMI of 30. These margins tell a more complete story. The probability of high blood pressure is much lower for both men and women who maintain a BMI of 20. More interesting is that the relationship between men and women differs depending on BMI. While young men who maintain a BMI of 20 are still twice as likely as young women to have high blood pressure $(0.011/0.005)$ and youngish men are over 50% more likely $(0.016/0.010)$, the gap narrows substantially for men in the four older groups. The story is worse for those with a BMI of 30. Both men and women with a high BMI have a substantially increased risk of high blood pressure, with men ages 50–69 almost 10 percentage points higher than women. Before you dismiss these differences as caused by the usual attenuation of the logistic curve in the tails, recall that when we fit the model, we allowed the effect of bmi to be different for each combination of sex and agegrp.

You may have noticed that the header of the prior results says "Adjusted predictions" rather than "Predictive margins". That is because our model has only three covariates, and we have fixed the values of each. margins is no longer averaging over the data, but is instead evaluating the margins at fixed points that we have requested. It lets us know that by changing the header.

We could post the results of margins and form linear combinations or perform tests about any of the assertions above; see *Example 10: Testing margins* in [R] **margins**.

We could have used the vce(unconditional) option on our survey examples if we wished to account for the sampling variation of the covariates in our sample as well as the sampling variation of the estimated coefficients. It makes little difference in our example.

There is much more to know about margins and the margins command. Consider the headings for the *Remarks* section of [R] **margins**:

> *Introduction*
> *Obtaining margins of responses*
>   *Example 1: A simple case after regress*
>   *Example 2: A simple case after logistic*
>   *Example 3: Average response versus response at average*
>   *Example 4: Multiple margins from one command*
>   *Example 5: Margins with interaction terms*
>   *Example 6: Margins with continuous variables*
>   *Example 7: Margins of continuous variables*
>   *Example 8: Margins of interactions*
>   *Example 9: Decomposing margins*
>   *Example 10: Testing margins*
>   *Example 11: Margins of a specified prediction*
>   *Example 12: Margins of a specified expression*
>   *Example 13: Margins with multiple outcomes (responses)*
>   *Example 14: Margins with multiple equations*
>   *Example 15: Margins evaluated out of sample*
> *Obtaining margins of derivatives of responses (a.k.a. marginal effects)*
>   *Do not specify marginlist when you mean over()*
>   *Use at() freely, especially with continuous variables*
>   *Expressing derivatives as elasticities*
>   *Derivatives versus discrete differences*
>   *Example 16: Average marginal effect (partial effects)*
>   *Example 17: Average marginal effect of all covariates*
>   *Example 18: Evaluating marginal effects over the response surface*
> *Obtaining margins with survey data and representative samples*
>   *Example 19: Inferences for populations, margins of response*
>   *Example 20: Inferences for populations, marginal effects*
>   *Example 21: Inferences for populations with svyset data*
> *Standardizing margins*
> *Obtaining margins as though the data were balanced*
>   *Balancing using asbalanced*
>   *Balancing by standardization*
>   *Balancing nonlinear responses*
>   *Treating a subset of covariates as balanced*
>   *Using fvset design*
>   *Balancing in the presence of empty cells*
> *Obtaining margins with nested designs*
>   *Introduction*
>   *Margins with nested designs as though the data were balanced*
>   *Coding of nested designs*
> *Special topics*
>   *Requirements for model specification*
>   *Estimability of margins*
>   *Manipulability of tests*
>   *Using margins after the estimates use command*
>   *Syntax of at()*
>   *Estimation commands that may be used with margins*
> *Glossary*

20.15   Obtaining conditional and average marginal effects

Marginal effects measure the change in a response given a change in a covariate, which is to say that marginal effects are derivatives. As used here, marginal effects can also be the discrete change in a response as an indicator goes from 0 to 1. Some authors reserve the term marginal effect for the continuous change and use partial effect for the discrete change. We will not make that distinction. Regardless, marginal effects are most often used to make it easier to interpret how changes in covariates affect a nonlinear response from a fitted model—a probability, a censored dependent variable, a survival time, a hazard, etc.

Marginal effects can either be evaluated at a specified point for all the covariates in our model (conditional marginal effects) or be evaluated at the observed values of the covariates in a dataset and then averaged (average marginal effects).

To Stata, marginal effects are just margins whose response happens to be the derivative of another response. Those interested in marginal effects will be interested in all or most of [R] **margins**.

20.15.1   Obtaining conditional marginal effects

We call a marginal effect conditional when we fix the values of all the covariates and then take the derivative of the response with respect to a covariate. The mean of all covariates is often used as the fixed point, and this is sometimes called the marginal effect at the means.

Consider a simple probit model of union membership for women as a function of having graduated from college (collgrad), living in the South (south), tenure on the job (tenure), and the interaction of south and tenure. We are interested in how being in the South affects union membership. We fit the model by using an extract from 1988 of the U.S. National Longitudinal Survey of Labor Market Experience (see [XT] **xt**).

```
. use http://www.stata-press.com/data/r11/nlsw88, clear
(NLSW, 1988 extract)

. probit union i.collgrad i.south tenure south#c.tenure

Iteration 0:   log likelihood = -1042.6816
Iteration 1:   log likelihood = -997.71809
Iteration 2:   log likelihood = -997.60984
Iteration 3:   log likelihood = -997.60983
```

```
Probit regression                               Number of obs   =       1868
                                                LR chi2(4)      =      90.14
                                                Prob > chi2     =     0.0000
Log likelihood = -997.60983                     Pseudo R2       =     0.0432
```

union	Coef.	Std. Err.	z	P>|z|	[95% Conf. Interval]	
1.collgrad	.2783278	.0726167	3.83	0.000	.1360018	.4206539
1.south	-.2534964	.1050552	-2.41	0.016	-.4594008	-.0475921
tenure	.0362944	.0068205	5.32	0.000	.0229264	.0496624
south# c.tenure 1	-.0239785	.0119533	-2.01	0.045	-.0474065	-.0005504
_cons	-.8497418	.0664524	-12.79	0.000	-.9799862	-.7194974

Clearly, being located in the South decreases union membership. Using the dydx() and atmeans options of margins, we can ask how much it decreases membership by evaluating the marginal effect of being southern at the mean of all covariates:

```
. margins, dydx(south) atmeans
```

```
Conditional marginal effects                     Number of obs   =       1868
Model VCE    : OIM

Expression   : Pr(union), predict()
dy/dx w.r.t. : 1.south
at           : 0.collgrad      =     .7521413 (mean)
               1.collgrad      =     .2478587 (mean)
               0.south         =     .5744111 (mean)
               1.south         =     .4255889 (mean)
               tenure          =     6.571065 (mean)
```

	dy/dx	Delta-method Std. Err.	z	P>|z|	[95% Conf. Interval]	
1.south	-.1236055	.019431	-6.36	0.000	-.1616896	-.0855215

Note: dy/dx for factor levels is the discrete change from the base level.

At the means of all the covariates, southern women are 12 percentage points less likely to be members of a union. This marginal effect includes both the direct effect of i.south and the interaction south#c.tenure.

As margins reports below the table, this change in the response is for the discrete change of going from not southern (0) to southern (1).

The header of margins tells us where the marginal effect was estimated. This margin includes 75% of the effect of college graduates and fixes tenure to be 6.6 years. There is nothing special about this point. We could also evaluate the marginal effect at the median of tenure:

```
. margins, dydx(south) atmeans at((medians) _continuous)
```

```
Conditional marginal effects                     Number of obs   =       1868
Model VCE    : OIM

Expression   : Pr(union), predict()
dy/dx w.r.t. : 1.south
at           : 0.collgrad      =     .7521413 (mean)
               1.collgrad      =     .2478587 (mean)
               0.south         =     .5744111 (mean)
               1.south         =     .4255889 (mean)
               tenure          =     4.666667 (median)
```

	dy/dx	Delta-method Std. Err.	z	P>|z|	[95% Conf. Interval]	
1.south	-.1061338	.0201722	-5.26	0.000	-.1456706	-.066597

Note: dy/dx for factor levels is the discrete change from the base level.

With tenure at its median of 4.67, the marginal effect is about 2 percentage points less than it was at the mean of 6.6.

When examining conditional marginal effects, it is often useful to evaluate them at a range of values for the covariates. We can do that by asking both for values of the indicator covariate collgrad and for a range of values for tenure:

(Continued on next page)

```
. margins collgrad, dydx(south) at(tenure=(0(5)25))
```

Conditional marginal effects   Number of obs   =   1868
Model VCE   : OIM

Expression   : Pr(union), predict()
dy/dx w.r.t. : 1.south

1._at	: tenure	=	0
2._at	: tenure	=	5
3._at	: tenure	=	10
4._at	: tenure	=	15
5._at	: tenure	=	20
6._at	: tenure	=	25

	dy/dx	Delta-method Std. Err.	z	P>|z|	[95% Conf. Interval]	
1.south _at#collgrad						
1 0	-.0627725	.0254161	-2.47	0.014	-.112587	-.0129579
1 1	-.0791483	.0321151	-2.46	0.014	-.1420928	-.0162038
2 0	-.1031957	.0189184	-5.45	0.000	-.140275	-.0661164
2 1	-.1256566	.0232385	-5.41	0.000	-.1712031	-.0801101
3 0	-.1496772	.0222259	-6.73	0.000	-.1932392	-.1061151
3 1	-.1760137	.0266874	-6.60	0.000	-.2283202	-.1237073
4 0	-.2008801	.036154	-5.56	0.000	-.2717407	-.1300196
4 1	-.2282	.0419237	-5.44	0.000	-.3103689	-.146031
5 0	-.2549707	.0546355	-4.67	0.000	-.3620543	-.1478872
5 1	-.2799495	.0613127	-4.57	0.000	-.4001201	-.1597789
6 0	-.3097656	.0747494	-4.14	0.000	-.4562717	-.1632594
6 1	-.3289702	.0816342	-4.03	0.000	-.4889703	-.1689701

Note: dy/dx for factor levels is the discrete change from the base level.

We now have a more complete picture of the effect that being in the South has on union participation. For those with no tenure and without a college degree (the first line in the table), being in the South decreases union participation by only 6.3 percentage points. For those with 25 years of tenure and with a college degree (the last line in the table), being in the South decreases participation by almost 33 percentage points. We can read the effect for any combination of tenure and college graduation status from the other lines in the table.

20.15.2   Obtaining average marginal effects

To compute average marginal effects, the marginal effect is first computed for each observation in the dataset and then averaged. If the sample over which we compute the average marginal effect represents a population, then we have estimated the marginal effect for the population.

We continue with our example of labor union participation.

```
. use http://www.stata-press.com/data/r11/nlsw88
(NLSW, 1988 extract)
. probit union i.collgrad i.south tenure south#c.tenure
  (output omitted)
```

To estimate the average marginal effect for each of our regressors, we type

```
. margins, dydx(*)
Average marginal effects                        Number of obs    =    1868
Model VCE     : OIM

Expression    : Pr(union), predict()
dy/dx w.r.t.  : 1.collgrad 1.south tenure
```

	dy/dx	Delta-method Std. Err.	z	P>|z|	[95% Conf. Interval]	
1.collgrad	.0878847	.0238065	3.69	0.000	.0412248	.1345447
1.south	-.126164	.0191504	-6.59	0.000	-.1636981	-.0886299
tenure	.0083571	.0016521	5.06	0.000	.005119	.0115951

Note: dy/dx for factor levels is the discrete change from the base level.

For this sample, the average marginal effect is very close to the marginal effect at the mean that we computed earlier. That is not always true; it depends on the distribution of the other covariates. The results also tell us that on average, for populations like the one from which our sample was drawn, union participation increases 0.8 percentage points for every year of tenure on the job. College graduates are, on average, 8.8 percentage points more likely to participate.

In the examples above, we treated the covariates in the sample as fixed and known. We could have accounted for the fact that this sample was drawn from a population and the covariates represent just one sample from that population. We do that by adding the vce(robust) or vce(cluster *clustvar*) option when fitting the model and the vce(unconditional) option when estimating the margins; see *Obtaining margins with survey data and representative samples* in [R] **margins**. It makes little difference in the examples above.

20.16   Obtaining robust variance estimates

Estimates of variance refer to estimated standard errors or, more completely, the estimated variance–covariance matrix of the estimators of which the standard errors are a subset, being the square root of the diagonal elements. Call this matrix the variance. All estimation commands produce an estimate of variance and, using that, produce confidence intervals and significance tests.

In addition to the conventional estimator of variance, there is another estimator that has been called by various names because it has been derived independently in different ways by different authors. Two popular names associated with the calculation are Huber and White, but it is also known as the sandwich estimator of variance (because of how the calculation formula physically appears) and the robust estimator of variance (because of claims made about it). Also, this estimator has an independent and long tradition in the survey literature.

The conventional estimator of variance is derived by starting with a model. Let's start with the regression model

$$y_i = \mathbf{x}_i \beta + \epsilon_i, \qquad \epsilon_i \sim N(0, \sigma^2)$$

although it is not important for the discussion that we are using regression. Under the model-based approach, we assume that the model is true and thereby derive an estimator for β and its variance.

The estimator of the standard error of $\widehat{\beta}$ we develop is based on the assumption that the model is true in every detail. y_i is not exactly equal to $\mathbf{x}_i \beta$ (so that we would only need to solve an equation to obtain precisely that value of β) because the observed y_i has noise ϵ_i added to it, the noise is Gaussian, and it has constant variance. That noise leads to the uncertainty about β, and it is from the characteristics of that noise that we are able to calculate a sampling distribution for $\widehat{\beta}$.

The key thought here is that the standard error of $\widehat{\beta}$ arises because of ϵ and is valid only because the model is absolutely, without question, true; we just do not happen to know the particular values of β and σ^2 that make the model true. The implication is that, in an infinite-sized sample, the estimator $\widehat{\beta}$ for β would converge to the true value of β and that its variance would go to 0.

Now here is another interpretation of the estimation problem: We are going to fit the model

$$y_i = \mathbf{x}_i \mathbf{b} + e_i$$

and, to obtain estimates of $\mathbf{b}$, we are going to use the calculation formula

$$\widehat{\mathbf{b}} = (\mathbf{X}'\mathbf{X})^{-1}\mathbf{X}'\mathbf{y}$$

We have made no claims that the model is true or any claims about e_i or its distribution. We shifted our notation from β and ϵ_i to $\mathbf{b}$ and e_i to emphasize this. All we have stated are the physical actions we intend to carry out on the data. Interestingly, it is possible to calculate a standard error for $\widehat{\mathbf{b}}$ here. At least, it is possible if you will agree with us on what the standard error measures are.

We are going to define the standard error as measuring the standard error of the calculated $\widehat{\mathbf{b}}$ if we were to repeat the data collection followed by estimation over and over again.

This is a different concept of the standard error from the conventional, model-based ideas, but it is related. Both measure uncertainty about $\mathbf{b}$ (or β). The regression model–based derivation states from where the variation arises and so can make grander statements about the applicability of the measured standard error. The weaker second interpretation makes fewer assumptions and so produces a standard error suitable for one purpose.

There is a subtle difference in interpretation of these identically calculated point estimates. $\widehat{\beta}$ is the estimate of β under the assumption that the model is true. $\widehat{\mathbf{b}}$ is the estimate of $\mathbf{b}$, which is merely what the estimator would converge to if we collected more and more data.

Is the estimate of $\mathbf{b}$ unbiased? If we mean, "Does $\mathbf{b} = \beta$?" that depends on whether the model is true. $\widehat{\mathbf{b}}$ is, however, an unbiased estimate of $\mathbf{b}$, which admittedly is not saying much.

What if $\mathbf{x}$ and e are correlated? Don't we have a problem then? We may have an interpretation problem—$\mathbf{b}$ may not measure what we want to measure, namely, β—but we measure $\widehat{\mathbf{b}}$ to be such and such and expect, if the experiment and estimation were repeated, that we would observe results in the range we have reported.

So, we have two different understandings of what the parameters mean and how the variance in their estimators arises. However, both interpretations must confront the issue of how to make valid statistical inference about the coefficient estimates when the data do not come from either a simple random sample or the distribution of $(\mathbf{x}_i, \epsilon_i)$ is not independent and identically distributed (i.i.d.). In essence, we need an estimator of the standard errors that is robust to this deviation from the standard case.

Hence, the name *the robust estimate of variance*; its associated authors are Huber (1967) and White (1980, 1982) (who developed it independently), although many others have extended its development, including Gail, Tan, and Piantadosi (1988); Kent (1982); Royall (1986); and Lin and Wei (1989). In the survey literature, this same estimator has been developed; see Kish and Frankel (1974), Fuller (1975), and Binder (1983).

Many of Stata's estimation commands can produce this alternative estimate of variance, and, if they can, they have a vce(robust) option. Without vce(robust), we get one measure of variance:

```
. use http://www.stata-press.com/data/r11/auto7
(1978 Automobile Data)

. regress mpg weight foreign
```

Source	SS	df	MS		Number of obs =	74
					F(2, 71) =	69.75
Model	1619.2877	2	809.643849		Prob > F =	0.0000
Residual	824.171761	71	11.608053		R-squared =	0.6627
					Adj R-squared =	0.6532
Total	2443.45946	73	33.4720474		Root MSE =	3.4071

mpg	Coef.	Std. Err.	t	P>|t|	[95% Conf. Interval]	
weight	-.0065879	.0006371	-10.34	0.000	-.0078583	-.0053175
foreign	-1.650029	1.075994	-1.53	0.130	-3.7955	.4954422
_cons	41.6797	2.165547	19.25	0.000	37.36172	45.99768

With vce(robust), we get another:

```
. regress mpg weight foreign, vce(robust)
```

Linear regression

					Number of obs =	74
					F(2, 71) =	73.81
					Prob > F =	0.0000
					R-squared =	0.6627
					Root MSE =	3.4071

mpg	Coef.	Robust Std. Err.	t	P>|t|	[95% Conf. Interval]	
weight	-.0065879	.0005462	-12.06	0.000	-.007677	-.0054988
foreign	-1.650029	1.132566	-1.46	0.150	-3.908301	.6082424
_cons	41.6797	1.797553	23.19	0.000	38.09548	45.26392

Either way, the point estimates are the same. (See [R] **regress** for an example where specifying vce(robust) produces strikingly different standard errors.)

How do we interpret these results? Let's consider the model-based interpretation. Suppose that

$$y_i = \mathbf{x}_i \boldsymbol{\beta} + \epsilon_i,$$

where $(\mathbf{x}_i, \epsilon_i)$ are independently and identically distributed (i.i.d.) with variance σ^2. For the model-based interpretation, we also must assume that $\mathbf{x}_i$ and ϵ_i are uncorrelated. With these assumptions and a few technical regularity conditions, our first regression gives us consistent parameter estimates and standard errors that we can use for valid statistical inference about the coefficients. Now suppose that we weaken our assumptions so that $(\mathbf{x}_i, \epsilon_i)$ are independently and—but not necessarily—identically distributed. Our parameter estimates are still consistent, but the standard errors from the first regression can no longer be used to make valid inference. We need estimates of the standard errors that are robust to the fact that the error term is not identically distributed. The standard errors in our second regression are just what we need. We can use them to make valid statistical inference about our coefficients, even though our data are not identically distributed.

Now consider a non–model-based interpretation. If our data come from a survey design that ensures that $(\mathbf{x}_i, e_i)$ are i.i.d., then we can use the nonrobust standard errors for valid statistical inference about the population parameters $\mathbf{b}$. For this interpretation, we do not need to assume that $\mathbf{x}_i$ and e_i are uncorrelated. If they are uncorrelated, the population parameters $\mathbf{b}$ and the model parameters $\boldsymbol{\beta}$ are the same. However, if they are correlated, then the population parameters $\mathbf{b}$ that we are estimating are not the same as the model-based β. So, what we are estimating is different, but we still need standard errors that allow us to make valid statistical inference. So, if the process that we used to collect the data caused $(\mathbf{x}_i, e_i)$ to be independently but not identically distributed, then we need to use the robust standard errors to make valid statistical inference about the population parameters **b**.

The robust estimator of variance has one feature that the conventional estimator does not have: the ability to relax the assumption of independence of the observations. That is, if you specify the vce(cluster *clustvar*) option, it can produce "correct" standard errors (in the measurement sense), even if the observations are correlated.

For the automobile data, it is difficult to believe that the models of the various manufacturers are truly independent. Manufacturers, after all, use common technology, engines, and drive trains across their model lines. The VW Dasher in the above regression has a measured residual of -2.80. Having been told that, do you really believe that the residual for the VW Rabbit is as likely to be above 0 as below? (The residual is -2.32.) Similarly, the measured residual for the Chevrolet Malibu is 1.27. Does that provide information about the expected value of the residual of the Chevrolet Monte Carlo (which turns out to be 1.53)?

We need to be careful about picking examples from data; we have not told you about the Datsun 210 and 510 (residuals $+8.28$ and -1.01) or the Cadillac Eldorado and Seville (residuals -1.99 and $+7.58$), but you should, at least, question the assumption of independence. It may be believable that the measured mpg given the weight of one manufacturer's vehicles is independent of other manufacturers' vehicles, but it is at least questionable whether a manufacturer's vehicles are independent of one another.

In commands with the vce(robust) option, another option—vce(cluster *clustvar*)—relaxes the independence assumption and requires only that the observations be independent across the clusters:

```
. regress mpg weight foreign, vce(cluster manufacturer)
```

Linear regression				Number of obs =	74
				F(2, 22) =	90.93
				Prob > F =	0.0000
				R-squared =	0.6627
				Root MSE =	3.4071

(Std. Err. adjusted for 23 clusters in manufacturer)

mpg	Coef.	Robust Std. Err.	t	P>|t|	[95% Conf. Interval]	
weight	-.0065879	.0005339	-12.34	0.000	-.0076952	-.0054806
foreign	-1.650029	1.039033	-1.59	0.127	-3.804852	.5047939
_cons	41.6797	1.844559	22.60	0.000	37.85432	45.50508

It turns out that, in these data, whether or not we specify vce(cluster *clustvar*) makes little difference. The VW and Chevrolet examples above were not representative; had they been, the confidence intervals would have widened. (In the above, manuf is a variable that takes on values such as "Chev." or "VW", recording the manufacturer of the vehicle. This variable was created from variable make, which contains values such as "Chev. Malibu" or "VW Rabbit", by extracting the first word.)

As a demonstration of how well clustering can work, in [R] **regress** we fit a random-effects model with regress, vce(robust) and then compared the results with ordinary least squares and the GLS random-effects estimator. Here we will simply summarize the results.

We start with a dataset on 4,711 women aged 14–46 years. Subjects appear an average of 6.056 times in the data; there are a total of 28,534 observations. The model we use is log wage on age,

age-squared, and job tenure. The focus of the example is the estimated coefficient on tenure. We obtain the following results:

Estimator	point estimate	confidence interval
(inappropriate) least squares	.039	[.038, .041]
robust clusterered	.039	[.036, .042]
GLS random effects	.026	[.025, .027]

Notice how well the robust clustered estimate does compared with the GLS random-effects model. We then run a Hausman specification test, obtaining $\chi^2(3) = 336.62$, which casts grave doubt on the assumptions justifying the use of the GLS estimator and hence on the GLS results. At this point, we will simply quote our comments:

> Meanwhile, our robust regression results still stand, as long as we are careful about the interpretation. The correct interpretation is that, if the data collection were repeated (on women sampled the same way as in the original sample), and if we were to refit the model, 95% of the time we would expect the estimated coefficient on tenure to be in the range $[.036, .042]$.

> Even with robust regression, we must be careful about going beyond that statement. Here the Hausman test is probably picking up something that differs within and between person, which would cast doubt on our robust regression model in terms of interpreting $[.036, .042]$ to contain the rate of return for keeping a job, economywide, for all women, without exception.

The formula for the robust estimator of variance is

$$\widehat{\mathcal{V}} = \widehat{\mathbf{V}} \left(\sum_{j=1}^{N} \mathbf{u}_j' \mathbf{u}_j \right) \widehat{\mathbf{V}}$$

where $\widehat{\mathbf{V}} = (-\partial^2 \ln L / \partial \beta^2)^{-1}$ (the conventional estimator of variance) and $\mathbf{u}_j$ (a row vector) is the contribution from the jth observation to $\partial \ln L / \partial \beta$.

In the example above, observations are assumed to be independent. Assume for a moment that the observations denoted by j are not independent but that they can be divided into M groups G_1, G_2, ..., G_M that are independent. The robust estimator of variance is

$$\widehat{\mathcal{V}} = \widehat{\mathbf{V}} \left(\sum_{k=1}^{M} \mathbf{u}_k^{(G)'} \mathbf{u}_k^{(G)} \right) \widehat{\mathbf{V}}$$

where $\mathbf{u}_k^{(G)}$ is the contribution of the kth group to $\partial \ln L / \partial \beta$. That is, application of the robust variance formula merely involves using a different decomposition of $\partial \ln L / \partial \beta$, namely, $\mathbf{u}_k^{(G)}$, $k = 1, \dots, M$ rather than $\mathbf{u}_j$, $j = 1, \dots, N$. Moreover, if the log-likelihood function is additive in the observations denoted by j

$$\ln L = \sum_{j=1}^{N} \ln L_j$$

then $\mathbf{u}_j = \partial \ln L_j / \partial \beta$, so

$$\mathbf{u}_k^{(G)} = \sum_{j \in G_k} \mathbf{u}_j$$

That is what the vce(cluster *clustvar*) option does. (This point was first made in writing by Rogers [1993], although he considered the point an obvious generalization of Huber [1967] and the calculation—implemented by Rogers—had appeared in Stata a year earlier.)

❑ Technical note

What is written above is asymptotically correct but ignores a finite-sample adjustment to $\widehat{\mathcal{V}}$. For maximum likelihood estimators, when you specify vce(robust) but not vce(cluster *clustvar*), a better estimate of variance is $\widehat{\mathcal{V}}^* = \{N/(N-1)\}\widehat{\mathcal{V}}$. When you also specify the vce(cluster *clustvar*) option, this becomes $\widehat{\mathcal{V}}^* = \{M/(M-1)\}\widehat{\mathcal{V}}$.

For linear regression, the finite-sample adjustment is $N/(N-k)$ without vce(cluster *clustvar*)—where k is the number of regressors—and $\{M/(M-1)\}\{(N-1)/(N-k)\}$ with vce(cluster *clustvar*). Also, two data-dependent modifications to the calculation for $\widehat{\mathcal{V}}^*$, suggested by MacKinnon and White (1985), are also provided by regress; see [R] **regress**. Angrist and Pischke (2009, chap. 8) is devoted to robust covariance matrix estimation and offers practical guidance on the use of vce(robust) and vce(cluster *clustvar*) in both cross-sectional and panel-data applications.

❑

20.17   Obtaining scores

Many of the estimation commands that provide the vce(robust) option also provide the ability to generate equation-level score variables via the predict command. With the score option, predict returns an important ingredient into the robust variance calculation that is sometimes useful in its own right. As explained in [U] **20.16 Obtaining robust variance estimates** above, ignoring the finite-sample corrections, the robust estimate of variance is

$$\widehat{\mathcal{V}} = \widehat{\mathbf{V}} \left(\sum_{j=1}^{N} \mathbf{u}_j' \mathbf{u}_j \right) \widehat{\mathbf{V}}$$

where $\widehat{\mathbf{V}} = (-\partial^2 \ln L/\partial \beta^2)^{-1}$ is the conventional estimator of variance. Let's consider likelihood functions that are additive in the observations

$$\ln L = \sum_{j=1}^{N} \ln L_j$$

then $\mathbf{u}_j = \partial \ln L_j/\partial \beta$. In general, function L_j is a function of $\mathbf{x}_j$ and β, $L_j(\beta; \mathbf{x}_j)$. For many likelihood functions, however, it is only the linear form $\mathbf{x}_j\beta$ that enters the function. In those cases,

$$\frac{\partial \ln L_j(\mathbf{x}_j\beta)}{\partial \beta} = \frac{\partial \ln L_j(\mathbf{x}_j\beta)}{\partial(\mathbf{x}_j\beta)} \frac{\partial(\mathbf{x}_j\beta)}{\partial \beta} = \frac{\partial \ln L_j(\mathbf{x}_j\beta)}{\partial(\mathbf{x}_j\beta)} \mathbf{x}_j$$

By writing $u_j = \partial \ln L_j(\mathbf{x}_j\beta)/\partial(\mathbf{x}_j\beta)$, this becomes simply $u_j\mathbf{x}_j$. Thus the formula for the robust estimate of variance can be rewritten as

$$\widehat{\mathcal{V}} = \widehat{\mathbf{V}} \left(\sum_{j=1}^{N} u_j^2 \mathbf{x}_j' \mathbf{x}_j \right) \widehat{\mathbf{V}}$$

We refer to u_j as the equation-level score (in the singular), and it is u_j that is returned when you use predict with the score option. u_j is like a residual in that

1. $\sum_j u_j = 0$ and

2. correlation of u_j and $\mathbf{x}_j$, calculated over $j = 1, \ldots, N$, is 0.

In fact, for linear regression, u_j is the residual, normalized,

$$\frac{\partial \ln L_j}{\partial (\mathbf{x}_j \boldsymbol{\beta})} = \frac{\partial}{\partial (\mathbf{x}_j \boldsymbol{\beta})} \ln f \left\{ (y_j - \mathbf{x}_j \boldsymbol{\beta})/\sigma \right\}$$
$$= (y_j - \mathbf{x}_j \boldsymbol{\beta})/\sigma$$

where $f()$ is the standard normal density.

▷ Example 19

probit provides both the vce(robust) option and predict, score. Equation-level scores play an important role in calculating the robust estimate of variance, but we can use predict, score regardless of whether we specify vce(robust):

```
. use http://www.stata-press.com/data/r11/auto
. probit foreign mpg weight
Iteration 0:   log likelihood =  -45.03321
Iteration 1:   log likelihood = -29.244141
Iteration 2:   log likelihood = -27.041557
Iteration 3:   log likelihood =  -26.84658
Iteration 4:   log likelihood = -26.844189
Iteration 5:   log likelihood = -26.844189
```

Probit regression				Number of obs	=	74
				LR chi2(2)	=	36.38
				Prob > chi2	=	0.0000
Log likelihood = -26.844189				Pseudo R2	=	0.4039

foreign	Coef.	Std. Err.	z	P>|z|	[95% Conf. Interval]	
mpg	-.1039503	.0515689	-2.02	0.044	-.2050235	-.0028772
weight	-.0023355	.0005661	-4.13	0.000	-.003445	-.0012261
_cons	8.275464	2.554142	3.24	0.001	3.269438	13.28149

```
. predict double u, scores
. summarize u
```

Variable	Obs	Mean	Std. Dev.	Min	Max
u	74	-3.87e-16	.5988325	-1.655439	1.660787

```
. correlate u mpg weight
(obs=74)
```

	u	mpg	weight
u	1.0000		
mpg	-0.0000	1.0000	
weight	-0.0000	-0.8072	1.0000

```
. list make foreign mpg weight u if abs(u)>1.65
```

	make	foreign	mpg	weight	u
24.	Ford Fiesta	Domestic	28	1,800	-1.6554395
64.	Peugeot 604	Foreign	14	3,420	1.6607871

The light, high-mileage Ford Fiesta is surprisingly domestic, whereas the heavy, low-mileage Peugeot 604 is surprisingly foreign.   ◁

❏ Technical note

For some estimation commands, one score is not enough. Consider a likelihood that can be written as $L_j(\mathbf{x}_j\boldsymbol{\beta}_1, \mathbf{z}_j\boldsymbol{\beta}_2)$, a function of two linear forms (or linear equations). Then $\partial\ln L_j/\partial\boldsymbol{\beta}$ can be written $(\partial\ln L_j/\partial\boldsymbol{\beta}_1, \partial\ln L_j/\partial\boldsymbol{\beta}_2)$. Each of the components can in turn be written as $[\partial\ln L_j/\partial(\beta_1\mathbf{x})]\mathbf{x} = u_1\mathbf{x}$ and $[\partial\ln L_j/\partial(\beta_2\mathbf{z})]\mathbf{z} = u_2\mathbf{z}$. There are then two equation-level scores, u_1 and u_2, and, in general, there could be more.

Stata's `streg, distribution(weibull)` command is an example of this: it estimates $\boldsymbol{\beta}$ and a shape parameter, $\ln p$, the latter of which can be thought of as a degenerate linear form $(\ln p)\mathbf{z}$ with $\mathbf{z} = \mathbf{1}$. `predict, scores` after this command requires that you specify two new variable names, or you can specify *stub*, which will generate two variables, *stub1* and *stub2*; the first will be defined containing u_1—the score associated with $\boldsymbol{\beta}$—and the second will be defined containing u_2—the score associated with $\ln p$.

❏

❏ Technical note

Using Stata's matrix commands—see [P] **matrix**—we can make the robust variance calculation for ourselves and then compare it with that made by Stata.

```
. use http://www.stata-press.com/data/r11/auto, clear
(1978 Automobile Data)
. quietly probit foreign mpg weight, score(u)
. matrix accum S = mpg weight [iweight=u^2*74/73]
(obs=26.53642547)
. matrix rV = e(V)*S*e(V)
. matrix list rV
symmetric rV[3,3]
                    foreign:     foreign:     foreign:
                        mpg       weight        _cons
   foreign:mpg     .00352299
foreign:weight     .00002216    2.434e-07
 foreign:_cons   -.14090346    -.00117031    6.4474174
. quietly probit foreign mpg weight, vce(robust)
. matrix list e(V)
symmetric e(V)[3,3]
                    foreign:     foreign:     foreign:
                        mpg       weight        _cons
   foreign:mpg     .00352299
foreign:weight     .00002216    2.434e-07
 foreign:_cons   -.14090346    -.00117031    6.4474174
```

The results are the same.

There is an important lesson here for programmers. Given the scores, conventional variance estimates can be easily transformed to robust estimates. If we were writing a new estimation command, it would not be difficult to include a `vce(robust)` option.

It is, in fact, easy if we ignore clustering. With clustering, it is more work because the calculation involves forming sums within clusters. For programmers interested in implementing robust variance calculations, Stata provides an _robust command to ease the task. This is documented in [P] **_robust**.

To use _robust, you first produce conventional results (a vector of coefficients and covariance matrix) along with a variable containing the scores u_j (or variables if the likelihood function has more than one stub). You then call _robust, and it will transform your conventional variance estimate into the robust estimate. _robust will handle the work associated with clustering and the details of the finite-sample adjustment, and it will even label your output so that the word *Robust* appears above the standard error when the results are displayed.

Of course, this is all even easier if you write your commands with Stata's ml maximum likelihood optimization, in which case you merely pass the vce(robust) option on to ml. ml will then call _robust itself and do all the work for you.

❏

❏ Technical note

For some estimation commands, predict, score computes parameter-level scores $\partial L_j / \partial \beta$ instead of equation-level scores $\partial L_j / \partial \mathbf{x}_j \beta$. Those commands are

    asclogit

    asmprobit

    asroprobit

    nlogit

    stcox

    stcrreg

These models share the characteristic that there are multiple observations per independent event.

In making the robust variance calculation, what are really needed are parameter-level scores $\partial L_j / \partial \beta$, and so you may be asking yourself why predict, score does not always produce parameter-level scores. In the usual case we can obtain them from equation-level scores via the chain rule, and fewer variables are required if we adopt this approach. In the cases above, however, the likelihood is calculated at the group level and is not split into contributions from the individual observations. Thus the chain rule cannot be used and we must use the parameter level scores directly.

_robust can be tricked into using them if each parameter appears to be in its own equation as a constant. This requires resetting the row and column stripes on the covariance matrix before _robust is called. The equation names for each row and column must each be unique and the variable names must all be _cons.

❏

20.18   Weighted estimation

[U] **11.1.6 weight** introduced the syntax for weights. Stata provides four kinds of weights: fweights, or frequency weights; pweights, or sampling weights; aweights, or analytic weights; and iweights, or importance weights. The syntax for using each is the same. Type

    . regress y x1 x2

and you obtain unweighted estimates; type

    . regress y x1 x2 [pweight=pop]

and you obtain (in this example) pweighted estimation.

The sections below explain how each type of weight is used in estimation.

20.18.1 Frequency weights

Frequency weights—fweights—are integers and are nothing more than replication counts. The weight is statistically uninteresting, but from a data processing perspective it is important. Consider the following data

```
   y      x1      x2
  22      1       0
  22      1       0
  22      1       1
  23      0       1
  23      0       1
  23      0       1
```

and the estimation command

. regress y x1 x2

Equivalent is the following, more compressed data

```
   y      x1      x2      pop
  22      1       0        2
  22      1       1        1
  23      0       1        3
```

and the corresponding estimation command

. regress y x1 x2 [fweight=pop]

When you specify frequency weights, you are treating each observation as one or more real observations.

❏ Technical note

You might occasionally run across a command that does not allow weights at all, especially among user-written commands. expand (see [D] **expand**) can be used with such commands to obtain frequency-weighted results. The expand command duplicates observations so that the data become self-weighting. Suppose that you want to run the command usercmd, which does something or other, and you would like to type usercmd y x1 x2 [fw=pop]. Unfortunately, usercmd does not allow weights. Instead, you type

. expand pop
. usercmd y x1 x2

to obtain your result. Moreover, there is an important principle here: the results of running any command with frequency weights should be the same as running the command on the unweighted, expanded data. Unweighted, duplicated data and frequency-weighted data are merely two ways of recording identical information.

❏

20.18.2 Analytic weights

Analytic weights—*analytic* is a term we made up—statistically arise in one particular problem: linear regression on data that are themselves observed means. That is, think of the model

$$y_i = \mathbf{x}_i \boldsymbol{\beta} + \epsilon_i, \qquad \epsilon_i \sim N(0, \sigma^2)$$

and now think about fitting this model on data $(\overline{y}_j, \overline{\mathbf{x}}_j)$ that are themselves observed averages. For instance, a piece of the underlying data for $(y_i, \mathbf{x}_i)$ might be $(3, 1)$, $(4, 2)$, and $(2, 2)$, but you do not know that. Instead, you have one observation $\{(3 + 4 + 2)/3, (1 + 2 + 2)/3\} = (3, 1.67)$ and know only that the $(3, 1.67)$ arose as the average of 3 underlying observations. All your data are like that.

`regress` with `aweights` is the solution to that problem:

    . regress y x [aweight=pop]

There is a history of misusing such weights. A researcher does not have cell-mean data but instead has a probability-weighted random sample. Long before Stata existed, some researchers were using `aweights` to produce estimates from such samples. We will come back to this point in [U] **20.18.3 Sampling weights** below.

Anyway, the statistical problem that `aweights` resolve can be written as

$$y_i = \mathbf{x}_i \boldsymbol{\beta} + \epsilon_i, \qquad \epsilon_i \sim N(0, \sigma^2/w_i)$$

where the w_i are the analytic weights. The details of the solution are to make linear regression calculations using the weights as if they were `fweights` but to normalize them to sum to N before doing that.

Most commands that allow `aweights` handle them in this manner. That is, if you specify `aweights`, they are

1. normalized to sum to N and then

2. inserted in the calculation formulas in the same way as `fweights`.

20.18.3 Sampling weights

Sampling weights—probability weights or `pweights`—refer to probability-weighted random samples. Actually, what you specify in `[pweight=...]` is a variable recording the number of subjects in the full population that the sampled observation in your data represents. That is, an observation that had probability $1/3$ of being included in your sample has pweight 3.

Some researchers have used `aweights` with this kind of data. If they do, they are probably making a mistake. Consider the regression model

$$y_i = \mathbf{x}_i \boldsymbol{\beta} + \epsilon_i, \qquad \epsilon_i \sim N(0, \sigma^2)$$

Begin by considering the exact nature of the problem of fitting this model on cell-mean data—for which `aweights` are the solution: heteroskedasticity arising from the grouping. The error term ϵ_i is homoskedastic (meaning that it has constant variance σ^2). Say that the first observation in the data is the mean of 3 underlying observations. Then

$$y_1 = \mathbf{x}_1 \boldsymbol{\beta} + \epsilon_1, \qquad \epsilon_i \sim N(0, \sigma^2)$$
$$y_2 = \mathbf{x}_2 \boldsymbol{\beta} + \epsilon_2, \qquad \epsilon_i \sim N(0, \sigma^2)$$
$$y_3 = \mathbf{x}_3 \boldsymbol{\beta} + \epsilon_3, \qquad \epsilon_i \sim N(0, \sigma^2)$$

and taking the mean

$$(y_1 + y_2 + y_3)/3 = \{(\mathbf{x}_1 + \mathbf{x}_2 + \mathbf{x}_3)/3\}\boldsymbol{\beta} + (\epsilon_1 + \epsilon_2 + \epsilon_3)/3$$

For another observation in the data—which may be the result of summing of a different number of observations—the variance will be different. Hence, the model for the data is

$$\overline{y}_j = \overline{x}_j\boldsymbol{\beta} + \overline{\epsilon}_j, \qquad \overline{\epsilon}_j \sim N(0, \sigma^2/N_j)$$

This makes intuitive sense. Consider 2 observations, one recording means over two subjects and the other means over 100,000 subjects. You would expect the variance of the residual to be less in the 100,000-subject observation; i.e., there is more information in the 100,000-subject observation than in the two-subject observation.

Now instead say that you are fitting the same model, $y_i = \mathbf{x}_i\boldsymbol{\beta} + \epsilon_i$, $\epsilon_i \sim N(0, \sigma^2)$, on probability-weighted data. Each observation in your data is one subject, but the different subjects have different chances of being included in your sample. Therefore, for each subject in your data

$$y_i = \mathbf{x}_i\boldsymbol{\beta} + \epsilon_i, \qquad \epsilon_i \sim N(0, \sigma^2)$$

That is, there is no heteroskedasticity problem. The use of the `aweighted` estimator cannot be justified on these grounds.

As a matter of fact, from the argument just given, you do not need to adjust for the weights at all, although the argument does not justify not making an adjustment. If you do not adjust, you are holding tightly to the assumed truth of your model. Two issues arise when considering adjustment for sampling weights:

1. the efficiency of the point estimate $\widehat{\boldsymbol{\beta}}$ of $\boldsymbol{\beta}$ and

2. the reported standard errors (and, more generally, the variance matrix of $\widehat{\boldsymbol{\beta}}$).

Efficiency argues in favor of adjustment, and that, by the way, is why many researchers have used `aweights` with `pweighted` data. The adjustment implied by `pweights` to the point estimates is the same as the adjustment implied by `aweights`.

With regard to the second issue, the use of `aweights` produces incorrect results because it interprets larger weights as designating more accurately measured points. For `pweights`, however, the point is no more accurately measured—it is still just one observation with one residual ϵ_j and variance σ^2. In [U] **20.16 Obtaining robust variance estimates** above, we introduced another estimator of variance that measures the variation that would be observed if the data collection followed by the estimation were repeated. Those same formulas provide the solution to `pweights`, and they have the added advantage that they are not conditioned on the model's being true. If we have any hopes of measuring the variation that would be observed were the data collection followed by estimation repeated, we must include the probability of the observations being sampled in the calculation.

In Stata, when you type

```
. regress y x1 x2 [pw=pop]
```

the results are the same as if you had typed

```
. regress y x1 x2 [pw=pop], vce(robust)
```

That is, specifying `pweights` implies the `vce(robust)` option and, hence, the robust variance calculation (but weighted). In this example, we use `regress` simply for illustration. The same is true of `probit` and all of Stata's estimation commands. Estimation commands that do not have a `vce(robust)` option (there are a few) do not allow `pweights`.

`pweights` are adequate for handling random samples where the probability of being sampled varies. `pweights` may be all you need. If, however, the observations are not sampled independently but are sampled in groups—called clusters in the jargon—you should specify the estimator's `vce(cluster clustvar)` option as well:

```
. regress y x1 x2 [pw=pop], vce(cluster block)
```

There are two ways of thinking about this:

1. The robust estimator answers the question of which variation would be observed were the data collection followed by the estimation repeated; if that question is to be answered, the estimator must account for the clustered nature of how observations are selected. If observations 1 and 2 are in the same cluster, then you cannot select observation 1 without selecting observation 2 (and, by extension, you cannot select observations like 1 without selecting observations like 2).

2. If you prefer, you can think about potential correlations. Observations in the same cluster may not really be independent—that is an empirical question to be answered by the data. For instance, if the clusters are neighborhoods, it would not be surprising that the individual neighbors are similar in their income, their tastes, and their attitudes, and even more similar than two randomly drawn persons from the area at large with similar characteristics, such as age and sex.

Either way of thinking leads to the same (robust) estimator of variance.

Sampling weights usually arise from complex sampling designs, which often involve not only unequal probability sampling and cluster sampling but also stratified sampling. There is a family of commands in Stata designed to work with the features of complex survey data, and those are the commands that begin with `svy`. To fit a linear regression model with stratification, for example, you would use the `svy:regress` command.

Non-`svy` commands that allow `pweights` and clustering give essentially identical results to the `svy` commands. If the sampling design is simple enough that it can be accommodated by the non-`svy` command, that is a fine way to perform the analysis. The `svy` commands differ in that they have more features, and they do all the little details correctly for real survey data. See [SVY] **survey** for a brief discussion of some of the issues involved in the analysis of survey data and a list of all the differences between the `svy` and non-`svy` commands.

Not all model estimation commands in Stata allow `pweights`. This is often because they are computationally or statistically difficult to implement.

20.18.4 Importance weights

Stata's `iweights`—importance weights—are the emergency exit. These weights are for those who want to take control and create special effects. For example, programmers have used `regress` with `iweights` to compute iteratively reweighted least-squares solutions for various problems.

iweights are treated much like aweights, except that they are not normalized. Stata's iweight rule is that

1. the weights are not normalized and

2. they are generally inserted into calculation formulas in the same way as fweights. There are exceptions; see the *Methods and formulas* for the particular command.

iweights are used mostly by programmers who are often on the way to implementing one of the other kinds of weights.

20.19   A list of postestimation commands

The following commands can be used after estimation:

[R]	**estat**	AIC, BIC, VCE, and estimation sample summary
[R]	**estimates**	cataloging estimation results
[R]	**hausman**	Hausman specification test
[R]	**lincom**	point estimates, standard errors, testing, and inference for linear combinations of coefficients
[R]	**linktest**	specification link test for single-equation models
[R]	**lrtest**	likelihood-ratio test
[R]	**margins**	marginal means, predictive margins, and marginal effects
[R]	**nlcom**	point estimates, standard errors, testing, and inference for generalized predictions
[R]	**predict**	predictions, residuals, influence statistics, and other diagnostic measures
[R]	**predictnl**	point estimates, standard errors, testing, and inference for generalized predictions
[R]	**suest**	seemingly unrelated estimation
[R]	**test**	Wald tests of simple and composite linear hypotheses
[R]	**testnl**	Wald tests of nonlinear hypotheses

Also see [U] **13.5 Accessing coefficients and standard errors** for accessing coefficients and standard errors.

The commands above are general-purpose postestimation commands that can be used after almost all estimation commands. Many estimation commands provide other estimator-specific postestimation commands. The full list of postestimation commands available for an estimator can be found in an entry titled *estimator* postestimation that immediately follows each estimator's entry in the [R], [MI], [MV], [ST], [SVY], [TS], and [XT] reference manuals.

Halbert Lynn White Jr. (1950–) was born in Kansas City. After receiving economics degrees at Princeton and MIT, he has taught and researched economics at the University of Rochester and, since 1980, at the University of California, San Diego. He is also active as a consultant. White's research interests include artificial neural networks, finance, econometrics, and forecasting, and his hobbies include music and antiques.

Peter Jost Huber (1934–) was born in Wohlen (Aargau, Switzerland). He gained mathematics degrees from ETH Zürich, including a PhD thesis on homotopy theory, and then studied statistics at Berkeley on postdoctoral fellowships. This visit yielded a celebrated 1964 paper on robust estimation, and Huber's later monographs on robust statistics were crucial in directing that field. Thereafter his career took him back and forth across the Atlantic, with periods at Cornell, ETH Zürich, Harvard, MIT, and Bayreuth. His work has touched several other major parts of statistics, theoretical and applied, including regression, exploratory multivariate analysis, large datasets, and statistical computing. Huber also has a major long-standing interest in Babylonian astronomy.

20.20   References

Afifi, A. A., and S. P. Azen. 1979. *Statistical Analysis: A Computer Oriented Approach.* 2nd ed. New York: Academic Press.

Angrist, J. D., and J.-S. Pischke. 2009. *Mostly Harmless Econometrics: An Empiricist's Companion.* Princeton, NJ: Princeton University Press.

Baum, C. F. 2009. *An Introduction to Stata Programming.* College Station, TX: Stata Press.

Binder, D. A. 1983. On the variances of asymptotically normal estimators from complex surveys. *International Statistical Review* 51: 279–292.

Deaton, A. 1997. *The Analysis of Household Surveys: A Microeconometric Approach to Development Policy.* Baltimore, MD: Johns Hopkins University Press.

Fuller, W. A. 1975. Regression analysis for sample survey. *Sankhyā, Series C* 37: 117–132.

Gail, M. H., W. Y. Tan, and S. Piantadosi. 1988. Tests for no treatment effect in randomized clinical trials. *Biometrika* 75: 57–64.

Hampel, F. R. 1992. Introduction to Huber (1964) "Robust estimation of a location parameter". In *Breakthroughs in Statistics. Volume II: Methodology and Distribution*, ed. S. Kotz and N. L. Johnson, 479–491. New York: Springer.

Huber, P. J. 1967. The behavior of maximum likelihood estimates under nonstandard conditions. In Vol. 1 of *Proceedings of the Fifth Berkeley Symposium on Mathematical Statistics and Probability*, 221–233. Berkeley: University of California Press.

Kent, J. T. 1982. Robust properties of likelihood ratio tests. *Biometrika* 69: 19–27.

Kish, L., and M. R. Frankel. 1974. Inference from complex samples. *Journal of the Royal Statistical Society, Series B* 36: 1–37.

Lin, D. Y., and L. J. Wei. 1989. The robust inference for the Cox proportional hazards model. *Journal of the American Statistical Association* 84: 1074–1078.

Long, J. S., and J. Freese. 2000a. sg145: Scalar measures of fit for regression models. *Stata Technical Bulletin* 56: 34–40. Reprinted in *Stata Technical Bulletin Reprints*, vol. 10, pp. 197–205. College Station, TX: Stata Press.

——. 2000b. sg152: Listing and interpreting transformed coefficients from certain regression models. *Stata Technical Bulletin* 57: 27–34. Reprinted in *Stata Technical Bulletin Reprints*, vol. 10, pp. 231–240. College Station, TX: Stata Press.

MacKinnon, J. G., and H. White. 1985. Some heteroskedasticity-consistent covariance matrix estimators with improved finite sample properties. *Journal of Econometrics* 29: 305–325.

Rogers, W. H. 1993. sg17: Regression standard errors in clustered samples. *Stata Technical Bulletin* 13: 19–23. Reprinted in *Stata Technical Bulletin Reprints*, vol. 3, pp. 88–94. College Station, TX: Stata Press.

Royall, R. M. 1986. Model robust confidence intervals using maximum likelihood estimators. *International Statistical Review* 54: 221–226.

Weesie, J. 2000. sg127: Summary statistics for estimation sample. *Stata Technical Bulletin* 53: 32–35. Reprinted in *Stata Technical Bulletin Reprints*, vol. 9, pp. 275–277. College Station, TX: Stata Press.

White, H. 1980. A heteroskedasticity-consistent covariance matrix estimator and a direct test for heteroskedasticity. *Econometrica* 48: 817–838.

——. 1982. Maximum likelihood estimation of misspecified models. *Econometrica* 50: 1–25.

Advice

21 Inputting data

Contents

21.1 Overview

To input data into Stata, you can use

[D] **edit** and [D] **input**	to enter data from the keyboard
[D] **insheet**	to read tab- or comma-separated data
[D] **infile (free format)**	to read unformatted data
[D] **infile (fixed format)** or [D] **infix (fixed format)**	to read formatted data
[D] **xmlsave** (where `xmluse` is documented)	to use datasets in XML and Excel format
[D] **odbc**	to read from an ODBC source
[D] **fdasave** (where `fdause` is documented)	to read datasets in SAS XPORT format
[TS] **haver**	to read data in Haver Analytics' format
[U] **21.4 Transfer programs**	to transfer data

Because dataset formats differ, you should familiarize yourself with each method.

[D] **infile (fixed format)** and [D] **infix (fixed format)** are two different commands that do the same thing. Read about both, and then use whichever appeals to you.

Alternatively, `edit` and `input` both allow you to enter data from the keyboard. `edit` opens a Viewer, and `input` allows you to type as the command line.

After you have read this chapter, also see [D] **infile** for more examples of the different commands to input data.

21.2 Determining which input method to use

Below are several rules that, when applied sequentially, will direct you to the appropriate method for entering your data. After the rules is a description of each command, as well as a reference to the corresponding entry in the *Reference* manuals.

1. If you have a few data and simply wish to type the data directly into Stata at the keyboard, see [D] **input**—there are many examples, and doing so should be easy. Also see [D] **edit**.

2. If your dataset is in binary format or the internal format of some software package, you have several options:

   a. If the data are in a spreadsheet, copy and paste the data into Stata's Data Editor; see [D] **edit** for details.

   b. If the data are in an Excel spreadsheet, use Excel to export the data as XML, and then use Stata's xmluse command to read them; see [D] **xmlsave**.

   c. If the data are in SAS XPORT format, use fdause to read the data; see [D] **fdasave**.

   d. If the data in Haver Analytics' .dat format (Haver Analytics provides economics and financial databases), and you are using Stata for Windows, use haver to read the data; see [TS] **haver**.

   e. Translate the data into ASCII (also known as character) format by using the other software. For instance, in Excel you can save spreadsheets as tab-delimited or comma-separated text. Then, see [D] **insheet**.

   f. Other software packages are available that will convert non–Stata format data files into Stata-format files; see [U] **21.4 Transfer programs**.

   g. If the data are located in an ODBC source, which typically includes databases and spreadsheets, you can use the odbc load command to import the data; see [D] **odbc**. Currently odbc is available for Windows, Mac, and Linux versions of Stata.

3. If the dataset has one observation per line and the data are tab- or comma separated, use insheet; see [D] **insheet**. This is the easiest way to read data.

4. If the dataset is formatted and that formatting information is required to interpret the data, you can use infile with a dictionary or infix; see [D] **infile (fixed format)** or [D] **infix (fixed format)**.

5. If there are no string variables, you can use infile without a dictionary: see [D] **infile (free format)**.

6. If all the string variables in the data are enclosed in (single or double) quotes, you can use infile without a dictionary; see [D] **infile (free format)**.

7. If the undelimited string variables have no blanks, you can use infile without a dictionary; see [D] **infile (free format)**.

8. If you make it to here, see [D] **infile (fixed format)** or [D] **infix (fixed format)**.

21.2.1 Entering data interactively

If you have a few data, you can type the data directly into Stata; see [D] **input** or [D] **edit**. Otherwise, we assume that your data are stored on disk.

21.2.2   Copying and pasting data

If your data are in another program and you wish to analyze them with Stata, first see if the program you are using allows you to copy the data to the clipboard. If it does, do so, and then open the Data Editor in Stata and select **Edit** > **Paste** to paste the data into Stata.

21.2.3   If the dataset is in binary format

Stata can read ASCII datasets, which is technical jargon for datasets composed of characters—datasets that can be typed on your screen or printed on your printer. The alternative, binary datasets, cannot be read by Stata. Binary datasets are popular, and almost every software package has its own binary format. Stata .dta datasets are an example of a binary format that Stata can read. The Excel format is a binary format that Stata cannot read.

If your dataset is in binary format or in the internal format of another software package, you must translate it into an XML format that Stata can understand (see [D] **xmlsave**), translate it into ASCII, or use some other program for conversion to Stata format. If this dataset is located in a database or an ODBC source, see [U] **21.5 ODBC sources**. If the dataset is in SAS XPORT format, you can read it by using Stata's fdause command; see [D] **fdasave**. If the dataset is in Haver Analytics' .dat format, you can read it by using Stata's haver command; see [TS] **haver**.

Detecting whether data are stored in binary format can be tricky. For instance, many Windows users wish to read data that have been entered into a word processor—let's assume Word. Unwittingly, they have stored the dataset as a Word document. The dataset looks like ASCII to them: When they look at it in Word, they see readable characters. The dataset seems to even pass the printing test in that Word can print it. Nevertheless, the dataset is not ASCII; it is stored in an internal Word format, and the data cannot really pass the printing test because only Word can print it. To read the dataset, Windows users must use it in Word and then store it as an MS-DOS text file, MS-DOS text being the term Word decided to use to mean ASCII.

So, how do you know whether your dataset is binary? Here's a simple test: regardless of the operating system you use, start Stata and type type followed by the name of the file:

```
. type myfile.raw
output will appear
```

You do not have to print the entire file; press *Break* when you have seen enough.

Do you see things that look like hieroglyphics? If so, the dataset is binary. See [U] **21.4 Transfer programs** below.

If it looks like data, however, the file is (probably) ASCII.

Let's assume that you have an ASCII dataset that you wish to read. The data's format will determine the command you need to use. The different formats are discussed in the following sections.

21.2.4   If the data are simple

The easiest way to read data is with insheet; see [D] **insheet**.

insheet is smart: it looks at the dataset, determines what it contains, and then reads it. That is, insheet is smart given certain restrictions, such as that the dataset has one observation per line and that the values are tab- or comma separated. insheet can read this

```
——————————————————————————————————— begin data1.raw ———————
M,Joe Smith,288,14
M,K Marx,238,12
F,Farber,211,7
——————————————————————————————————— end data1.raw ———————
```

or this (which has variable names on the first line)

```
——————————————————————————————————— begin data2.raw ———————
sex, name, dept, division
M,Joe Smith,288,14
M,K Marx,238,12
F,Farber,211,7
——————————————————————————————————— end data2.raw ———————
```

or this (which has one tab character separating the values):

```
——————————————————————————————————— begin data3.raw ———————
M       Joe Smith      288      14
M       K Marx   238   12
F       Farber   211   7
——————————————————————————————————— end data3.raw ———————
```

This looks odd because of how tabs work; data3.raw could similarly have a variable header, but insheet cannot read

```
——————————————————————————————————— begin data4.raw ———————
M       Joe Smith      288      14
M       K Marx         238      12
F       Farber         211      7
——————————————————————————————————— end data4.raw ———————
```

which has spaces rather than tabs.

There is a way to tell data3.raw from data4.raw: Ask Stata to type the data and show the tabs by typing

```
. type data3.raw, showtabs
M<T>Joe Smith<T>288<T>14
M<T>K Marx<T>238<T>12
F<T>Farber<T>211<T>7

. type data4.raw, showtabs
M       Joe Smith      288      14
M       K Marx         238      12
F       Farber         211      7
```

21.2.5   If the dataset is formatted and the formatting is significant

If the dataset is formatted and formatting information is required to interpret the data, see [D] **infile (fixed format)** or [D] **infix (fixed format)**.

Using infix or infile with a data dictionary is something new users want to avoid if at all possible.

The purpose of this section is only to take you to the most complicated of all cases if there is no alternative. Otherwise, you should wait and see if it is necessary. Do not misinterpret this section and say, "Ah, my dataset is formatted, so at last I have a solution."

Just because a dataset is formatted does not mean that you have to exploit the formatting information. The following dataset is formatted

```
──────────────────────────────────────────────── begin data5.raw ───────────
    1    27.39    12
    2     1.00     4
    3   100.10   100
──────────────────────────────────────────────── end data5.raw ───────────
```

in that the numbers line up in neat columns, but you do not need to know the information to read it. Alternatively, consider the same data run together:

```
──────────────────────────────────────────────── begin data6.raw ───────────
    1 27.39 12
    2  1.00  4
    3100.10100
──────────────────────────────────────────────── end data6.raw ───────────
```

This dataset is formatted, too, and you must know the formatting information to make sense of "3100.10100". You must know that variable 2 starts in column 4 and is six characters long to extract the 100.10. It is datasets like data6.raw that you should be looking for at this stage—datasets that make sense only if you know the starting and ending columns of data elements. To read data such as data6.raw, you must use either infix or infile with a data dictionary.

Reading unformatted data is easier. If you need the formatting information to interpret the data, then you must communicate that information to Stata, which means that you will have to type it. This is the hardest kind of data to read, but Stata can do it. See [D] **infile (fixed format)** or [D] **infix (fixed format)**.

Looking back at data4.raw,

```
──────────────────────────────────────────────── begin data4.raw ───────────
    M       Joe Smith      288    14
    M       K Marx         238    12
    F       Farber         211    7
──────────────────────────────────────────────── end data4.raw ───────────
```

you may be uncertain whether you have to read it with a data dictionary. If you are uncertain, do not jump yet.

Finally, here is an obvious example of unformatted data:

```
──────────────────────────────────────────────── begin data7.raw ───────────
    1 27.39            12
    2 1 4
    3 100.1 100
──────────────────────────────────────────────── end data7.raw ───────────
```

Here blanks separate one data element from the next and, in one case, many blanks, although there is no special meaning attached to more than one blank.

The following sections discuss datasets that are unformatted or formatted in a way that do not require a data dictionary.

21.2.6   If there are no string variables

If there are no string variables, see [D] **infile (free format)**.

Although the dataset data7.raw is unformatted, it can still be read using infile without a dictionary. This is not the case with data4.raw because this dataset contains undelimited string variables with embedded blanks.

❑ Technical note

Some Stata users prefer to read data with a data dictionary, even when we suggest differently, as above. They like the convenience of the data dictionary—they can sit in front of an editor and carefully compose the list of variables and attach variable labels rather than having to type the variable list (correctly) on the Stata command line. However, they can create a do-file containing the infile statement and thus have all the advantages of a data dictionary without some of the (extremely technical) disadvantages of data dictionaries.

Nevertheless, we do tend to agree with such users—we, too, prefer data dictionaries. Our recommendations, however, are designed to work in all cases. If the dataset is unformatted and contains no string variables, it can always be read without a data dictionary, whereas only sometimes can it be read with a data dictionary.

The distinction is that infile without a data dictionary performs stream I/O, whereas with a data dictionary it performs record I/O. The difference is intentional—it guarantees that you will be able to read your data into Stata somehow. Some datasets require stream I/O, others require record I/O, and still others can be read either way. Recommendations 1–5 identify datasets that either require stream I/O or can be read either way.

❑

We are now left with datasets that contain at least one string variable.

21.2.7   If all the string variables are enclosed in quotes

If all the string variables in the data are enclosed in (single or double) quotes, see [D] **infile (free format)**.

See [U] **23 Working with strings** for a formal definition of strings, but as a quick guide, a string variable is a variable that takes on values like "bob" or "joe", as opposed to numeric variables that take on values like 1, 27.5, and –17.393. Undelimited strings—strings not enclosed in quotes—can be difficult to read.

Here is an example including delimited string variables:

```
───────────────────────────────────────────── begin data8.raw ─────────
"M" "Joe Smith" 288 14
"M" "K Marx" 238 12
"F" "Farber" 211 7
───────────────────────────────────────────── end data8.raw ─────────
```

or

```
───────────────────────────── begin data8.raw, alternative format ─────────
"M" "Joe Smith" 288   14
"M" "K Marx"     238   12
"F" "Farber"     211    7
───────────────────────────── end data8.raw, alternative format ─────────
```

Both of these are merely variations on data4.raw except that the strings are enclosed in quotes. Here infile without a dictionary can be used to read the data.

Here is another version of data4.raw without delimiters or even formatting:

```
───────────────────────────────────────────── begin data9.raw ─────────
M Joe Smith 288 14
M K Marx 238 12
F Farber 211 7
───────────────────────────────────────────── end data9.raw ─────────
```

What makes these data difficult? Blanks sometimes separate values and sometimes are nothing more than a blank within a string. For instance, you cannot tell whether Farber has first initial F with missing sex or is instead female with a missing first initial.

Fortunately, such data rarely happen. Either the strings are delimited, as we showed in `data8.raw`, or the data are in columns, as in `data4.raw`.

21.2.8   If the undelimited strings have no blanks

There is a case in which uncolumnized, undelimited strings cause no confusion—when they contain no blanks. For instance, if our data contained only last names,

```
──────────────────────────────────────── begin data10.raw ────────────
    Smith 288 14
    Marx 238 12
    Farber 211 7
──────────────────────────────────────── end data10.raw ────────────
```

Stata could read it without a data dictionary. Caution: the last names must contain no blanks—no Van Owen's or von Beethoven's.

If the undelimited string variables have no blanks, see [D] **infile (free format)**.

21.2.9   If you make it to here

If you make it to here, see [D] **infile (fixed format)** or [D] **infix (fixed format)**.

Remember `data4.raw`?

```
──────────────────────────────────────── begin data4.raw ────────────
    M        Joe Smith        288      14
    M        K Marx           238      12
    F        Farber           211       7
──────────────────────────────────────── end data4.raw ────────────
```

It can be read using either `infile` with a dictionary or `infix`.

21.3   If you run out of memory

You can increase the amount of memory allocated to Stata; see [U] **6 Setting the size of memory**.

You can also try to conserve memory.

When you read the data, did you specify variable types? Stata can store integers more compactly than floats and small integers more compactly than large integers; see [U] **12 Data**.

If that is not sufficient, you will have to resort to reading the data in pieces. Both `infile` and `infix` allow you to specify an in *range* modifier, and, here the range is interpreted as the observation range to read. Thus, `infile ... in 1/100` would read observations 1–100 of your data and stop.

`infile ... in 101/200` would read observations 101–200. The end of the range may be specified as larger than the actual number of observations in the data. If the dataset contained only 150 observations, `infile ... in 101/200` would read observations 101–150.

Another way of reading the data in pieces is to specify the if *exp* modifier. Say that your data contained an equal number of males and females, coded as the variable sex (which you will read) being 0 or 1, respectively. You could type infile ... if sex==0 to read the males. infile will read an observation, determine if sex is zero, and if not, throw the observation away. You could read just the females by typing infile ... if sex==1.

If the dataset is really big, perhaps you need only a random sample of the data—you never intended to analyze the entire dataset. Because infile and infix allow if *exp*, you could type infile ... if runiform()<.1. runiform() is the uniformly distributed random-number generator; see [D] **functions**. This method would read an approximate 10% sample of the data. If you are serious about using random samples, do not forget to set the seed before using runiform(); see [R] **set seed**.

The final approach is to read all the observations but only some of the variables. When reading data without a data dictionary, you can specify _skip for variables, indicating that the variable is to be skipped. When reading with a data dictionary or using infix, you can specify the actual columns to read, skipping any columns you wish to ignore.

21.4   Transfer programs

To import data from, say, Excel, you can save the data as a text file and then read it into Stata according to the rules above, read it via an ODBC source, or purchase a program to translate the dataset from Excel's format to Stata's format.

One such program is Stat/Transfer, which is available for Windows, Mac OS X, and Unix. It reads and writes data in a variety of formats, including Microsoft Access, dBASE, Epi Info, Excel, FoxPro, GAUSS, JMP, LIMDEP, Lotus 1-2-3, MATLAB, MineSet, ODBC, Paradox, Quattro Pro, S-Plus, SAS, SPSS, Statistica, SYSTAT, and, of course, Stata.

Stat/Transfer, available from...	is manufactured by...
StataCorp	Circle Systems
4905 Lakeway Drive	1001 Fourth Avenue Plaza, Suite 3200
College Station, Texas 77845	Seattle, Washington 98154
Telephone: 979-696-4600	Telephone: 206-682-3783
Fax: 979-696-4601	Fax: 206-328-4788
Email: stata@stata.com	sales@circlesys.com

There are other transfer programs available, too. Our web site, http://www.stata.com, lists programs available from other sources.

21.5   ODBC sources

If your dataset is located in a network database or shared spreadsheet, you may be able to import your data via ODBC. Open Database Connectivity (ODBC) is a standard for exchanging data between programs. Stata supports the ODBC standard for importing data via the odbc command and can read from any ODBC source on your computer.

This process requires a data source, such as a database located on a network. To use the odbc command to import data from a database requires that the database first be set up as an ODBC source on the same machine that is running Stata. The database itself does not have to be on the same machine, just the definition of that database as the ODBC source. On a Windows machine, an ODBC source is added via a Control Panel called "Data Sources". Also, typing odbc list from Stata displays all the ODBC sources that are provided by the computer.

If the database is functioning and the appropriate data source has been set up on the same machine as Stata, one call using `odbc load` is all that is needed to import data. For a more thorough description of this process, see [D] **odbc**.

21.6 Reference

Swagel, P. 1994. os14: A program to format raw data files. *Stata Technical Bulletin* 20: 10–12. Reprinted in *Stata Technical Bulletin Reprints*, vol. 4, pp. 80–82. College Station, TX: Stata Press.

22 Combining datasets

You have two datasets that you wish to combine. Below, we will draw a dataset as a box where, in the box, the variables go across and the observations go down.

See [D] **append** if you want to combine datasets vertically:

append adds observations to the existing variables. That is an oversimplification because append does not require that the datasets have the same variables. append is appropriate, for instance, when you have data on hospital patients and then receive data on more patients.

See [D] **merge** if you want to combine datasets horizontally:

merge adds variables to the existing observations. That is an oversimplification because merge does not require that the datasets have the same observations. merge is appropriate, for instance, when you have data on survey respondents and then receive data on part 2 of the questionnaire.

See [D] *joinby* when you want to combine datasets horizontally but form all pairwise combinations within group:

joinby is similar to merge but forms all combinations of the observations where it makes sense. joinby would be appropriate, for instance, where A contained data on parents and B contained data on their children. joinby *familyid* would form a dataset of each parent joined with each of his or her children.

Also see [D] **cross** for a less frequently used command that forms every pairwise combination of two datasets.

23 Working with strings

Contents

Please read [U] **12 Data** before reading this entry.

23.1 Description

The word *string* is shorthand for a string of characters. "Male" and "Female", "yes" and "no", and "R. Smith" and "P. Jones" are examples of strings. The alternative to strings is numbers—0, 1, 2, 5.7, and so on. Variables containing strings—called *string variables*—occur in data for a variety of reasons. Four of these reasons are listed below.

A variable might contain strings because it is an identifying variable. Employee names in a payroll file, patient names in a hospital file, and city names in a city data file are all examples of this. This is a proper use of string variables.

A variable might contain strings because it records categorical information. "Male" and "Female" and "yes" and "no" are examples of such use, but this is not an appropriate use of string variables. It is not appropriate because the same information could be coded numerically, and, if it were, it would take less memory to store the data and the data would be more useful. We will explain how to convert categorical strings to categorical numbers below.

Also, a variable might contain strings because of a mistake. For example, the variable contains things like 1, 5, 8.2, but because of an error in reading the data, the data were mistakenly put into a string variable. We will explain how to fix such mistakes.

Finally, a variable might contain strings because the data simply could not be coerced into being stored numerically. "15 Jan 1992", "1/15/92", and "1A73" are examples of such use. We will explain how to deal with such complexities.

23.2 Categorical string variables

A variable might contain strings because it records categorical information.

Suppose that you have read in a dataset that contains a variable called sex, recorded as "male" and "female", yet when you attempt to run an ANOVA, the following message is displayed:

```
. use http://www.stata-press.com/data/r11/hbp2

. anova hbp sex
no observations
r(2000);
```

There are no observations because anova, along with most of Stata's "analytic" commands, cannot deal with string variables. Commands want to see numbers, and when they do not, they treat the variable as if it contained numeric missing values. Despite this limitation, it is possible to obtain tables:

```
. encode sex, gen(gender)
. anova hbp gender
```

		Number of obs =	1128	R-squared	=	0.0123
		Root MSE = .214223		Adj R-squared =		0.0114

Source	Partial SS	df	MS	F	Prob > F
Model	.644485682	1	.644485682	14.04	0.0002
gender	.644485682	1	.644485682	14.04	0.0002
Residual	51.6737767	1126	.045891454		
Total	52.3182624	1127	.046422593		

The magic here is to convert the string variable sex into a numeric variable called gender with an associated value label, a trick accomplished by encode; see [U] **12.6.3 Value labels** and [D] **encode**.

23.3   Mistaken string variables

A variable might contain strings because of a mistake.

Suppose that you have numeric data in a variable called x, but because of a mistake, x was made a string variable when you read the data. When you list the variable, it looks fine:

```
. list x
```

	x
1.	2
2.	2.5
3.	17

(*output omitted*)

Yet, when you attempt to obtain summary statistics on x,

```
. summarize x
```

Variable	Obs	Mean	Std. Dev.	Min	Max
x	0				

If this happens to you, type describe to confirm that x is stored as a string:

```
. describe
Contains data
  obs:          10
  vars:          3
  size:        160 (99.9% of memory free)
```

variable name	storage type	display format	value label	variable label
x	str4	%9s		
y	float	%9.0g		
z	float	%9.0g		

```
Sorted by:
```

x is stored as a str4.

The problem is that `summarize` does not know how to calculate the mean of string variables—how to calculate the mean of "Joe" plus "Bill" plus "Roger"—even when the string variable contains what could be numbers. By using the `destring` command ([D] **destring**), the variable mistakenly stored as a `str4` can be converted to a numeric variable.

```
. destring x, replace
. summarize x
```

Variable	Obs	Mean	Std. Dev.	Min	Max
newx	10	1.76	.8071899	.7	3

An alternative to using the `destring` command is to use `generate` with the `real()` function; see [D] **functions**.

23.4   Complex strings

A variable might contain strings because the data simply could not be coerced into being stored numerically.

A complex string is a string that contains more than one piece of information. The most common example of a complex string is a date: "15 Jan 1992" contains three pieces of information—a day, a month, and a year. If your complex strings are dates or times, see [U] **24 Working with dates and times**.

Although Stata has functions for dealing with dates, you will have to deal with other complex strings yourself. Assume that you have data that include part numbers:

```
. list partno
```

```
     partno

1.   5A2713
2.   2B1311
3.   8D2712
   (output omitted )
```

The first digit of the part number is a division number, and the character that follows identifies the plant at which the part was manufactured. The next three digits represent the major part number and the last digit is a modifier indicating the color. This complex variable can be decomposed using the `substr()` and `real()` functions described in [D] **functions**:

```
. gen byte div = real(substr(partno,1,1))
. gen str1 plant = substr(partno,2,1)
. gen int part = real(substr(partno,3,3))
. gen byte color = real(substr(partno,6,1))
```

We use the `substr()` function to extract pieces of the string and use the `real()` function, when appropriate, to translate the piece into a number.

For an extended discussion of numeric and string data types and how to convert from one kind to another, see Cox (2002).

23.5   Reference

Cox, N. J. 2002. Speaking Stata: On numbers and strings. *Stata Journal* 2: 314–329.

24 Working with dates and times

Contents

24.1   Overview

Full documentation on Stata's date and time capabilities—including documentation on relevant functions and display formats—can be found in [D] **dates and times**.

Stata can work with dates such as 21nov2006, with times such as 13:42:02.213, and with dates and times such as 21nov2006 13:42:02.213. You can write these dates and times however you wish, such as 11/21/2006, November 21, 2006, and 1:42 p.m.

Stata stores dates, times, and dates and times as integers such as −4,102, 0, 82, 4,227, and 1,479,735,745,213. It works like this:

1. You begin with the date/time variables in your data however they are recorded, such as 21nov2006 or 11/21/2006 or November 21, 2006, or 13:42:02.213 or 1:42 p.m. The original values are usually best stored in string variables.

2. Using functions we will describe below, you translate the original into the integers that Stata understands and store those values in a new variable.

3. You specify the appropriate display format for the new variable so that, rather than displaying as the integer values that they are, they display in a way you can read them such as 21nov2006 or 11/21/2006 or November 21, 2006, or 13:42:02.213 or 1:42 p.m.

The numeric encoding that Stata uses is centered around the first millisecond of 01jan1960, i.e., 01jan1960 00:00:00.000. That date/time is assigned integer value 0.

Integer value 1 is the millisecond after that: 01jan1960 00:00:00.001.

Integer value −1 is the millisecond before that: 31dec1959 23:59:59.999.

By that logic, 21nov2006 13:42:02.213 is integer value 1,479,735,722,213 or, at least, it is if we ignore the leap seconds that have been inserted to keep clocks in alignment with astronomical observation. If we account for leap seconds, 21nov2006 13:42:02.213 would be 23 seconds later, namely, 1,479,735,745,213. Stata can work either way.

Obtaining the number of milliseconds associated with a date/time is easy because Stata provides functions that translate things like 21nov2006 13:42:02.213 (written however you wish) to 1,479,735,722,213 or 1,479,735,745,213.

Just remember, Stata records data/time values as the number of milliseconds since the first millisecond of 01jan1960.

331

Stata records pure time values (clock times independent of date) the same way. Rather than thinking of the numeric value as the number of milliseconds since 01jan1960, however, think of it as the number of milliseconds since the beginning of the day. For instance, at 2 p.m. every day, the airplane takes off from Houston for London. The numeric value associated with 2 p.m. is 50,400,000 because there are that many milliseconds between the beginning of the day (00:00:00.000) and 2 p.m.

The advantage of thinking this way is that you can add dates and times. What is the date/time value for when the plane takes off on 21nov2006? Well, 21nov2006 00:00:00.000 is 1,479,686,400,000 (ignoring leap seconds), and 1,479,686,400,000 + 50,400,000 is 1,479,736,800,000.

Subtracting date/time values is useful, too. How many hours are there between 21jan1952 7:23 a.m. and 21nov2006 3:14 p.m.? Answer: $(1,479,741,240,000 - (-250,706,220,000))/3,600,000 =$ 480,679.85 hours.

Variables that record the number of milliseconds since 01jan1960 and ignore leap seconds are called %tc variables.

Variables that record the number of milliseconds since 01jan1960 and account for leap seconds are called %tC variables.

Stata has seven other kinds of %t variables.

In many applications, calendar dates by themselves are sufficient. The applicant was hired on 15jan2006, for instance. You could use a %tc variable to record that value, assigning some arbitrary time that you would ignore, but it is better and easier to use a %td variable. In %td variables, 0 still corresponds to 01jan1960, but a unit change now represents an entire day rather than a millisecond. The value 1 represents 02jan1960. The value −1 represents 31dec1959. When you subtract %td variables, you obtain the number of days between dates.

In a financial application, you might use %tq variables. In %tq, 0 represents the first quarter of 1960, 1 represents the second quarter, and −1 represents the last quarter of 1959. When you subtract %tq variables, you obtain the number of quarters between dates.

Stata understands nine %t formats:

format	base	units	comment
%tc	01jan1960	milliseconds	ignores leap seconds
%tC	01jan1960	milliseconds	accounts for leap seconds
%td	01jan1960	days	calendar date format
%tw	1960-w1	weeks	52nd week may have more than 7 days
%tm	jan1960	months	calendar month format
%tq	1960-q1	quarters	financial quarter
%th	1960-h1	half-years	1 half-year = 2 quarters
%ty	0 A.D	year	1960 means year 1960
%tg	?	?	whatever you wish

All formats except %ty and %tg are based on the beginning of January 1960. The value 0 means the first millisecond, day, week, month, quarter, or half-year of 1960, depending on format. The value 1 is the millisecond, day, week, month, quarter, or half-year after that. The value −1 is the millisecond, day, week, month, quarter, or half-year before that.

Stata's %ty format records years as numeric values and it codes them the natural way: rather than 0 meaning 1960, 1960 means 1960, and so 2006 also means 2006.

Stata's %tg format is for use when none of the other formats fit your date/time data. The value 0, 1, and −1 mean whatever you want them to mean.

24.2   Inputting dates and times

Dates and time variables are best read as strings. You then use one of the string-to-numeric conversion functions to convert the string to an appropriate %t value:

format	string-to-numeric conversion function
%tc	clock(*string*, *mask*)
%tC	Clock(*string*, *mask*)
%td	date(*string*, *mask*)
%tw	weekly(*string*, *mask*)
%tm	monthly(*string*, *mask*)
%tq	quarterly(*string*, *mask*)
%th	halfyearly(*string*, *mask*)
%ty	yearly(*string*, *mask*)
%tg	no function necessary; read as numeric

The full documentation of these functions can be found in *String-to-numeric translation functions* in [D] **dates and times**.

In the above table, *string* is the string variable to be translated, and *mask* specifies the order in which the components of the date and/or time appear in *string*. For instance, the *mask* in %td function date() is made up of the letters M, D, and Y.

date(*string*, "DMY") specifies *string* contains dates in the order of day, month, year. With that specification, date() can translate 21nov2006, 21 November 2006, 21-11-2006, 21112006, and other strings that contain dates in the order day, month, year.

date(*string*, "MDY") specifies *string* contains dates in the order of month, day, year. With that specification, date() can translate November 21, 2006, 11/21/2006, 11212006, and other strings that contain dates in the order month, day, year.

You can specify a two-digit prefix in front of Y to handle two-digit years. date(*string*, "MD19Y") specifies *string* contains dates in the order of month, day, and year, and that if the year contains only two digits, it is to be prefixed with 19. With that specification, date() could not only translate November 21, 2006, 11/21/2006, and 11212006, but also Feb. 15 '98, 2/15/98, and 21598. (There is another way to deal with two-digit years so that 98 becomes 1998 while 06 becomes 2006; it involves specifying an optional third argument.)

Let's consider some %td data. We have the following raw-data file:

```
 ─────────────────────────────────────────── begin bdays.raw ───────────
   Bill   21 Jan 1952   22
   May    11 Jul 1948   18
   Sam    12 Nov 1960   25
   Kay     9 Aug 1975   16
 ──────────────────────────────────────────── end bdays.raw ───────────
```

We could read these data by typing

```
. infix str name 1-5  str bday 7-17  x 20-21 using bdays
(4 observations read)
```

We read the date not as three separate variables but as one variable. Variable bday contains the entire date:

```
. list
```

	name	bday	x
1.	Bill	21 Jan 1952	22
2.	May	11 Jul 1948	18
3.	Sam	12 Nov 1960	25
4.	Kay	9 Aug 1975	16

The data look fine, but if we set about using them, we would quickly discover there is not much we could do with variable bday. Variable bday looks like a date, but it is just a string. We need to turn bday into a %t variable that Stata understands:

```
. gen birthday = date(bday, "DMY")
. list
```

	name	bday	x	birthday
1.	Bill	21 Jan 1952	22	-2902
2.	May	11 Jul 1948	18	-4191
3.	Sam	12 Nov 1960	25	316
4.	Kay	9 Aug 1975	16	5699

New variable birthday is a %td variable. The problem now is that, whereas the new variable is perfectly understandable to Stata, it is not understandable to us. Naturally enough, a %td variable needs a %td format:

```
. format birthday %td
. list
```

	name	bday	x	birthday
1.	Bill	21 Jan 1952	22	21jan1952
2.	May	11 Jul 1948	18	11jul1948
3.	Sam	12 Nov 1960	25	12nov1960
4.	Kay	9 Aug 1975	16	09aug1975

Using our new %td variable, we can create a variable recording how old each of these subjects was on 01jan2000:

```
. gen age2000 = (td(1jan2000)-birthday)/365.25
. list
```

	name	bday	x	birthday	age2000
1.	Bill	21 Jan 1952	22	21jan1952	47.94524
2.	May	11 Jul 1948	18	11jul1948	51.47433
3.	Sam	12 Nov 1960	25	12nov1960	39.13484
4.	Kay	9 Aug 1975	16	09aug1975	24.39699

td() is a function that makes it easy to type %td dates. There are also functions tc(), tC(), tw(), tm(), tq(), and th() for the other %t formats; see [D] **dates and times**.

Let's consider one more example. We have the following data:

```
. use http://www.stata-press.com/data/r11/datexmpl2
. list
```

	id	timestamp	action
1.	1001	Tue Nov 14 08:59:43 CST 2006	15
2.	1002	Wed Nov 15 07:36:49 CST 2006	15
3.	1003	Wed Nov 15 09:21:07 CST 2006	11
4.	1002	Wed Nov 15 14:57:36 CST 2006	16
5.	1005	Thu Nov 16 08:22:53 CST 2006	12
6.	1001	Thu Nov 16 08:36:44 CST 2006	16

Variable timestamp is a string which we want to convert to a %tc variable. From the table above, we know we will use function clock(). The *mask* in clock() uses the letters D, M, Y, and h, m, s, which specify the order of the day, month, year and hours, minutes, seconds. timestamp contains more than that and so cannot directly be converted using clock. First, we must create a variable that clock() understands:

```
. gen str ts = substr(timestamp, 5, 15) + " " + substr(timestamp, 25, 4)
. list ts
```

	ts
1.	Nov 14 08:59:43 2006
2.	Nov 15 07:36:49 2006
3.	Nov 15 09:21:07 2006
4.	Nov 15 14:57:36 2006
5.	Nov 16 08:22:53 2006
6.	Nov 16 08:36:44 2006

New variable ts can be translated using clock(ts, "MD hms Y"). "MD hms Y" specifies that the order of the components in ts is month, day, hours, minutes, seconds, and year. There is no meaning to the spaces; we could just as well have specified clock(ts, "MDhmsY"). You can specify spaces when they help to make what you type more readable.

Because %tc values can be so large, whenever you use the function clock(), you must store the results in a double, as we do below:

```
. gen double dt = clock(ts, "MD hms Y")
. list id dt action
```

	id	dt	action
1.	1001	1.479e+12	15
2.	1002	1.479e+12	15
3.	1003	1.479e+12	11
4.	1002	1.479e+12	16
5.	1005	1.479e+12	12
6.	1001	1.479e+12	16

Don't panic. New variable dt contains numeric values, and large ones, which is why it was so important that we stored the values as doubles. That output above just shows us what a %tc variable looks like with default formatting. If we wanted to see the numeric values better, we could change dt to have a %20.0gc format. We would then see that the first value is 1,479,113,983,000, the second 1,479,195,409,000, and so on. We will not do that. Instead, we will put a %tc format on our %tc variable:

```
. format dt %tc
. list id dt action
```

	id	dt	action
1.	1001	14nov2006 08:59:43	15
2.	1002	15nov2006 07:36:49	15
3.	1003	15nov2006 09:21:07	11
4.	1002	15nov2006 14:57:36	16
5.	1005	16nov2006 08:22:53	12
6.	1001	16nov2006 08:36:44	16

Variable dt is a variable we can use. Say we wanted to know how many hours it had been since the previous action:

```
. sort dt
. gen hours = hours(dt - dt[_n-1])
(1 missing value generated)
. format hours %9.2f
. list id dt action hours
```

	id	dt	action	hours
1.	1001	14nov2006 08:59:43	15	.
2.	1002	15nov2006 07:36:49	15	22.62
3.	1003	15nov2006 09:21:07	11	1.74
4.	1002	15nov2006 14:57:36	16	5.61
5.	1005	16nov2006 08:22:53	12	17.42
6.	1001	16nov2006 08:36:44	16	0.23

We subtracted dt from its previous value, which results in the number of milliseconds. Converting milliseconds to hours is easy enough; we just have to divide by $60 \times 60 \times 1{,}000 = 3{,}600{,}000$. It is easy to forget or mistype that constant, so we used Stata's hours() function, which converts milliseconds to hours. hours(), and other useful functions, are documented in [D] **dates and times**.

24.3   Displaying dates and times

A %td variable should have a %td format, a %tc variable should have a %tc format, and so on for all the other %t variable–format pairs. You do that by typing format *varname* %td, format *varname* %tc, etc.

Formats %tc, %tC, %td, %tw, %tm, %tq, %th, and %ty are called the default %t formats. By specifying codes following them, you can control how the variable is to be displayed.

In the previous example, we started with a string variable that contained a time stamp and looked like "Tue Nov 14 08:59:43 CST 2006". After creating a %tc variable from it, and putting the default %tc format on it, our date/times looked like "14nov2006 08:59:43". Below we specify a %tc format that makes our new variable look just like the original:

```
. format dt %tcDay_Mon_DD_HH:MM:SS_!C!D!T_CCYY
. list id dt action hours
```

	id	dt	action	hours
1.	1001	Tue Nov 14 08:59:43 CDT 2006	15	.
2.	1002	Wed Nov 15 07:36:49 CDT 2006	15	22.62
3.	1003	Wed Nov 15 09:21:07 CDT 2006	11	1.74
4.	1002	Wed Nov 15 14:57:36 CDT 2006	16	5.61
5.	1005	Thu Nov 16 08:22:53 CDT 2006	12	17.42
6.	1001	Thu Nov 16 08:36:44 CDT 2006	16	0.23

%t display formats are documented under *Formatting date and time values* in [D] **dates and times**.

24.4   Typing dates and times (date/time literals)

You will sometimes need to type dates and times in expressions. When we needed to calculate the age of subjects as of 01jan2000 in a previous example, for instance, we typed,

```
. gen age2000 = (td(1jan2000)-birthday)/365.25
```

although we could just as well have typed,

```
. gen age2000 = (14610-birthday)/365.25
```

because 14,610 is the %td value of 01jan2000. Typing td(1jan2000) is easier and less error prone.

Similarly, if we needed 10:55 a.m. on 01jan1960 as a %tc value, rather than typing 39,300,000, we could type tc(01jan1960 10:55). See *Typing dates and times* in [D] **dates and times** for details.

24.5   Extracting components of dates and times

Once you have a %t variable, you can use the extraction functions to obtain components of the variable. For instance, the following functions are appropriate for use with %td variables:

year(*date*)	returns four-digit year; e.g., 1980, 2002
month(*date*)	returns month; 1, 2, . . . , 12
day(*date*)	returns day within month; 1, 2, . . . , 31
halfyear(*date*)	returns the half of year; 1 or 2
quarter(*date*)	returns quarter of year; 1, 2, 3, or 4
week(*date*)	returns week of year; 1, 2, . . . , 52
dow(*date*)	returns day of week; 0, 1, . . . , 6; 0 = Sunday
doy(*date*)	returns day of year; 1, 2, . . . , 366

There are other functions useful with other %t variables. See *Extracting date and time components* in [D] **dates and times**.

24.6   Converting between date and time values

You can convert between %t values. For instance, function cofd() converts a %td value to a %tc value. cofd() of 17,126 (21nov2006) returns 1,479,686,400,000 (21nov2006 00:00:00). Function dofc() of 1,479,736,920,000 (21nov2006 14:02) returns 17,126 (21nov2006).

There are other functions for converting between other %t values; see *Converting date and time values* in [D] **dates and times**.

24.7   Reference

Cox, N. J. 2006. Speaking Stata: Time of day. *Stata Journal* 6: 124–137.

25 Working with categorical data and factor variables

Contents

25.1 Continuous, categorical, and indicator variables

Although to Stata a variable is a variable, it is helpful to distinguish among three conceptual types:

- A *continuous variable* measures something. Such a variable might measure a person's age, height, or weight; a city's population or land area; or a company's revenues or costs.

- A *categorical variable* identifies a group to which the thing belongs. You could categorize persons according to their race or ethnicity, cities according to their geographic location, or companies according to their industry. Sometimes, categorical variables are stored as strings.

- An *indicator variable* denotes whether something is true. For example, is a person a veteran, does a city have a mass transit system, or is a company profitable?

Indicator variables are a special case of categorical variables. Consider a variable that records a person's sex. Examined one way, it is a categorical variable. A categorical variable identifies the group to which a thing belongs, and here the thing is a person and the basis for categorization is anatomy. Looked at another way, however, it is an indicator variable. It indicates whether the person is female.

We can use the same logic on any categorical variable that divides the data into two groups. It is a categorical variable because it identifies whether an observation is a member of this or that group; it is an indicator variable because it denotes the truth value of the statement "the observation is in this group".

All indicator variables are categorical variables, but the opposite is not true. A categorical variable might divide the data into more than two groups. For clarity, let's reserve the term *categorical variable* for variables that divide the data into more than two groups, and let's use the term *indicator variable* for categorical variables that divide the data into exactly two groups.

Stata can convert continuous variables to categorical and indicator variables and categorical variables to indicator variables.

25.1.1   Converting continuous variables to indicator variables

Stata treats logical expressions as taking on the values *true* or *false*, which it identifies with the numbers 1 and 0; see [U] **13 Functions and expressions**. For instance, if you have a continuous variable measuring a person's age and you wish to create an indicator variable denoting persons aged 21 and over, you could type

```
. generate age21p = age>=21
```

The variable age21p takes on the value 1 for persons aged 21 and over and 0 for persons under 21.

Because age21p can take on only 0 or 1, it would be more economical to store the variable as a byte. Thus it would be better to type

```
. generate byte age21p = age>=21
```

This solution has a problem. The value of age21 is set to 1 for all persons whose age is missing because Stata defines missing to be larger than all other numbers. In our data, we might have no such missing ages, but it still would be safer to type

```
. generate byte age21p = age>=21 if age<.
```

That way, persons whose age is missing would also have a missing age21p.

❏ Technical note

Put aside missing values and consider the following alternative to generate age21p = age>=21 that may have occurred to you:

```
. generate age21p = 1 if age>=21
```

That does not produce the desired result. This statement makes age21p 1 (*true*) for all persons aged 21 and above but makes age21p missing for everyone else.

If you followed this second approach, you would have to combine it with

```
. replace age21p = 0 if age<21
```

❏

25.1.2   Converting continuous variables to categorical variables

Suppose that you wish to categorize persons into four groups on the basis of their age. You want a variable to denote whether a person is 21 or under, between 22 and 38, between 39 and 64, or 65 and above. Although most people would label these categories 1, 2, 3, and 4, there is really no reason to restrict ourselves to such a meaningless numbering scheme. Let's call this new variable agecat and make it so that it takes on the topmost value for each group. Thus persons in the first group will be identified with an agecat of 21, persons in the second with 38, persons in the third with 64, and persons in the last (drawing a number out of the air) with 75. Here is a way to create the variable that will work, but it is not the best method for doing so:

```
. use http://www.stata-press.com/data/r11/agexmpl

. generate byte agecat=21 if age<=21
(176 missing values generated)

. replace agecat=38 if age>21 & age<=38
(148 real changes made)

. replace agecat=64 if age>38 & age<=64
(24 real changes made)

. replace agecat=75 if age>64 & age<.
(4 real changes made)
```

We created the categorical variable according to the definition by using the generate and replace commands. The only thing that deserves comment is the opening generate. We (wisely) told Stata to generate the new variable agecat as a byte, thus conserving memory.

We can create the same result with one command using the recode() function:

```
. use http://www.stata-press.com/data/r11/agexmpl, clear

. generate byte agecat=recode(age,21,38,64,75)
```

recode() takes three or more arguments. It examines the first argument (here age) against the remaining arguments in the list. It returns the first element in the list that is greater than or equal to the first argument or, failing that, the last argument in the list. Thus, for each observation, recode() asked if age was less than or equal to 21. If so, the value is 21. If not, is it less than or equal to 38? If so, the value is 38. If not, is it less than or equal to 64? If so, the value is 64. If not, the value is 75.

Most researchers typically make tables of categorical variables, so we will tabulate the result:

```
. tabulate agecat
```

agecat	Freq.	Percent	Cum.
21	28	13.73	13.73
38	148	72.55	86.27
64	24	11.76	98.04
75	4	1.96	100.00
Total	204	100.00	

There is another way to convert continuous variables into categorical variables, and it is even more automated: autocode() works like recode(), except that all you tell the function is the range and the total number of cells that you want that range broken into:

```
. use http://www.stata-press.com/data/r11/agexmpl, clear

. generate agecat=autocode(age,4,18,65)

. tabulate agecat
```

agecat	Freq.	Percent	Cum.
29.75	82	40.20	40.20
41.5	96	47.06	87.25
53.25	16	7.84	95.10
65	10	4.90	100.00
Total	204	100.00	

In one instruction, we told Stata to break age into four evenly spaced categories from 18 to 65. When we tabulate agecat, we see the result. In particular, we see that the breakpoints of the four categories are 29.75, 41.5, 53.25, and 65. The first category contains everyone aged 29.75 years or less; the second category contains persons over 29.75 who are 41.5 years old or less; the third category contains persons over 41.5 who are 53.25 years old or less; and the last category contains all persons over 53.25.

❑ Technical note

We chose the range 18–65 arbitrarily. Although you cannot tell from the table above, there are persons in this dataset who are under 18, and there are persons over 65. Those persons are counted in the first and last cells, but we have not divided the age range in the data evenly. We could split the full age range into four categories by obtaining the overall minimum and maximum ages (by typing summarize) and substituting the overall minimum and maximum for the 18 and 65 in the autocode() function:

```
. use http://www.stata-press.com/data/r11/agexmpl, clear
. summarize age
```

Variable	Obs	Mean	Std. Dev.	Min	Max
age	204	31.57353	10.28986	2	66

```
. generate agecat2=autocode(age,4,2,66)
```

We could also sort the data into ascending order of age and tell Stata to construct four categories over the range age[1] (the minimum) to age[_N] (the maximum):

```
. use http://www.stata-press.com/data/r11/agexmpl, clear
. sort age
. generate agecat2=autocode(age,4,age[1],age[_N])
. tabulate agecat2
```

agecat2	Freq.	Percent	Cum.
18	10	4.90	4.90
34	138	67.65	72.55
50	41	20.10	92.65
66	15	7.35	100.00
Total	204	100.00	

❑

25.2 Estimation with factor variables

Stata handles categorical variables as factor variables; see [U] 11.4.3 Factor variables. Categorical variables refer to the variables in your data that take on categorical values, variables such as sex, group, and region. Factor variables refer to Stata's treatment of categorical variables. Factor variables create indicator variables for the levels (categories) of categorical variables and, optionally, for their interactions.

In what follows, the word level means the value that a categorical variable takes on. The variable sex might take on levels 0 and 1, with 0 representing male and 1 representing female. We could say that sex is a two-level factor variable.

The regressors created by factor variables are called indicators or, more explicitly, virtual indicator variables. They are called virtual because the machinery for factor variables seldom creates new variables in your dataset, even though the indicators will appear just as if they were variables in your estimation results.

To be used as a factor variable, a categorical variable must take on nonnegative integer values. If you have variables with negative values, recode them; see [D] **recode**. If you have string variables, you can use egen's group() function to recode them,

. egen *newcatvar*= group(*mystringcatvar*)

If you also specify the label option, egen will create a value label for the numeric code it produces so that your output will be subsequently more readable:

. egen *newcatvar*= group(*mystringcatvar*), label

Alternatively, you can use encode to convert string categorical variables to numeric ones:

. encode *mystringcatvar*, generate(*newcatvar*)

egen group(), label and encode do the same thing. We tend to use egen group(), label. See [D] **egen** and [D] **encode**.

In the unlikely event that you have a noninteger categorical variable, use the egen solution. More likely, however, is that you need to read [U] **25.1.2 Converting continuous variables to categorical variables**.

❏ Technical note

If you should ever need to create your own indicator variables from a string or numeric variable—and it is difficult to imagine why you would—type

. tabulate *var*, gen(*newstub*)

Typing that will create indicator variables named *newstub*1, *newstub*2, . . . ; see [R] **tabulate oneway**.
❏

We will be using linear regression in the examples that follow just because it is so easy to explain and to interpret. We could, however, just as well have used logistic regression, Heckman selectivity, or even Cox proportional-hazards regression with shared frailties. Stata's factor-variable features work with nearly every estimation command.

25.2.1   Including factor variables

The fundamental building block of factor variables is the treatment of each factor variable as if it represented a collection of indicators, with one indicator for each level of the variable. To treat a variable as a factor variable, you add i. in front of the variable's name:

(Continued on next page)

```
. use http://www.stata-press.com/data/r11/fvex
(Artificial factor variables' data)

. regress y  i.group age
```

Source	SS	df	MS		
Model	42767.8126	3	14255.9375		
Residual	1348665.19	2996	450.155272		
Total	1391433.01	2999	463.965657		

				Number of obs =	3000
				F(3, 2996) =	31.67
				Prob > F =	0.0000
				R-squared =	0.0307
				Adj R-squared =	0.0298
				Root MSE =	21.217

y	Coef.	Std. Err.	t	P>|t|	[95% Conf. Interval]
group					
2	-2.395169	.9497756	-2.52	0.012	-4.257447 -.5328905
3	.2966833	1.200423	0.25	0.805	-2.057054 2.65042
age	-.318005	.039939	-7.96	0.000	-.3963157 -.2396943
_cons	83.2149	1.963939	42.37	0.000	79.3641 87.06571

In these data, variable group takes on the values 1, 2, and 3.

Because we typed

```
. regress y  i.group age
```

rather than

```
. regress y    group age
```

instead of fitting the regression as a continuous function of group's values, regress fit the regression on indicators for each level of group included as a separate covariate. In the left column of the coefficient table in the output, the numbers 2 and 3 identify the coefficients that correspond to the values of 2 and 3 of the group variable. Using the more precise terminology of [U] **11.4.3 Factor variables**, the coefficients reported for 2 and 3 are the coefficients for virtual variables 2.group and 3.group, the indicator variables for group = 2 and group = 3.

If group took on the values 2, 10, 11, and 125 rather than 1, 2, and 3, then we would see 2, 10, 11, and 125 below group in the table, corresponding to virtual variables 2.group, 10.group, 11.group, and 125.group.

We can use as many sets of indicators as we need in a varlist. Thus we can type

```
. regress y  i.group i.sex i.arm ...
```

25.2.2 Specifying base levels

In the above results, group = 1 was used as the base level and regress omitted reporting that fact in the output. Somehow, you are just supposed to know that, and usually you do. We can see base levels identified explicitly, however, if we specify the baselevels option, either at the time we estimate the model or, as we do now, when we replay results:

```
. regress, baselevels
```

Source	SS	df	MS
Model	42767.8126	3	14255.9375
Residual	1348665.19	2996	450.155272
Total	1391433.01	2999	463.965657

```
                                    Number of obs =     3000
                                    F(  3,  2996) =    31.67
                                    Prob > F      =   0.0000
                                    R-squared     =   0.0307
                                    Adj R-squared =   0.0298
                                    Root MSE      =   21.217
```

y	Coef.	Std. Err.	t	P>|t|	[95% Conf. Interval]
group					
1	(base)				
2	-2.395169	.9497756	-2.52	0.012	-4.257447 -.5328905
3	.2966833	1.200423	0.25	0.805	-2.057054 2.65042
age	-.318005	.039939	-7.96	0.000	-.3963157 -.2396943
_cons	83.2149	1.963939	42.37	0.000	79.3641 87.06571

The smallest value of the factor variable is used as the base by default. Using the notation explained in [U] **11.4.3.2 Base levels**, we can request another base level, such as group = 2, by typing

```
. regress y  ib2.group age
```

or, such as the largest value of group,

```
. regress y  ib(last).group age
```

Changing the base does not fundamentally alter the estimates in the sense that predictions from the model would be identical no matter which base levels we use. Changing the base does change the interpretation of coefficients. In the regression output above, the reported coefficients measure the differences from group = 1. Group 2 differs from group 1 by −2.4, and that difference is significant at the 5% level. Group 3 is not significantly different from group 1.

If we fit the above using group = 3 as the base,

```
. regress y  ib3.group age
  (output omitted )
```

the coefficients on group = 1 and group = 2 would be −0.297 and −2.692. Note that the difference between group 2 and group 1 would still be −2.692 − (−0.296) = −2.4. Results may look different, but when looked at correctly, they are the same. Similarly, the significance of group = 2 would now be 0.805 rather than 0.012, but that is because what is being tested is different. In the output above, the test against 0 is a test of whether group 2 differs from group 1. In the output that we omit, the test is whether group 2 differs from group 3. If, after running the ib3.group specification, we were to type

```
. test 2.group = 1.group
```

we would obtain the same 0.012 result. Similarly, after running the shown result, if we typed test 3.group = 1.group, we would obtain 0.805.

25.2.3   Setting base levels permanently

As explained directly above, you can temporarily change the base level by using the ib. operator; also see [U] **11.4.3.2 Base levels**. You can change the base level permanently by using the fvset command; see [U] **11.4.3.3 Setting base levels permanently**.

25.2.4   Testing significance of a main effect

In the example we have been using,

```
. use http://www.stata-press.com/data/r11/fvex
. regress y  i.group age
```

many disciplines refer to the coefficients on the set of indicators for `i.group` as a main effect. Because we have no interactions, the main effect of `i.group` refers to the effect of the levels of group taken as a whole. We can test the significance of the indicators by using `testparm` (see [R] **test**):

```
. testparm i.group
 ( 1)   2.group = 0
 ( 2)   3.group = 0
       F(  2,  2996) =    4.89
           Prob > F =    0.0076
```

Just as we type `i.group` with `regress` to include the entire set of indicators, we type `i.group` with `testparm` to test whether the coefficients for the group are jointly zero. We reject the hypothesis.

25.2.5   Specifying indicator (dummy) variables as factor variables

We are using the model

```
. use http://www.stata-press.com/data/r11/fvex
. regress y  i.group age
```

We are going to add `sex` to our model. Variable `sex` is a 0/1 variable in our data, a type of variable we call an indicator variable and which many people call a dummy variable. We could type

```
. regress y    sex i.group age
```

but we are going to type

```
. regress y  i.sex i.group age
```

It is better to include indicator variables as factor variables, which is to say, to include indicator variables with the `i.` prefix.

You will obtain the same estimation results either way, but by specifying `i.sex` rather than `sex`, you will communicate to postestimation commands that care that `sex` is not a continuous variable, and that will save you typing later should you use one of those postestimation commands. `margins` (see [R] **margins**) is an example of a postestimation command that cares.

Below we type `regress y i.sex i.group age`, and we will specify the `baselevels` option just to make explicit how `regress` is interpreting our request. Ordinarily, we would not specify the `baselevels` option.

```
. regress y  i.sex i.group age, baselevels
```

Source	SS	df	MS
Model	214569.509	4	53642.3772
Residual	1176863.5	2995	392.942737
Total	1391433.01	2999	463.965657

Number of obs =	3000
F(4, 2995) =	136.51
Prob > F =	0.0000
R-squared =	0.1542
Adj R-squared =	0.1531
Root MSE =	19.823

y	Coef.	Std. Err.	t	P>|t|	[95% Conf. Interval]
sex					
0	(base)				
1	18.44069	.8819175	20.91	0.000	16.71146 20.16991
group					
1	(base)				
2	5.178636	.9584485	5.40	0.000	3.299352 7.057919
3	13.45907	1.286127	10.46	0.000	10.93729 15.98085
age	-.3298831	.0373191	-8.84	0.000	-.4030567 -.2567094
_cons	68.63586	1.962901	34.97	0.000	64.78709 72.48463

As with all factor variables, by default the first level of sex serves as its base, so the coefficient 18.4 measures the increase in y for sex = 1 as compared with sex = 0. In these data, sex = 1 represents females and sex = 0 represents males.

25.2.6 Including interactions

We are using the model

```
. use http://www.stata-press.com/data/r11/fvex
. regress y  i.sex i.group age
```

If we are not certain that the levels of group have the same effect for females as they do for males, we should add to our model interactions for each combination of the levels in sex and group. We would need to add indicators for

$$\text{sex} = 0 \quad \text{and} \quad \text{group} = 1$$
$$\text{sex} = 0 \quad \text{and} \quad \text{group} = 2$$
$$\text{sex} = 0 \quad \text{and} \quad \text{group} = 3$$
$$\text{sex} = 1 \quad \text{and} \quad \text{group} = 1$$
$$\text{sex} = 1 \quad \text{and} \quad \text{group} = 2$$
$$\text{sex} = 1 \quad \text{and} \quad \text{group} = 3$$

Doing this would allow each combination of sex and group to have a different effect on y.

Interactions like those listed above are produced using the # operator. We could type

```
. regress y  i.sex i.group i.sex#i.group age
```

The # operator assumes that the variables on either side of it are factor variables, so we can omit the i. prefixes and obtain the same result by typing

```
. regress y  i.sex i.group sex#group age
```

We must continue to specify the prefix on the main effects i.sex and i.group, however.

In the output below, we add the allbaselevels option to that. The allbaselevels option is much like baselevels, except allbaselevels lists base levels in interactions as well as in main effects. Specifying allbaselevels will make the output easier to understand the first time, and after that, you will probably never specify it again.

```
. regress y  i.sex i.group sex#group age, allbaselevels
```

Source	SS	df	MS		Number of obs =	3000
					F(6, 2993) =	92.52
Model	217691.706	6	36281.9511		Prob > F =	0.0000
Residual	1173741.3	2993	392.162145		R-squared =	0.1565
					Adj R-squared =	0.1548
Total	1391433.01	2999	463.965657		Root MSE =	19.803

y	Coef.	Std. Err.	t	P>|t|	[95% Conf. Interval]	
sex						
0	(base)					
1	21.71794	1.490858	14.57	0.000	18.79473	24.64115
group						
1	(base)					
2	8.420661	1.588696	5.30	0.000	5.305615	11.53571
3	16.47226	1.6724	9.85	0.000	13.19309	19.75143
sex#group						
0 1	(base)					
0 2	(base)					
0 3	(base)					
1 1	(base)					
1 2	-4.658322	1.918195	-2.43	0.015	-8.419436	-.8972081
1 3	-6.736936	2.967391	-2.27	0.023	-12.55527	-.9186038
age	-.3305546	.0373032	-8.86	0.000	-.4036972	-.2574121
_cons	65.97765	2.198032	30.02	0.000	61.66784	70.28745

Look at the sex#group term in the output. There are six combinations of sex and group, just as we expected. That four of the cells are labeled base and that only two extra coefficients were estimated should not surprise us, at least after we think about. There are 3×2 sex#age groups, and thus $3 \times 2 = 6$ means to be estimated, and we indeed estimated six coefficients, including a constant, plus a seventh for continuous variable age. Now look at which combinations were treated as base. Treated as base were all combinations that were the base of sex, plus all combinations that were the base of group. The sex = 0-and-group = 1 combination was omitted for both reasons, and the other combinations were omitted for one or the other reason.

We entered a two-way interaction between sex and group. If we believed that the effects of sex#group were themselves dependent on the treatment arm of an experiment, we would want the three-way interaction, which we could obtain by typing sex#group#arm. Stata allows up to eight-way interactions among factor variables and another eight-ways of interaction among continuous covariates.

❏ Technical note

The virtual variables associated with the interaction terms have the names 1.sex#2.group and 1.sex#3.group.

❏

25.2.7   Testing significance of interactions

We are using the model

```
. use http://www.stata-press.com/data/r11/fvex
. regress y  i.sex i.group sex#group age
```

We can test the overall significance of the sex#group interaction by typing

```
. testparm sex#group
 ( 1)   1.sex#2.group = 0
 ( 2)   1.sex#3.group = 0
       F(  2,  2993) =    3.98
           Prob > F =    0.0188
```

Just as with testing the main effects, we type the term to be tested—sex#group—in the same way as we typed it to include it in the regression. The interaction is significant beyond the 5% level. That is not surprising because both interaction indicators were significant in the regression.

testparm relies on having sex#group mean the same thing as sex#group meant at the time the model was fit. If the relevant dataset were no longer in memory, we could not use testparm. We would need to use the test command and specify the individual coefficients for ourselves:

```
. test 1.sex#2.group 1.sex#3.group
  (output omitted )
```

Results would be the same. How did we know what to type after test? If you have been following the technical notes, you knew already what to type—you type the name of the corresponding virtual variables. Typing regress, coeflegend will remind you of the names of the virtual variables.

The testparm command did not save us much typing in this example. Using the same dataset, try fitting the regression

```
. regress y  i.sex i.age sex#age
  (output omitted )
```

In the above, we are treating age as if it were a categorical variable. The result is that there will be forty coefficients in the interaction! Now type

```
. testparm sex#age
```

You could perform the same command using test, but we would need to type out the forty coefficients:

```
. test 1.sex#21.age 1.sex#22.age ... 1.sex#60.age
```

25.2.8   Including factorial specifications

We have the model

```
. use http://www.stata-press.com/data/r11/fvex
. regress y  i.sex i.group sex#group age
```

The above model is called a factorial specification with respect to sex and group because sex and group appear by themselves and an interaction. Were it not for age being included in the model, we could call this model a full-factorial specification. In any case, Stata provides a shorthand for factorial specifications. We could fit the model above by typing

```
. regress y  sex##group age
```

When you type *A##B*, Stata takes that to mean *A B A#B*.

When you type *A##B##C*, Stata takes that to mean *A B C A#B A#C B#C A#B#C*.

And so on. Up to eight-way interactions are allowed.

The ## notation is just a shorthand. Estimation results are unchanged. This time we will not specify the allbaselevels option:

```
. regress y  sex##group age
```

Source	SS	df	MS		
Model	217691.706	6	36281.9511		
Residual	1173741.3	2993	392.162145		
Total	1391433.01	2999	463.965657		

	Number of obs	=	3000
	F(6, 2993)	=	92.52
	Prob > F	=	0.0000
	R-squared	=	0.1565
	Adj R-squared	=	0.1548
	Root MSE	=	19.803

y	Coef.	Std. Err.	t	P>|t|	[95% Conf. Interval]	
1.sex	21.71794	1.490858	14.57	0.000	18.79473	24.64115
group						
2	8.420661	1.588696	5.30	0.000	5.305615	11.53571
3	16.47226	1.6724	9.85	0.000	13.19309	19.75143
sex#group						
1 2	-4.658322	1.918195	-2.43	0.015	-8.419436	-.8972081
1 3	-6.736936	2.967391	-2.27	0.023	-12.55527	-.9186038
age	-.3305546	.0373032	-8.86	0.000	-.4036972	-.2574121
_cons	65.97765	2.198032	30.02	0.000	61.66784	70.28745

25.2.9   Including squared terms and polynomials

may be used to interact continuous variables if you specify the c. indicator in front of them. The command

```
. regress y  age c.age#c.age
```

fits y as a quadratic function of age. Similarly,

```
. regress y  age c.age#c.age c.age#c.age#c.age
```

fits a third-order polynomial.

Using the # operator is preferable to generating squared and cubed variables of age because when # is used, Stata understands the relationship between age and c.age#c.age and c.age#c.age#c.age. Postestimation commands can take advantage of this to produce smarter answers; see, for example, *Requirements for model specification* in [R] **margins**.

25.2.10   Including interactions with continuous variables

and ## may be used to create interactions of categorical variables with continuous variables if the continuous variables are prefixed with c., such as sex#c.age in

```
. regress y  i.sex age sex#c.age
. regress y  sex##c.age
. regress y  i.sex sex#c.age
```

The result of fitting the first of these models (equivalent to the second) is shown below. We include `allbaselevels` to make results more understandable the first time you see them.

```
. regress y  i.sex age sex#c.age, allbaselevels

      Source |       SS       df       MS              Number of obs =    3000
-------------+------------------------------           F(  3,  2996) =  139.91
       Model | 170983.675      3  56994.5583           Prob > F      =  0.0000
    Residual | 1220449.33   2996   407.35959           R-squared     =  0.1229
-------------+------------------------------           Adj R-squared =  0.1220
       Total | 1391433.01   2999  463.965657           Root MSE      =  20.183

-------------+----------------------------------------------------------------
           y |      Coef.   Std. Err.      t    P>|t|     [95% Conf. Interval]
-------------+----------------------------------------------------------------
         sex |
          0  |   (base)
          1  |   14.92308   2.789012     5.35   0.000     9.454508    20.39165
             |
         age |  -.4929608   .0480944   -10.25   0.000    -.5872622   -.3986595
             |
    sex#c.age |
          0  |   (base)
          1  |  -.0224116   .0674167    -0.33   0.740    -.1545994    .1097762
             |
       _cons |   82.36936   1.812958    45.43   0.000      78.8146    85.92413
-------------+----------------------------------------------------------------
```

The coefficient on the interaction (-0.022) is the difference in the slope of age for females (sex = 1) as compared with the slope for males. It is far from significant at any reasonable level, so we cannot distinguish the two slopes.

A different but equivalent parameterization of this model would be to omit the main effect of age, the result of which would be that we would estimate the separate slope coefficients of age for males and females:

```
. regress y  i.sex sex#c.age

      Source |       SS       df       MS              Number of obs =    3000
-------------+------------------------------           F(  3,  2996) =  139.91
       Model | 170983.675      3  56994.5583           Prob > F      =  0.0000
    Residual | 1220449.33   2996   407.35959           R-squared     =  0.1229
-------------+------------------------------           Adj R-squared =  0.1220
       Total | 1391433.01   2999  463.965657           Root MSE      =  20.183

-------------+----------------------------------------------------------------
           y |      Coef.   Std. Err.      t    P>|t|     [95% Conf. Interval]
-------------+----------------------------------------------------------------
       1.sex |   14.92308   2.789012     5.35   0.000     9.454508    20.39165
             |
    sex#c.age |
          0  |  -.4929608   .0480944   -10.25   0.000    -.5872622   -.3986595
          1  |  -.5153724   .0472435   -10.91   0.000    -.6080054   -.4227395
             |
       _cons |   82.36936   1.812958    45.43   0.000      78.8146    85.92413
-------------+----------------------------------------------------------------
```

It is now easier to see the slopes themselves, although the test of the equality of the slopes no longer appears in the output. We can obtain the comparison of slopes by using the `lincom` postestimation command:

```
. lincom 1.sex#c.age - 0.sex#c.age
( 1)  - 0b.sex#c.age + 1.sex#c.age = 0
```

y	Coef.	Std. Err.	t	P>|t|	[95% Conf. Interval]
(1)	-.0224116	.0674167	-0.33	0.740	-.1545994 .1097762

As noted earlier, it can be difficult at first to know how to refer to individual parameters when you need to type them on postestimation commands. The solution is to replay your estimation results specifying the `coeflegend` option:

```
. regress, coeflegend
```

Source	SS	df	MS		
Model	170983.675	3	56994.5583		
Residual	1220449.33	2996	407.35959		
Total	1391433.01	2999	463.965657		

Number of obs =   3000
F(3, 2996) = 139.91
Prob > F   = 0.0000
R-squared   = 0.1229
Adj R-squared = 0.1220
Root MSE   = 20.183

y	Coef.	Legend
1.sex	14.92308	_b[1.sex]
sex#c.age		
0	-.4929608	_b[0b.sex#c.age]
1	-.5153724	_b[1.sex#c.age]
_cons	82.36936	_b[_cons]

The legend suggests that we type

```
. lincom _b[1.sex#c.age] - _b[0b.sex#c.age]
```

instead of `lincom 1.sex#c.age - 0.sex#c.age`. That is, the legend suggests that we bracket terms in `_b[]` and explicitly recognize base levels. The latter does not matter. Concerning bracketing, some commands allow you to omit brackets, and others do not. All commands will allow bracketing, which is why the legend suggests it.

25.2.11   Parentheses binding

Factor-variable operators can be applied to groups of variables if those variables are bound in parentheses. For instance, you can type

```
. regress y  sex##(group c.age c.age#c.age)
```

rather than

```
. regress y  i.sex i.group sex#group age sex#c.age c.age#c.age sex#c.age#c.age
```

Parentheses may be nested. The parenthetically bound notation does not let you specify anything you could not specify without it, but it can save typing and, as importantly, make what you type more understandable. Consider

```
. regress y  i.sex i.group sex#group age sex#c.age c.age#c.age sex#c.age#c.age
. regress y  sex##(group c.age c.age#c.age)
```

The second specification is shorter and easier to read. We can see that all the covariates have different parameters for males and females.

25.2.12   Including indicators for single levels

Consider the following regression of statewide marriage rates (marriages per 100,000) on the median age in the state of the United States:

```
. use http://www.stata-press.com/data/r11/censusfv
(1980 Census data by state)
. regress marriagert medage
```

Source	SS	df	MS
Model	148.944706	1	148.944706
Residual	173402855	48	3612559.48
Total	173403004	49	3538836.82

```
Number of obs =      50
F(  1,    48) =    0.00
Prob > F      = 0.9949
R-squared     = 0.0000
Adj R-squared = -0.0208
Root MSE      = 1900.7
```

marriagert	Coef.	Std. Err.	t	P>|t|	[95% Conf. Interval]
medage	1.029541	160.3387	0.01	0.995	-321.3531 323.4122
_cons	1301.307	4744.027	0.27	0.785	-8237.199 10839.81

There appears to be no effect of median age. We know, however, that couples from around the country flock to Nevada to be married in Las Vegas, which skews our results. Nevada corresponds to state = 30 in these data. We can add a single indicator for state = 30 by typing

```
. regress marriagert medage i30.state
```

Source	SS	df	MS
Model	171657575	2	85828787.6
Residual	1745428.85	47	37136.784
Total	173403004	49	3538836.82

```
Number of obs =      50
F(  2,    47) = 2311.15
Prob > F      = 0.0000
R-squared     = 0.9899
Adj R-squared = 0.9895
Root MSE      = 192.71
```

marriagert	Coef.	Std. Err.	t	P>|t|	[95% Conf. Interval]
medage	-61.23095	16.2825	-3.76	0.000	-93.98711 -28.47479
30.state	13255.81	194.9742	67.99	0.000	12863.57 13648.05
_cons	2875.366	481.5533	5.97	0.000	1906.606 3844.126

These results are more reasonable. By the way, we learned that Nevada corresponds to state = 30 by 1) describing our data, from which we learned that variable state had a value label named st, and 2) using label list st to see the list of value labels.

There is a subtlety to specifying individual levels. Let's add another indicator, this time for California. The following will not produce the desired results, and we specify the baselevels option to help you understand the issue. First, however, here is the result:

(Continued on next page)

```
. regress marriagert  medage i6.state i30.state, baselevels
```

Source	SS	df	MS		
Model	171657575	2	85828787.6		
Residual	1745428.85	47	37136.784		
Total	173403004	49	3538836.82		

Number of obs = 50
F(2, 47) = 2311.15
Prob > F = 0.0000
R-squared = 0.9899
Adj R-squared = 0.9895
Root MSE = 192.71

marriagert	Coef.	Std. Err.	t	P>|t|	[95% Conf. Interval]	
medage	-61.23095	16.2825	-3.76	0.000	-93.98711	-28.47479
state						
6	(base)					
30	13255.81	194.9742	67.99	0.000	12863.57	13648.05
_cons	2875.366	481.5533	5.97	0.000	1906.606	3844.126

Look at the result for state. Rather than obtaining a coefficient for 6.state as we expected, Stata instead chose to omit it as the base category.

Stata considers all the individual specifiers for a factor variable together as being related. In our command, we specified that we wanted i6.state and i30.state by typing

```
. regress marriagert  medage i6.state i30.state
```

and Stata put that together as "include state, levels 6 and 30". Then Stata applied its standard logic for dealing with factor variables: treat the smallest level as the base category.

To achieve the desired result, we need to tell Stata that we want no base, which we do by typing the "base none" (bn) modifier:

```
. regress marriagert  medage i6bn.state i30.state
```

We need to specify bn only once, and it does not matter where we specify it. We could type

```
. regress marriagert  medage i6.state i30bn.state
```

and we would obtain the same result. We can specify bn more than once:

```
. regress marriagert  medage i6bn.state i30bn.state
```

The result of typing any one of these commands is

```
. regress marriagert  medage i6bn.state i30.state, baselevels
```

Source	SS	df	MS		
Model	171664796	3	57221598.6		
Residual	1738208.24	46	37787.1357		
Total	173403004	49	3538836.82		

Number of obs = 50
F(3, 46) = 1514.31
Prob > F = 0.0000
R-squared = 0.9900
Adj R-squared = 0.9893
Root MSE = 194.39

marriagert	Coef.	Std. Err.	t	P>|t|	[95% Conf. Interval]	
medage	-60.66128	16.47607	-3.68	0.001	-93.82589	-27.49667
state						
6	86.12456	197.0209	0.44	0.664	-310.4578	482.707
30	13257.18	196.6991	67.40	0.000	12861.25	13653.12
_cons	2856.788	487.6072	5.86	0.000	1875.286	3838.29

25.2.13   Including subgroups of levels

We just typed

```
. regress marriagert  medage i6bn.state i30.state
```

You can specify specific levels by using numlists. We could have typed

```
. regress marriagert  medage i(6 30)bn.state
```

There may be a tendency to think of i(6 30)bn.state as specifying something extra to be added to the regression. In the example above, it is just that. But consider

```
. regress y  i.arm i.agegroup arm#i(3/4)bn.agegroup
```

The goal may be to restrict the interaction term just to levels 3 and 4 of agegroup, but the effect will be to restrict agegroup to levels 3 and 4 throughout, which includes the term i.agegroup.

Try the example for yourself:

```
. use http://www.stata-press.com/data/r11/fvex
. regress y  i.arm i.agegroup arm#i(3/4)bn.agegroup
```

If you really wanted to restrict the interaction term arm#agegroup to levels 3 and 4 of agegroup, while leaving i.agegroup to include all the levels, you need to fool Stata:

```
. generate agegrp = agegroup
. regress y i.arm i.agegroup arm#i(3/4)bn.agegrp
```

In the above, we use agegroup for the main effect, but agegrp in the interaction.

25.2.14   Combining factor variables and time-series operators

You can combine factor-variable operators with the time-series operators L. and F. to lag and lead factor variables. Terms like iL.group (or Li.group), cL.age#cL.age (or Lc.age#Lc.age), and F.arm#L.group are all legal as long as the data are tsset or xtset. See [U] **11.4.3.6 Using factor variables with time-series operators**.

25.2.15   Treatment of empty cells

Consider the following data:

```
. use http://www.stata-press.com/data/r11/estimability, clear
(margins estimability)
. table sex group
```

sex	group				
	1	2	3	4	5
0	2	9	27	8	2
1	9	9	3		

In these data, there are no observations for sex = 1 and group = 4, and for sex = 1 and group = 5. Here is what happens when you use these data to fit an interacted model:

```
. regress y  sex##group
note: 1.sex#4.group identifies no observations in the sample
note: 1.sex#5.group identifies no observations in the sample
```

Source	SS	df	MS			
Model	839.550121	7	119.935732			
Residual	1500.65278	61	24.6008652			
Total	2340.2029	68	34.4147485			

Number of obs =	69
F(7, 61) =	4.88
Prob > F =	0.0002
R-squared =	0.3588
Adj R-squared =	0.2852
Root MSE =	4.9599

y	Coef.	Std. Err.	t	P>|t|	[95% Conf.	Interval]
1.sex	-5.666667	3.877352	-1.46	0.149	-13.41991	2.086579
group						
2	-13.55556	3.877352	-3.50	0.001	-21.3088	-5.80231
3	-13	3.634773	-3.58	0.001	-20.26818	-5.731822
4	-12.875	3.921166	-3.28	0.002	-20.71586	-5.034145
5	-11	4.959926	-2.22	0.030	-20.91798	-1.082015
sex#group						
1 2	12.11111	4.527772	2.67	0.010	3.057271	21.16495
1 3	10	4.913786	2.04	0.046	.1742775	19.82572
1 4	(empty)					
1 5	(empty)					
_cons	32	3.507197	9.12	0.000	24.98693	39.01307

Stata reports that the results for sex = 1 and group = 4 and for sex = 1 and group = 5 are empty; no coefficients can be estimated.

Empty cells are of no concern when fitting models and interpreting results. If, however, you subsequently perform tests or form linear or nonlinear combinations involving any of the coefficients in the interaction, you should be aware that those tests or combinations may depend on how you parameterized your model. See *Estimability of margins* in [R] **margins**.

26 Overview of Stata estimation commands

Contents

26.1 Introduction

Estimation commands fit models such as linear regression and probit. Stata has many such commands, so it is easy to overlook a few. Some of these commands differ greatly from each other, others are gentle variations on a theme, and still others are equivalent to each other.

Estimation commands share features that this chapter will not discuss; see [U] **20 Estimation and postestimation commands**. Especially see [U] **20.16 Obtaining robust variance estimates**, which discusses an alternative calculation for the estimated variance matrix (and hence standard errors) that many of Stata's estimation commands provide, and [U] **20.11 Performing hypothesis tests on the coefficients**.

Here, however, this chapter will put aside all of that—and all issues of syntax—and deal solely with matching commands to their statistical concepts. Nor will it cross-reference specific commands. To find the details on a particular command, look up its name in the index.

26.2   Linear regression with simple error structures

Consider models of the form

$$y_j = \mathbf{x}_j \boldsymbol{\beta} + \epsilon_j$$

for a continuous y variable. In this category, estimation is restricted to when σ_ϵ^2 is constant across observations j. The model is called the linear regression model, and the estimator is often called the (ordinary) least-squares estimator.

regress is Stata's linear regression command. (regress produces the robust estimate of variance as well as the conventional estimate, and regress has a collection of commands that can be run after it to explore the nature of the fit.)

Also, the following commands will do linear regressions, as does regress, but offer special features:

1. ivregress fits models in which some of the regressors are endogenous, using either instrumental variables or generalized method of moments (GMM) estimators.

2. areg fits models $y_j = \mathbf{x}_j \boldsymbol{\beta} + \mathbf{d}_j \boldsymbol{\gamma} + \epsilon_j$, where $\mathbf{d}_j$ is a mutually exclusive and exhaustive dummy variable set. areg obtains estimates of β (and associated statistics) without ever forming $\mathbf{d}_j$, meaning that it also does not report the estimated γ. If your interest is in fitting fixed-effects models, Stata has a better command—xtreg—discussed in [U] **26.15.1 Linear regression with panel data**. Most users who find areg appealing will probably want to use xtreg because it provides more useful summary and test statistics. areg duplicates the output that regress would produce if you were to generate all the dummy variables. This means, for instance, that the reported R^2 includes the effect of γ.

3. boxcox obtains maximum likelihood estimates of the coefficients and the Box–Cox transform parameters in a model of the form

$$y_i^{(\theta)} = \beta_0 + \beta_1 x_{i1}^{(\lambda)} + \beta_2 x_{i2}^{(\lambda)} + \cdots + \beta_k x_{ik}^{(\lambda)} + \gamma_1 z_{i1} + \gamma_2 z_{i2} + \cdots + \gamma_l z_{il} + \epsilon_i$$

where $\epsilon \sim N(0, \sigma^2)$. Here the *depvar* y is subject to a Box–Cox transform with parameter θ. Each of the *indepvars* $x_1, x_2, \ldots, x_k$ is transformed by a Box–Cox transform with parameter λ. The $z_1, z_2, \ldots, z_l$ are independent variables that are not transformed. In addition to the general form specified above, boxcox can fit three other versions of this model defined by the restrictions $\lambda = \theta$, $\lambda = 1$, and $\theta = 1$.

4. tobit allows estimation of linear regression models when y_i has been subject to left-censoring, right-censoring, or both. Say that y_i is not observed if $y_i < 1{,}000$, but for those observations, it is known that $y_i < 1{,}000$. tobit fits such models.

   ivtobit does the same but allows for endogenous regressors.

5. intreg (interval regression) is a generalization of tobit. In addition to allowing open-ended intervals, intreg allows closed intervals. Rather than observing y_j, it is assumed that y_{0j} and y_{1j} are observed, where $y_{0j} \le y_j \le y_{1j}$. Survey data might report that a subject's monthly income was in the range \$1,500–\$2,500. intreg allows such data to be used to fit a regression model. intreg allows $y_{0j} = y_{1j}$ and so can reproduce results reported by regress. intreg allows y_{0j} to be $-\infty$ and y_{1j} to be $+\infty$ and so can reproduce results reported by tobit.

6. `truncreg` fits the regression model when the sample is drawn from a restricted part of the population and so is similar to `tobit`, except that here the independent variables are not observed. Under the normality assumption for the whole population, the error terms in the truncated regression model have a truncated-normal distribution.

7. `cnsreg` allows you to place linear constraints on the coefficients.

8. `eivreg` adjusts estimates for errors in variables.

9. `nl` provides the nonlinear least-squares estimator of $y_j = f(\mathbf{x}_j, \boldsymbol{\beta}) + \epsilon_j$.

10. `rreg` fits robust regression models, which are not to be confused with regression with robust standard errors. Robust standard errors are discussed in [U] **20.16 Obtaining robust variance estimates**. Robust regression concerns point estimates more than standard errors, and it implements a data-dependent method for downweighting outliers.

11. `qreg` produces quantile-regression estimates, a variation that is not linear regression at all but is an estimator of $y_j = \mathbf{x}_j\boldsymbol{\beta} + \epsilon_j$. In the basic form of this model, sometimes called median regression, $\mathbf{x}_j\boldsymbol{\beta}$ measures not the predicted mean of y_j conditional on $\mathbf{x}_j$, but its median. As such, `qreg` is of most interest when ϵ_j does not have constant variance. `qreg` allows you to specify the quantile, so you can produce linear estimates for the predicted 1st, 2nd, ..., 99th percentile.

   Another command, `bsqreg`, is identical to `qreg` but presents bootstrap standard errors.

   The `sqreg` command estimates multiple quantiles simultaneously; standard errors are obtained via the bootstrap.

   The `iqreg` command estimates the difference between two quantiles; standard errors are obtained via the bootstrap.

12. `vwls` (variance-weighted least squares) produces estimates of $y_j = \mathbf{x}_j\boldsymbol{\beta} + \epsilon_j$, where the variance of ϵ_j is calculated from group data or is known a priori. `vwls` is therefore of most interest to categorical-data analysts and physical scientists.

26.3 ANOVA, ANCOVA, MANOVA, and MANCOVA

ANOVA and ANCOVA are related to linear regression, but we classify them separately. The related Stata commands are `anova`, `oneway`, and `loneway`. The `manova` command provides MANOVA and MANCOVA (multivariate ANOVA and ANCOVA).

`anova` fits ANOVA and ANCOVA models, one-way and up—including two-way factorial, three-way factorial, etc.—and fits nested and mixed-design models and repeated-measures models.

`oneway` fits one-way ANOVA models. It is quicker at producing estimates than `anova`, although `anova` is so fast that this probably does not matter. The important difference is that `oneway` can report multiple-comparison tests.

`loneway` is an alternative to `oneway`. The results are numerically the same, but `loneway` can deal with more levels (limited only by dataset size; `oneway` is limited to 376 levels and `anova` to 798, but for `anova` to reach 798 requires a lot of memory), and `loneway` reports some additional statistics, such as the intraclass correlation.

`manova` fits MANOVA and MANCOVA models, one-way and up—including two-way factorial, three-way factorial, etc.—and it fits nested and mixed-design models.

26.4   Generalized linear models

The generalized linear model is

$$g\{E(y_j)\} = \mathbf{x}_j\boldsymbol{\beta}, \qquad y_j \sim F$$

where $g()$ is called the link function and F is a member of the exponential family, both of which you specify before estimation. glm fits this model.

The GLM framework encompasses a surprising array of models known by other names, including linear regression, Poisson regression, exponential regression, and others. Stata provides dedicated estimation commands for many of these. Stata has, for instance, regress for linear regression, poisson for Poisson regression, and streg for exponential regression, and that is not all of the overlap.

glm by default uses maximum likelihood estimation and alternatively estimates via iterated reweighted least squares (IRLS) when the irls option is specified. For each family, F, there is a corresponding link function, $g()$, called the canonical link, for which IRLS estimation produces results identical to maximum likelihood estimation. You can, however, match families and link functions as you wish, and, when you match a family to a link function other than the canonical link, you obtain a different but valid estimator of the standard errors of the regression coefficients. The estimator you obtain is asymptotically equivalent to the maximum likelihood estimator, which, in small samples, produces slightly different results.

For example, the canonical link for the binomial family is logit. glm, irls with that combination produces results identical to the maximum-likelihood logit (and logistic) command. The binomial family with the probit link produces the probit model, but probit is not the canonical link here. Hence, glm, irls produces standard error estimates that differ slightly from those produced by Stata's maximum-likelihood probit command.

Many researchers feel that the maximum-likelihood standard errors are preferable to IRLS estimates (when they are not identical), but they would have a difficult time justifying that feeling. Maximum likelihood probit is an estimator with (solely) asymptotic properties; glm, irls with the binomial family and probit link is an estimator with (solely) asymptotic properties, and in finite samples, the standard errors differ a little.

Still, we recommend that you use Stata's dedicated estimators whenever possible. IRLS—the theory—and glm, irls—the command—are all encompassing in their generality, meaning that they rarely use the right jargon or provide things in the way you wish they would. The narrower commands, such as logit, probit, and poisson, focus on the issue at hand and are invariably more convenient.

glm is useful when you want to match a family to a link function that is not provided elsewhere.

glm also offers several estimators of the variance–covariance matrix that are consistent, even when the errors are heteroskedastic or autocorrelated. Another advantage of a glm version of a model over a model-specific version is that many of these VCE estimators are available only for the glm implementation. You can also obtain the ML–based estimates of the VCE from glm.

26.5   Binary-outcome qualitative dependent-variable models

There are many ways to write these models, one of which is

$$\Pr(y_j \neq 0) = F(\mathbf{x}_j\boldsymbol{\beta})$$

where F is some cumulative distribution. Two popular choices for $F()$ are the normal and logistic, and the models are called the probit and logit (or logistic regression) models. A third is the complementary log–log function; maximum likelihood estimates are obtained by Stata's `cloglog` command.

The two parent commands for the maximum likelihood estimator of probit and logit are `probit` and `logit`, although `logit` has a sibling, `logistic`, that provides the same estimates but displays results in a slightly different way. There is also an exact logistic estimator; see [U] **26.9 Exact estimators**.

Do not read anything into the names logit and logistic. Logit and logistic have two interchanged definitions in two scientific camps. In the medical sciences, logit means the minimum χ^2 estimator, and logistic means maximum likelihood. In the social sciences, it is the other way around. From our experience, it appears that neither reads the other's literature, because both talk (and write books) asserting that logit means one thing and logistic the other. Our solution is to provide both `logit` and `logistic`, which do the same thing, so that each camp can latch on to the maximum likelihood command under the name each expects.

There are two slight differences between `logit` and `logistic`. `logit` reports estimates in the coefficient metric, whereas `logistic` reports exponentiated coefficients—odds ratios. This is in accordance with the expectations of each camp and makes no substantial difference. The other difference is that `logistic` has a family of postlogistic commands that you can run to explore the nature of the fit. Actually, that is not exactly true because all the commands for use after `logistic` can also be used after `logit`.

If you have not already selected `logit` or `logistic` as your favorite, we recommend that you try `logistic`. Logistic regression (logit) models are more easily interpreted in the odds-ratio metric.

In addition to `logit` and `logistic`, Stata provides `glogit`, `blogit`, and `binreg` commands.

`blogit` is the maximum likelihood estimator (the same as `logit` or `logistic`) but applied on data organized in a different way. Rather than having individual observations, your data are organized so that each observation records the number of observed successes and failures.

`glogit` is the weighted-regression, grouped-data estimator.

`binreg` can be used to model either individual-level or grouped data in an application of the generalized linear model. The family is assumed to be binomial, and each link provides a distinct parameter interpretation. Also, `binreg` offers several options for setting the link function according to the desired biostatistical interpretation. The available links and interpretation options are

Option	Implied link	Parameter
or	logit	Odds ratios = $\exp(\beta)$
rr	log	Risk ratios = $\exp(\beta)$
hr	log complement	Health ratios = $\exp(\beta)$
rd	identity	Risk differences = β

Related to logit, the skewed logit estimator scobit adds a power to the logit link function and is estimated by Stata's `scobit` command.

Turning to probit, you have two choices: `probit` and `ivprobit`. `probit` fits a maximum-likelihood probit model. `ivprobit` fits a probit model where one or more of the regressors are endogenously determined.

Stata also provides bprobit and gprobit. The bprobit command is a maximum likelihood estimator—equivalent to probit—but works with data organized in the different way outlined above. gprobit is the weighted-regression, grouped-data estimator.

Continuing with probit: hetprob fits heteroskedastic probit models. In these models, the variance of the error term is parameterized.

heckprob fits probit models with sample selection.

Also, Stata's biprobit command fits bivariate probit models, meaning two correlated outcomes. biprobit also fits partial-observability models in which only the outcomes $(0,0)$ and $(1,1)$ are observed.

26.6   Conditional logistic regression

clogit is Stata's conditional logistic regression estimator. In this model, observations are assumed to be partitioned into groups, and a predetermined number of events occur in each group. The model measures the risk of the event according to the observation's covariates, x_j. The model is used in matched case–control studies (clogit allows $1:1$, $1:k$, and $m:k$ matching) and is used in natural experiments whenever observations can be grouped into pools in which a fixed number of events occur.

26.7   Multiple-outcome qualitative dependent-variable models

For more than two outcomes, Stata provides ordered logit, ordered probit, rank-ordered logit, multinomial logistic regression, multinomial probit regression, McFadden's choice model (conditional fixed-effects logistic regression), and nested logistic regression.

oprobit and ologit provide maximum-likelihood ordered probit and logit. These are generalizations of probit and logit models known as the proportional odds model and are used when the outcomes have a natural ordering from low to high. The idea is that there is an unmeasured $z_j = x_j\beta$, and the probability that the kth outcome is observed is $\Pr(c_{k-1} < z_j < c_k)$, where $c_0 = -\infty$, $c_k = +\infty$, and $c_1, \ldots, c_{k-1}$ along with β are estimated from the data.

rologit fits the rank-ordered logit model for rankings. This model is also known as the Plackett–Luce model, the exploded logit model, and choice-based conjoint analysis.

asroprobit fits the probit model for rankings, a more flexible estimator than rologit because asroprobit allows covariances among the rankings. asroprobit is also similar to asmprobit (below), which is used for outcomes that have no natural ordering. The as in the name signifies that asroprobit also allows alternative-specific regressors—variables that have different coefficients for each alternative.

slogit fits the stereotype logit model for data that are not truly ordered, as data are for ologit, but for which you are not sure that it is unordered, in which case mlogit would be appropriate.

mlogit fits maximum-likelihood multinomial logistic models, also known as polytomous logistic regression. It is intended for use when the outcomes have no natural ordering and you know only the characteristics of the outcome chosen (and, perhaps, the chooser).

asclogit fits McFadden's choice model, also known as conditional logistic regression. In the context denoted by the name *McFadden's choice model*, the model is used when the outcomes have no natural ordering, just as multinomial logistic regression, but the characteristics of the outcomes chosen and not chosen are known (along with, perhaps, the characteristics of the chooser).

In the context denoted by the name *conditional logistic regression*—mentioned above—subjects are members of pools, and one or more are chosen, typically to be infected by some disease or to have some other unfortunate event befall them. Thus the characteristics of the chosen and not chosen are known, and the issue of the characteristics of the chooser never arises. Either way, it is the same model.

In their choice-model interpretations, `mlogit` and `clogit` assume that the odds ratios are independent of other alternatives, known as the independence of irrelevant alternatives (IIA) assumption. This assumption is often rejected by the data and the nested logit model does not impose this condition. `nlogit` is also popular for fitting the random utility choice model.

`asmprobit` is for use with outcomes that have no natural ordering and with regressors that are alternative specific. It is weakly related to `mlogit`. Unlike `mlogit`, `asmprobit` does not assume the IIA.

`mprobit` is also for use with outcomes that have no natural ordering but with models that do not have alternative-specific regressors.

26.8   Count dependent-variable models

These models concern dependent variables that count the number of occurrences of an event. In this category, we include Poisson and negative binomial regression. For the Poisson model,

$$E(\text{count}) = E_j \exp(\mathbf{x}_j \boldsymbol{\beta})$$

where E_j is the exposure time. `poisson` fits this model. There is also an exact Poisson estimator; see [U] **26.9 Exact estimators**.

Negative-binomial regression refers to estimating with data that are a mixture of Poisson counts. One derivation of the negative binomial model is that individual units follow a Poisson regression model but there is an omitted variable that follows a gamma distribution with variance α. Negative-binomial regression estimates β and α. `nbreg` fits such models. A variation on this, unique to Stata, allows you to model α. `gnbreg` fits those models.

Zero inflation refers to count models in which the number of 0 counts is more than would be expected in the regular model, and that is due to there being a probit or logit process that must first generate a positive outcome before the counting process can begin.

Stata's `zip` command fits zero-inflated Poisson models.

Stata's `zinb` command fits zero-inflated negative binomial models.

`ztp` and `ztnb` fit zero-truncated Poisson and negative binomial models. In zero-inflated models, you observe too many zeros, so you fit a separate model to them. In zero-truncated models, you do not observe the zeros.

26.9   Exact estimators

Exact estimators refer to models which, rather than being estimated by asymptotic formulas, are estimated by enumerating the conditional distribution of the sufficient statistics and then computing the maximum likelihood estimate using that distribution. Standard errors cannot be estimated, but confidence intervals can be and are obtained from the enumerations.

`exlogistic` fits logistic models of binary data in this way.

`expoisson` fits Poisson models of count data in this way.

In small samples, exact estimates have better coverage than the asymptotic estimates, and exact estimates are the only way to obtain estimates, tests, and confidence intervals of covariates that perfectly predict the observed outcome.

26.10   Linear regression with heteroskedastic errors

We now consider the model $y_j = \mathbf{x}_j\boldsymbol{\beta} + \epsilon_j$, where the variance of ϵ_j is nonconstant.

First, `regress` can fit such models if you specify the `vce(robust)` option. What Stata calls robust is also known as the White correction for heteroskedasticity.

For scientists who have data where the variance of ϵ_j is known a priori, `vwls` is the command. `vwls` produces estimates for the model given each observation's variance, which is recorded in a variable in the data.

If you wish to model the heteroskedasticity on covariates, use the `het()` option of the `arch` command. Although `arch` is written primarily to analyze time-series data, it can be used with cross-sectional data. Before using `arch` with cross-sectional data, set the data as time series, by typing `gen faketime = _n` and then typing `tsset faketime`.

Finally, `qreg` performs quantile regression, which in the presence of heteroskedasticity is most of interest. Median regression (one of `qreg`'s capabilities) is an estimator of $y_j = \mathbf{x}_j\boldsymbol{\beta} + \epsilon_j$ when ϵ_j is heteroskedastic. Even more useful, you can fit models of other quantiles and so model the heteroskedasticity. Also see the `sqreg` and `iqreg` commands; `sqreg` estimates multiple quantiles simultaneously. `iqreg` estimates differences in quantiles.

26.11   Stochastic frontier models

`frontier` fits stochastic production or cost frontier models on cross-sectional data. The model can be expressed as

$$y_i = \mathbf{x}_i\boldsymbol{\beta} + v_i - su_i$$

where

$$s = \begin{cases} 1 & \text{for production functions} \\ -1 & \text{for cost functions} \end{cases}$$

u_i is a nonnegative disturbance standing for technical inefficiency in the production function or cost inefficiency in the cost function. Although the idiosyncratic error term v_i is assumed to have a normal distribution, the inefficiency term is assumed to be one of the three distributions: half-normal, exponential, or truncated-normal. Also, when the nonnegative component of the disturbance is assumed to be either half-normal or exponential, `frontier` can fit models in which the error components are heteroskedastic conditional on a set of covariates. When the nonnegative component of the disturbance is assumed to be from a truncated-normal distribution, `frontier` can also fit a conditional mean model, where the mean of the truncated-normal distribution is modeled as a linear function of a set of covariates.

For panel-data stochastic frontier models, see [U] **26.15.1 Linear regression with panel data**.

26.12   Regression with systems of equations

For systems of equations with endogenous covariates, use the three-stage least-squares (3SLS) estimator reg3. The reg3 command can produce constrained and unconstrained estimates.

When we have correlated errors across equations but no endogenous right-hand-side variables,

$$y_{1j} = \mathbf{x}_{1j}\boldsymbol{\beta} + \epsilon_{1j}$$
$$y_{2j} = \mathbf{x}_{2j}\boldsymbol{\beta} + \epsilon_{2j}$$
$$\vdots$$
$$y_{mj} = \mathbf{x}_{mj}\boldsymbol{\beta} + \epsilon_{mj}$$

where $\epsilon_{k\cdot}$ and $\epsilon_{l\cdot}$ are correlated with correlation ρ_{kl}, a quantity to be estimated from the data. This is called Zellner's seemingly unrelated regressions, and sureg fits such models. When $\mathbf{x}_{1j} = \mathbf{x}_{2j} = \cdots = \mathbf{x}_{mj}$, the model is known as multivariate regression, and the corresponding command is mvreg.

The equations need not be linear; if they are not linear, use nlsur.

26.13   Models with endogenous sample selection

What has become known as the Heckman model refers to linear regression in the presence of sample selection: $y_j = \mathbf{x}_j\boldsymbol{\beta} + \epsilon_j$ is not observed unless some event occurs that itself has probability $p_j = F(\mathbf{z}_j\boldsymbol{\gamma} + \nu_j)$, where ϵ and ν might be correlated and $\mathbf{z}_j$ and $\mathbf{x}_j$ may contain variables in common.

heckman fits such models by maximum likelihood or Heckman's original two-step procedure.

This model has recently been generalized to replace the linear regression equation with another probit equation, and that model is fit by heckprob.

Another important case of endogenous sample selection is the treatment-effects model, which considers the effect of an endogenously chosen binary treatment on another endogenous, continuous variable, conditional on two sets of independent variables. treatreg fits a treatment-effects model by using either a two-step consistent estimator or full maximum likelihood.

26.14   Models with time-series data

ARIMA refers to models with autoregressive integrated moving-average processes, and Stata's arima command fits models with ARIMA disturbances via the Kalman filter and maximum likelihood. These models may be fit with or without confounding covariates.

Stata's prais command performs regression with AR(1) disturbances by using the Prais–Winsten or Cochrane–Orcutt transformation. Both two-step and iterative solutions are available, as well as a version of the Hildreth–Lu search procedure. The Prais–Winsten estimates for the model are an improvement over the Cochrane–Orcutt estimates in that the first observation is preserved in the estimation. This is particularly important with trended data in small samples.

prais automatically produces the Durbin–Watson d statistic, which can also be obtained after regress by using estat dwatson.

newey produces linear regression estimates with the Newey–West variance estimates that are robust to heteroskedasticity and autocorrelation of specified order.

Stata provides estimators for regression models with autoregressive conditional heteroskedastic (ARCH) disturbances

$$y_t = \mathbf{x}_t \boldsymbol{\beta} + \mu_t$$

where μ_t is distributed $N(0, \sigma_t^2)$ and σ_t^2 is given by some function of the lagged disturbances.

Stata's `arch` command provides different parameterizations of the conditional heteroskedasticity, and it also allows ARMA disturbances and/or multiplicative heteroskedasticity.

For multivariate data with autoregressive conditional heteroskedasticity, the `dvech` command fits the diagonal vech model, allowing for multivariate ARCH and GARCH relationships among the variables.

Stata provides `var` and `svar` for fitting vector autoregressive (VAR) and structural vector autoregressive (SVAR) models. See [TS] **var** for information on Stata's suite of commands for forecasting, specification testing, and inference on VAR and SVAR models. Stata also provides `vec` for fitting vector error-correction models; see [TS] **vec**. See [TS] **irf** for information on Stata's suite of commands for estimating, analyzing, and presenting impulse–response functions and forecast error variance decompositions. There is also a set of commands for performing Granger causality tests, lag-order selection, and residual analysis.

`sspace` estimates the parameters of multivariate state-space models using the Kalman filter. The state-space representation of time-series models is extremely flexible and can be used to estimate the parameters of many different models, including vector autoregressive moving-average (VARMA) models, dynamic-factor (DF) models, and structural time-series (STS) models. It can also solve some stochastic dynamic-programming problems.

`dfactor` estimates the parameters of dynamic-factor models. These flexible models for multivariate time series provide for a vector-autoregressive structure in both observed outcomes and in unobserved factors. They also allow exogenous covariates for observed outcomes or unobserved factors.

26.15   Panel-data models

26.15.1   Linear regression with panel data

This section could just as well be called "linear regression with complex error structures". Commands in this class begin with the letters `xt`.

`xtreg` fits models of the form

$$y_{it} = \mathbf{x}_{it} \boldsymbol{\beta} + \nu_i + \epsilon_{it}$$

`xtreg` can produce the between-regression estimator, the within-regression (fixed effects) estimator, or the GLS random-effects (matrix-weighted average of between and within results) estimator. It can also produce the maximum-likelihood random-effects estimator.

`xtregar` can produce the within estimator and a GLS random-effects estimator when the ϵ_{it} are assumed to follow an AR(1) process.

`xtivreg` contains the between-2SLS estimator, the within-2SLS estimator, the first-differenced-2SLS estimator, and two GLS random-effects-2SLS estimators to handle cases in which some of the covariates are endogenous.

`xtmixed` is a generalization of `xtreg` that allows for multiple levels of panels, random coefficients, and variance-component estimation in general. In the `xtmixed` framework, residuals (random effects) can occur anywhere and have any level of subscript.

xtabond is for use with dynamic panel-data models (models in which there are lagged dependent variables) and can produce the one-step, one-step robust, and two-step Arellano–Bond estimators. xtabond can handle predetermined covariates, and it reports both the Sargan and autocorrelation tests derived by Arellano and Bond.

xtdpdsys is an extension of xtabond and produces estimates with smaller bias when the coefficients of the AR process are large. xtpdsys is also more efficient than xtabond. Whereas xtabond uses moment conditions based on the differenced errors, xtpdsys uses moment conditions based on both the differenced errors and their levels.

xtdpd is an extension of xtdpdsys and can be used to estimate the parameters of a broader class of dynamic panel-data models. xtdpd can be used to fit models with serially correlated idiosyncratic errors, whereas xtdpdsys and xtabond assume no serial correlation. Or xtdpd can be used with models where the structure of the predetermined variables is more complicated than that assumed by xtdpdsys or xtabond.

xtgls produces generalized least-squares estimates for models of the form

$$y_{it} = \mathbf{x}_{it}\boldsymbol{\beta} + \epsilon_{it}$$

where you may specify the variance structure of ϵ_{it}. If you specify that ϵ_{it} is independent for all i and t, xtgls produces the same results as regress up to a small-sample degrees-of-freedom correction applied by regress but not by xtgls.

You may choose among three variance structures concerning i and three concerning t, producing a total of nine different models. Assumptions concerning i deal with heteroskedasticity and cross-sectional correlation. Assumptions concerning t deal with autocorrelation and, more specifically, AR(1) serial correlation.

Alternative methods report the OLS coefficients and a version of the GLS variance–covariance estimator. xtpcse produces panel-corrected standard error (PCSE) estimates for linear cross-sectional time-series models, where the parameters are estimated by OLS or Prais–Winsten regression. When you are computing the standard errors and the variance–covariance estimates, the disturbances are, by default, assumed to be heteroskedastic and contemporaneously correlated across panels.

In the jargon of GLS, the random-effects model fit by xtreg has exchangeable correlation within i—xtgls does not model this particular correlation structure. xtgee, however, does.

xtgee fits population-averaged models, and it optionally provides robust estimates of variance. Moreover, xtgee allows other correlation structures. One that is of particular interest to those with many data goes by the name *unstructured*. The within-panel correlations are simply estimated in an unconstrained way. [U] **26.15.3 Generalized linear models with panel data** will discuss this estimator further because it is not restricted to linear regression models.

xthtaylor uses instrumental variables estimators to estimate the parameters of panel-data random-effects models of the form

$$y_{it} = \mathbf{X}_{1it}\boldsymbol{\beta}_1 + \mathbf{X}_{2it}\boldsymbol{\beta}_2 + \mathbf{Z}_{1i}\boldsymbol{\delta}_1 + \mathbf{Z}_{2i}\boldsymbol{\delta}_2 + u_i + e_{it}$$

The individual effects u_i are correlated with the explanatory variables $\mathbf{X}_{2it}$ and $\mathbf{Z}_{2i}$ but are uncorrelated with $\mathbf{X}_{1it}$ and $\mathbf{Z}_{1i}$, where $\mathbf{Z}_1$ and $\mathbf{Z}_2$ are constant within panel.

xtfrontier fits stochastic production or cost frontier models for panel data. You may choose from a time-invariant model or a time-varying decay model. In both models, the nonnegative inefficiency term is assumed to have a truncated-normal distribution. In the time-invariant model, the inefficiency term is constant within panels. In the time-varying decay model, the inefficiency term is modeled as a truncated-normal random variable multiplied by a specific function of time. In both models, the idiosyncratic error term is assumed to have a normal distribution. The only panel-specific effect is the random inefficiency term.

26.15.2 Censored linear regression with panel data

xttobit fits random-effects tobit models and generalizes that to observation-specific censoring.

xtintreg performs random-effects interval regression and generalizes that to observation-specific censoring. Interval regression, in addition to allowing open-ended intervals, also allows closed intervals.

26.15.3 Generalized linear models with panel data

[U] **26.4 Generalized linear models** above discussed the model

$$g\{E(y_j)\} = \mathbf{x}_j\boldsymbol{\beta}, \qquad y_j \sim F \tag{1}$$

where $g()$ is the link function and F is a member of the exponential family, both of which you specify before estimation.

There are two approaches to generalizing the above to panel data: one, in which the correlation within panel is modeled in general terms, and the other, in which the intrapanel correlation is itself modeled, and in detail. The former provides estimates of β; the latter provides estimates of β and the variance components.

The first is known as the generalized estimation equation (GEE) approach.

The second is known as the generalized linear mixed model (GLMM).

The corresponding commands in Stata are xtgee for GEE and xtmixed, xtmelogit, and xtmepoisson for GLMM.

26.15.4 Qualitative dependent-variable models with panel data

xtprobit fits random-effects probit regression via maximum likelihood. It also fits population-averaged models via GEE. This last is nothing more than xtgee with the binomial family, probit link, and exchangeable error structure.

xtlogit fits random-effects logistic regression models via maximum likelihood. It also fits conditional fixed-effects models via maximum likelihood. Finally, as with xtprobit, it fits population-averaged models via GEE.

xtcloglog estimates random-effects complementary log-log regression via maximum likelihood. It also fits population-averaged models via GEE.

xtmelogit fits mixed-effects models for binary/binomial responses.

26.15.5 Count dependent-variable models with panel data

xtpoisson fits two different random-effects Poisson regression models via maximum likelihood. The two distributions for the random effect are gamma and normal. It also fits conditional fixed-effects models, and it fits population-averaged models via GEE. This last is nothing more than xtgee with the Poisson family, log link, and exchangeable error structure.

xtnbreg fits random-effects negative binomial regression models via maximum likelihood (the distribution of the random effects is assumed to be beta). It also fits conditional fixed-effects models, and it fits population-averaged models via GEE.

26.15.6   Random-coefficient models with panel data

xtrc fits Swamy's random-coefficients linear regression model. In this model, rather than only the intercept varying across groups, all the coefficients are allowed to vary.

26.16   Survival-time (failure-time) models

Commands are provided to fit Cox proportional-hazards models, competing-risks regression, and several parametric survival models including exponential, Weibull, Gompertz, lognormal, loglogistic, and generalized gamma; see [ST] **stcox**, [ST] **stcrreg**, and [ST] **streg**. The commands for Cox and parametric regressions, stcox and streg, are appropriate for single- or multiple-failure-per-subject data. The command for competing-risks regression, stcrreg, is appropriate only for single-failure data. Conventional, robust, bootstrap, and jackknife standard errors are available with all three commands, with the exception that for stcrreg, robust standard errors are the conventional standard errors.

Both the Cox model and the parametric models (as fit using Stata) allow for two additional generalizations. First, the models may be modified to allow for latent random effects, or *frailties*. Second, the models may be stratified in that the baseline hazard function may vary completely over a set of strata. The parametric models also allow for the modeling of ancillary parameters.

Competing-risks regression, as fit using Stata, is a useful alternative to Cox regression for datasets where more than one type of failure occurs, in other words, for data where failure events compete with one another. In such situations, competing-risks regression allows you to easily assess covariate effects on the incidence of the failure type of interest without having to make strong assumptions concerning the independence of failure types.

stcox, stcrreg, and streg require that the data be stset so that the proper response variables may be established. After you stset the data, the time/censoring response is taken as understood, and you need only supply the regressors (and other options) to stcox, stcrreg, and streg. With stcrreg, one required option deals with specifying which events compete with the failure event of interest that was previously stset.

26.17   Generalized method of moments (GMM)

gmm fits models using generalized method of moments (GMM). With the interactive version of the command, you enter your moment equations directly into the dialog box or command line using substitutable expressions just like with nl or nlsur. The moment-evaluator program version gives you greater flexibility in exchange for increased complexity; with this version, you write a program that calculates the moments based on a vector of parameters passed to it.

gmm can fit both single- and multiple-equation models, and you can combine moment conditions of the form $E\{\mathbf{z}_i u_i(\beta)\} = \mathbf{0}$, where $\mathbf{z}_i$ is a vector of instruments and $u_i(\beta)$ is often an additive regression error term, as well as more general moment conditions of the form $E\{\mathbf{h}_i(\mathbf{z}_i; \beta)\} = \mathbf{0}$. In the former case, you specify the expression for $u_i(\beta)$ and use the instruments() and xtinstruments() options to specify $\mathbf{z}_i$. In the latter case, you specify the expression for $\mathbf{h}_i(\mathbf{z}_i; \beta)$; because that expression incorporates your instruments, you do not use the instruments() or xtinstruments() option.

gmm supports cross-sectional, time-series, and panel data. You can request weight matrices and VCEs that are suitable for independent and identically distributed errors, that are suitable for heteroskedastic errors, that are appropriate for clustered observations, or that are heteroskedasticity- and autocorrelation-consistent (HAC). For HAC weight matrices and VCEs, gmm lets you specify the bandwidth or request an automatic bandwidth selection algorithm.

26.18   Estimation with correlated errors

By correlated errors, we mean that observations are grouped, and that within group, the observations might be correlated but, across groups, they are uncorrelated. regress with the vce(cluster *clustvar*) option can produce "correct" estimates, i.e., inefficient estimates with correct standard errors and lots of robustness; see [U] **20.16 Obtaining robust variance estimates**. Obviously, if you know the correlation structure (and are not mistaken), you can do better, so xtreg and xtgls are also of interest here; we discuss them in [U] **26.15.1 Linear regression with panel data**.

Estimation in the presence of autocorrelated errors is discussed in [U] **26.14 Models with time-series data**.

26.19   Survey data

Stata's svy command fits statistical models for complex survey data. svy is a prefix command, so to obtain linear regression, you type

    . svy: regress ...

or to obtain probit regression, you type

    . svy: probit ...

but first you must type a svyset command to define the survey design characteristics. Prefix svy works with many estimation commands, and everything is documented together in the *Survey Data Reference Manual*.

svy supports the following variance-estimation methods:

- Taylor-series linearization
- Balanced repeated replication (BRR)
- Jackknife

See [SVY] **variance estimation** for details.

svy supports the following survey design characteristics:

- With- and without- replacement sampling
- Sampling weights
- Stratification
- Poststratification
- Clustering
- Multiple stages of clustering without replacement
- BRR and jackknife replication weights

See [SVY] **svyset** for details.

Subpopulation estimation is available for all estimation commands.

Tabulations and summary statistics are also available, including means, proportions, ratios, and totals over multiple subpopulations, and direct standardization of means, proportions, and ratios.

26.20   Multiple imputation

Multiple imputation (MI) is a statistical technique for estimation in the presence of missing data. If you fit the parameters of y on x_1, x_2, and x_3 using any of the other Stata estimation commands, parameters are fit on the data for which y, x_1, x_2, and x_3 contain no missing values. This process is known as listwise or casewise deletion because observations for which any of y, x_1, x_2, or x_3 contain missing values are ignored or, said differently, deleted from consideration. MI is a technique to recover the information in those ignored observations when the missing values are missing at random (MAR) or missing completely at random (MCAR). Data are MAR if the probability that a value is missing may depend on observed data but not on unobserved data. Data are MCAR if the probability of missingness is not even a function of the observed data.

MI is named for the imputations it produces to replace the missing values in the data. MI does not just form replacement values for the missing data, it produces multiple replacements. The purpose is not to create replacement values as close as possible to the true ones, but to handle missing data in a way resulting in valid statistical inference.

There are three steps in an MI analysis. First, one forms M imputations for each missing value in the data. Second, one fits the model of interest separately on each of the M resulting datasets. Finally, one combines those M estimation results into the desired single result.

The `mi` command does this for you. It can be used with most of Stata's estimation commands, including the survival and survey data commands. See [MI] **intro**.

26.21   Multivariate and cluster analysis

Most of Stata's multivariate capabilities are to be found in the *Multivariate Statistics Reference Manual*, although there are some exceptions.

1. `mvreg` fits multivariate regressions.

2. `manova` fits MANOVA and MANCOVA models, one-way and up—including two-way factorial, three-way factorial, etc.—and it fits nested and mixed-design models. Also see [U] **26.3 ANOVA, ANCOVA, MANOVA, and MANCOVA** above.

3. `canon` estimates canonical correlations and their corresponding loadings. Canonical correlation attempts to describe the relationship between two sets of variables.

4. `pca` extracts principal components and reports eigenvalues and loadings. Some people consider principal components a descriptive tool—in which case standard errors as well as coefficients are relevant—and others look at it as a dimension-reduction technique.

5. `factor` fits factor models and provides principal factors, principal-component factors, iterated principal-component factors, and maximum-likelihood solutions. Factor analysis is concerned with finding few common factors $\widehat{\mathbf{z}}_k$, $k = 1, \ldots, q$ that linearly reconstruct the original variables $\mathbf{y}_i$, $i = 1, \ldots, L$.

6. `tetrachoric`, in conjunction with `pca` or `factor`, allows you to perform PCA or factor analysis on binary data.

7. `rotate` provides a wide variety of orthogonal and oblique rotations after `factor` and `pca`. Rotations are often used to produce more interpretable results.

8. `procrustes` performs Procrustes analysis, one of the standard methods of multidimensional scaling. It can perform orthogonal or oblique rotations, as well as translation and dilation.

9. mds performs metric and nonmetric multidimensional scaling for dissimilarity between observations with respect to a set of variables. A wide variety of dissimilarity measures are available and, in fact, are the same as those for cluster.

10. ca performs correspondence analysis, an exploratory multivariate technique for analyzing cross-tabulations and the relationship between rows and columns.

11. mca performs multiple correspondence analysis (MCA) and joint correspondence analysis (JCA).

12. mvtest performs multivariate of multivariate normality along with tests of means, covariances, and correlations.

13. cluster provides cluster analysis; both hierarchical and partition clustering methods are available. Strictly speaking, cluster analysis does not fall into the category of statistical estimation. Rather, it is a set of techniques for exploratory data analysis. Stata's cluster environment has many different similarity and dissimilarity measures for continuous and binary data.

14. discrim and candisc perform discriminant analysis. candisc performs linear discriminant analysis (LDA). discrim also performs LDA, and it performs quadratic discriminant analysis (QDA), kth nearest neighbor (KNN), and logistic discriminant analysis. The two commands differ in default output. discrim shows the classification summary, candisc shows the canonical linear discriminant functions, and both will produce either.

26.22   Pharmacokinetic data

There are four estimation commands for analyzing pharmacokinetic data. See [R] **pk** for an overview of the pk system.

1. pkexamine calculates pharmacokinetic measures from time-and-concentration subject-level data. pkexamine computes and displays the maximum measured concentration, the time at the maximum measured concentration, the time of the last measurement, the elimination time, the half-life, and the area under the concentration–time curve (AUC).

2. pksumm obtains the first four moments from the empirical distribution of each pharmacokinetic measurement and tests the null hypothesis that the distribution of that measurement is normally distributed.

3. pkcross analyzes data from a crossover design experiment. When one is analyzing pharmaceutical trial data, if the treatment, carryover, and sequence variables are known, the omnibus test for separability of the treatment and carryover effects is calculated.

4. pkequiv performs bioequivalence testing for two treatments. By default, pkequiv calculates a standard confidence interval symmetric about the difference between the two treatment means. pkequiv also calculates confidence intervals symmetric about zero and intervals based on Fieller's theorem. Also, pkequiv can perform interval hypothesis tests for bioequivalence.

26.23   Specification search tools

There are three other commands that are not really estimation commands but are combined with estimation commands to assist in specification searches: stepwise, fracpoly, and mfp.

stepwise:, one of Stata's prefix commands, provides stepwise estimation. You can use the stepwise prefix with some, but not all, estimation commands. In [R] **stepwise** is a table of the estimation commands that are currently supported, but do not take it too literally. It was accurate as of the day that Stata 11 was released, but if you install the official updates, stepwise may now work with other commands, too. If you want to use stepwise with some estimation command, you should try it. Either it will work or you will get the message that the estimation command is not supported by stepwise.

fracpoly and mfp are commands to assist you in performing fractional-polynomial functional specification searches.

26.24   Obtaining new estimation commands

This chapter has discussed all the estimation commands included in Stata 11 the day that it was released; by now, there may be more. To obtain an up-to-date list, type search estimation.

And, of course, you can always write your own commands; see [R] **ml**.

26.25   Reference

Gould, W. W. 2000. sg124: Interpreting logistic regression in all its forms. *Stata Technical Bulletin* 53: 19–29. Reprinted in *Stata Technical Bulletin Reprints*, vol. 9, pp. 257–270. College Station, TX: Stata Press.

27 Commands everyone should know

27.1 43 commands

Putting aside the statistical commands that might particularly interest you, here are 43 commands that everyone should know:

Getting online help
    help, hsearch,
    net search, search   [U] **4 Stata's help and search facilities**

Keeping Stata up to date
    ado, net, update   [U] **28 Using the Internet to keep up to date**
    adoupdate   [R] **adoupdate**

Operating system interface
    pwd, cd   [D] **cd**

Using and saving data from disk
    save   [D] **save**
    use   [D] **use**
    append, merge   [U] **22 Combining datasets**
    compress   [D] **compress**

Inputting data into Stata   [U] **21 Inputting data**
    input   [D] **input**
    edit   [D] **edit**
    infile   [D] **infile (free format)**; [D] **infile (fixed format)**
    infix   [D] **infix (fixed format)**
    insheet   [D] **insheet**

Basic data reporting
    describe   [D] **describe**
    codebook   [D] **codebook**
    list   [D] **list**
    browse   [D] **edit**
    count   [D] **count**
    inspect   [D] **inspect**
    table   [R] **table**
    tabulate   [R] **tabulate oneway** and [R] **tabulate twoway**

(Continued on next page)

Data manipulation	[U] **13 Functions and expressions**
generate, replace	[D] **generate**
egen	[D] **egen**
rename	[D] **rename**
drop, keep	[D] **drop**
sort	[D] **sort**
encode, decode	[D] **encode**
order	[D] **order**
by	[U] **11.5 by varlist: construct**
reshape	[D] **reshape**
Keeping track of your work	
log	[U] **15 Saving and printing output—log files**
notes	[D] **notes**
Convenience	
display	[R] **display**

27.2   The by construct

If you do not understand the by *varlist*: construct, _n, and _N, and their interaction, and if you process data where observations are related, you are missing out on something. See

[U] **13.7 Explicit subscripting**
[U] **11.5 by varlist: construct**

Say that you have a dataset with multiple observations per person, and you want the average value of each person's blood pressure (bp) for the day. You could

```
. egen avgbp = mean(bp), by(person)
```

but you could also

```
. by person, sort: gen avgbp = sum(bp)/_N
. by person: replace avgbp = avgbp[_N]
```

Yes, typing two commands is more work than typing just one, but understanding the two-command construct is the key to generating more complicated things that no one ever thought about adding to egen.

Say that your dataset also contains time recording when each observation was made. If you want to add the total time the person is under observation (last time minus first time) to each observation, type

```
. by person (time), sort: gen ttl = time[_N]-time[1]
```

Or, suppose you want to add how long it has been since the person was last observed to each observation:

```
. by person (time), sort: gen howlong = time - time[_n-1]
```

If instead you wanted how long it would be until the next observation, type

```
. by person (time), sort: gen whennext = time[_n+1] - time
```

by *varlist*:, _n, and _N are often the solution to difficult calculations.

28 Using the Internet to keep up to date

Contents

28.1 Overview

Stata can read files over the Internet. Just to prove that to yourself, type the following:

```
. use http://www.stata.com/manual/chapter28, clear
```

You have just reached out and gotten a dataset from our web site. The dataset is not in HTML format, nor does this have anything to do with your browser. We just copied the Stata data file chapter28.dta onto our server, and now people all over the world can use it. If you have a web page, you can do the same thing. It is a convenient way to share datasets with colleagues.

Now type the following:

```
. update query
```

We promise that nothing bad will happen. update will read a short file from www.stata.com that will allow Stata to report whether your copy of Stata is up to date. Is your copy up to date? Now you know. If it is not, we will show you how to update it—it is no harder than typing update.

Now type the following:

```
. net from http://www.stata.com
```

That will go to www.stata.com and tell you what is available from our user-download site. The material there is not official, but it is useful. More useful is to type

```
. search kernel regression, net
```

or equivalently,

```
. net search kernel regression
```

That will search the entire web for additions to Stata having to do with kernel regression, whether it be from the *Stata Journal*, *Stata Technical Bulletin*, Statalist, archive sites, or private user sites.

To summarize: Stata can read files over the Internet:

1. You can share datasets, do-files, etc., with colleagues all over the world. This requires no special expertise, but you do need to have a web page.

2. You can update Stata; it is free, easy, and fast.

3. You can find and add new features to Stata; it is also free, easy, and fast.

Finally, you can create a site to distribute new features for Stata.

28.2   Sharing datasets (and other files)

There is just nothing to it: you copy the file as-is (in binary) onto the server and then let your colleagues know the file is there. This works for .dta files, .do files, .ado files, and, in fact, all files.

On the receiving end, you can use the file (if it is a .dta dataset) or you can copy it:

```
. use http://www.stata.com/manual/chapter28, clear
. copy http://www.stata.com/manual/chapter28.dta mycopy.dta
```

Stata includes a copy-file command and it works over the Internet just as use does; see [D] **copy**.

❏ Technical note

If you are concerned about transmission errors, you can create a checksum file before you copy the file onto the server. In placing chapter28.dta on our site, we started with chapter28.dta in our working directory and typed

```
. checksum chapter28.dta, save
```

This created the new file chapter28.sum. We then placed both files on our server. We did not have to create this second file, but because we did, when you use the data, Stata will be able to detect transmission errors and warn you if there are problems.

How would Stata know? chapter28.sum is a short file containing the result of a mathematical calculation made on the contents of chapter28.dta. When your Stata receives chapter28.dta, it repeats the calculation and then compares that result with what is recorded in chapter28.sum. If the results are different, then there must have been a transmission error.

Creating a checksum file is optional.

See [D] **checksum**.

❏

28.3   Official updates

Although we follow no formal schedule for the release of updates, the fact is that we update Stata about once every two weeks. You do not have to update that often, although we recommend that you do. There are two ways to check whether your copy of Stata is up to date:

type

```
. update query
```

or

Select **Help > Official Updates**
Click on **http://www.stata.com**

After that if an update is available, you should

type   or
. update all   click on *update*

After the updates have been downloaded, you may be prompted to type update swap. Be sure to do this if Stata asks you to, or the update will be incomplete.

After you have updated your Stata, to find out what has changed

type   or
. help whatsnew   Select **Help > What's New?**

28.3.1 Example

When you type update from http://www.stata.com or when you select **Help > Official Updates**, and click on **http://www.stata.com**, Stata presents a report:

```
. update from http://www.stata.com
(contacting http://www.stata.com)

Stata executable
    folder:                 C:\Program Files\Stata11\
    name of file:           Stata.exe
    currently installed:    28 Jul 2009
    latest available:       28 Jul 2009

Ado-file updates
    folder:                 C:\Program Files\Stata11\ado\updates\
    names of files:         (various)
    currently installed:    28 Jul 2009
    latest available:       28 Jul 2009

Recommendation
    Do nothing; all files up-to-date.
```

There are two components of official Stata: the binary Stata executable and the ado-files that we shipped with it. Ado-files are just programs written in Stata. For instance, when you use generate, you are using a command that was compiled into the Stata executable. When you use stcox, you are using a command that was implemented as an ado-file.

Both components of our Stata are up to date.

28.3.2 Updating ado-files

When you obtain the above report, you might see

```
. update from http://www.stata.com
(contacting http://www.stata.com)

Stata executable
    folder:                 C:\Program Files\Stata11\
    name of file:           Stata.exe
    currently installed:    28 Jul 2009
    latest available:       28 Jul 2009

Ado-file updates
    folder:                 C:\Program Files\Stata11\ado\updates\
    names of files:         (various)
    currently installed:    28 Jul 2009
    latest available:       08 Oct 2009

Recommendation
    Type -update all-
```

Stata tells you that your executable is up to date, but your ado-files need updating. Stata recommends that you update. If you go with the point-and-click alternative, at the bottom of the screen you will see

```
Recommendation
    update ado-files
```

where *update ado-files* is clickable.

Anyway, what you are to do next is type update ado-files or click on *update ado-files*. Either way, you will see something like the following:

```
. update ado-files
```

```
> update ado
(contacting http://www.stata.com)
Ado-file update log
    1.  verifying C:\Program Files\Stata11\ado\updates\ is writeable
    2.  obtaining list of files to be updated
    3.  downloading relevant files to temporary area
        downloading filename.ado
        downloading filename.sthlp
        ...
        downloading filename.ado
    4.  examining files
    5.  installing files
    6.  setting last date updated
Updates successfully installed.
Recommendation
    Type -help whatsnew- to learn about the new features
```

```
> update executable
(contacting http://www.stata.com)
executable already up to date
```

That is all there is to it, but do type help whatsnew to learn about the new features. (If you go the point-and-click path, click on *whatsnew*.)

Here is what happens if you type update all and you are already up to date:

```
. update all
```

```
> update ado
(contacting http://www.stata.com)
ado-files already up to date
```

```
> update executable
(contacting http://www.stata.com)
executable already up to date
```

28.3.3 Frequently asked questions about updating the ado-files

1. Could something go wrong and make my Stata become unusable?

    No. The updates are copied to a temporary place on your computer, Stata examines them to make sure they are complete before copying them to the official place. Thus either the updates are installed or they are not.

2. I do not believe you. Pretend that something you did not anticipate goes wrong, such as the power fails at the instant Stata is doing the local disk to local disk copy.

> If the improbable should happen, you can erase the update directory and then your Stata is back to being just as it was shipped. Updates go into a different directory from that of the originals and the originals are never erased.

> Stata tells you where it is installing your updates. You can also find out by typing sysdir. The directory you want is the one listed opposite UPDATES.

> (By the way, power failure should not cause a problem; the marker that the update is applied is set last, so you could also just type update all again and Stata would refetch the partially installed update.)

3. How much is downloaded?

> It depends on how many updates have been made since you last updated. Typical updates are only a few small files. If you wait 6 months between updates, you might have to download around 1 MB.

4. I am using Unix or a networked version of Stata. When I try to update all, I am told that the directory is not writeable. Can I copy the updates into another directory and then copy them to the official directory myself?

> Yes, assuming that you are a system administrator. Ordinarily, you would type update all and Stata would download whatever updates might be available, ado and/or executable. update ado allows you to download just the ado updates and to specify an alternate location for them to be installed. Type update ado, into(*dirname*). Stata will download the updates just as it would ordinarily but will place them in the directory you specify. We recommend that *dirname* be a new, empty directory, because later you will need to copy the entire contents of the directory to the official place. The official place is the directory listed next to UPDATES if you type sysdir. When you copy the files, copy over any existing files. Previously existing files in the official update directory are just previous updates. Also remember to make the files globally readable if necessary. See [R] **update**.

28.3.4 Updating the executable

Ado-file updates are released about every other week; updates for the executable are rarer than that. If the executable needs updating, Stata will mention it when you type update:

```
. update from http://www.stata.com
(contacting http://www.stata.com)

Stata executable
    folder:                 C:\Program Files\Stata11\
    name of file:           Stata.exe
    currently installed:    28 Jul 2009
    latest available:       12 Nov 2009

Ado-file updates
    folder:                 C:\Program Files\Stata11\ado\updates\
    names of files:         (various)
    currently installed:    28 Jul 2009
    latest available:       28 Jul 2009

Recommendation
    Type -update all-
```

Here is what happens when you type `update all`:

```
. update all
```

```
> update ado
(contacting http://www.stata.com)
ado-files already up to date
```

```
> update executable
(contacting http://www.stata.com)
Executable update log
    1.   verifying C:\Program Files\Stata11\ is writeable
    2.   downloading new executable
New executable successfully downloaded
Instructions
    1.   Type -update swap-
```

Just follow the instructions, which will vary depending on your computer. Here `update swap` is a command that automatically copies the newly downloaded executable over the current one. It then briefly restarts Stata to begin using the new executable. You must type `update swap` after downloading an executable update.

28.3.5 Frequently asked questions about updating the executable

1. If I understand this, `update all` does not really install the updated executable; it just copies one file onto my computer, and that one file happens to be the new executable, right?

    Probably. There can be more than one file such as a DLL. All the files are copied to the same place. When no DLLs are downloaded, this statement is true. On most systems, using the `update swap` command after downloading a new executable will perform the copy and actually install the executable.

2. How big is the downloaded file?

    Two to 35 MB, depending on the operating system.

3. What happens if I type `update all` and my executable is already up to date?

    Nothing. You are told "executable already up to date".

4. I am using Unix or a networked version of Stata. When Stata tries to update the executable, I am told that the directory is not writeable. Can I download the updated executable to another directory and then copy it to the official directory myself?

    Yes, assuming that you are a system administrator. Ordinarily, you would type `update all` and Stata would download whatever updates might be available, ado and/or executable. `update executable` allows you to download just the executable updates and to specify an alternate location for them to be installed. Type `update executable, into(`*dirname*`)`. We recommend that *dirname* be a new, empty directory, because there may be more than one file and later you will need to copy all of them to the official place. The official place is the directory listed next to STATA if you type `sysdir`. When you copy the files, copy over any existing files; we recommend that you make a backup of the originals first. See [R] **update**.

28.3.6   Updating both ado-files and the executable

When you type `update`, you may be told both the ado-files and executable need updating:

```
. update from http://www.stata.com
(contacting http://www.stata.com)

Stata executable
     folder:                C:\Program Files\Stata11\
     name of file:          Stata.exe
     currently installed:   28 Jul 2009
     latest available:      12 Nov 2009

Ado-file updates
     folder:                C:\Program Files\Stata11\ado\updates\
     names of files:        (various)
     currently installed:   28 Jul 2009
     latest available:      12 Nov 2009

Recommendation
     Type -update all-
```

Remember that if an executable update is downloaded, you will need to type `update swap` to finish installing it.

You could skip the `update from` step. You could just type `update all` and follow the instructions. If nothing needed updating, you would see

```
. update all
_____

> update ado
(contacting http://www.stata.com)
ado-files already up to date
_____

> update executable
(contacting http://www.stata.com)
executable already up to date

. _
```

28.4   Downloading and managing additions by users

Try the following:

type

     `. net from http://www.stata.com`

or

     Select **Help > SJ and User-written Programs**
     Click on one of the links

28.4.1   Downloading files

We are not the only ones developing additions to Stata. Stata is supported by a large and highly competent user community. An important part of this is the *Stata Journal* (SJ) and the *Stata Technical Bulletin* (STB). The *Stata Journal* is a refereed, quarterly journal containing articles of interest to Stata users. For more details and subscription information, visit the *Stata Journal* web site at http://www.stata-journal.com.

The *Stata Journal* is a printed and electronic journal with corresponding software. If you want the journal, you must subscribe, but the software is available for free from our web site at http://www.stata-journal.com.

The predecessor to the *Stata Journal* was the *Stata Technical Bulletin* (STB). The STB was also a printed and electronic journal with corresponding software. Individual STB issues may still be purchased. The STB software is available for free from our web site at http://www.stata.com.

Below are instructions for installing the *Stata Journal* and the *Stata Technical Bulletin* software from our web site.

Installing the Stata Journal software

1. Select **Help > SJ and User-written Programs**.

2. Click on *Stata Journal*.

3. Click on *sj2-2*.

4. Click on *st0001_1*.

5. Click on *click here to install*.

or type

1. Type: . net from http://www.stata-journal.com/software

2. Type: . net cd sj2-2

3. Type: . net describe st0001_1

4. Type: . net install st0001_1

The above could be shortened to

```
. net from http://www.stata-journal.com/software/sj2-2
. net describe st0001_1
. net install st0001_1
```

You could also type

```
. net sj 2-2
. net describe st0001_1
. net install st0001_1
```

Installing the STB software

1. Select **Help > SJ and User-written Programs**.

2. Click on *STB*.

3. Click on *stb58*.

4. Click on *sg84_3*.

5. Click on *click here to install*.

or type

1. Type: . net from http://www.stata.com

2. Type: . net cd stb

3. Type: . net cd stb58

4. Type: . net describe sg84_3

5. Type: . net install sg84_3

The above could be shortened to

```
. net from http://www.stata.com/stb/stb58
. net describe sg84_3
. net install sg84_3
```

28.4.2 Managing files

You now have the `concord` command, because we just downloaded and installed it. Convince yourself of this by typing

```
. help concord
```

and you might try it out, too. Let's now list the additions you have installed—that is probably just `concord`—and then get rid of `concord`.

In command mode, you can type

```
. ado dir
[1] package sg84_3 from http://www.stata.com/stb/stb58
      STB-58 sg84_3.  Concordance correlation coefficient: minor corrections
```

If you had more additions installed, they would be listed. Now knowing that you have *sg84_3* installed, you can obtain a more thorough description by typing

```
. ado describe sg84_3
```

```
[1] package sg84_3 from http://www.stata.com/stb/stb58
```

```
TITLE
      STB-58 sg84_3.  Concordance correlation coefficient:  minor corrections
DESCRIPTION/AUTHOR(S)
      STB insert by Thomas J. Steichen, RJRT
                  Nicholas J. Cox, University of Durham, UK
      Support:  steicht@rjrt.com, n.j.cox@durham.ac.uk
      After installation, see help concord
INSTALLATION FILES
      c/concord.ado
      c/concord.sthlp
INSTALLED ON
      5 Oct 2002
```

You can erase *sg84_3* by typing

```
. ado uninstall sg84_3
package sg84_3 from http://www.stata.com/stb/stb58
      STB-58 sg84_3.  Concordance correlation coefficient:  minor corrections

(package uninstalled)
```

You can do all of this from the point-and-click interface, too. Pull down **Help** and select **SJ and User-written Programs** and then click on *List*. From there, you can click on *sg84_3* to see the detailed description of the package and from there you can click on *click here to uninstall* if you want to erase it.

For more information on the `ado` command and the corresponding menu, see [R] **net**.

28.4.3   Finding files to download

There are two ways to find useful files to download. One is simply to thumb through sites. That is inefficient but entertaining. If you want to do that,

1. Select **Help > SJ and User-written Programs**.

2. Click on *Other Locations*.

3. Click on *links*.

What you are doing is starting at our download site and then working out from there. We maintain a list of other sites and those sites will have more links. You can do this from command mode, too:

```
. net from http://www.stata.com
. net cd links
```

The efficient way to find files—at least if you know what you are looking for—is to search. There are two ways to do that. If you suspect what you are looking for might already be in Stata (or published in the SJ), use Stata's `search` command:

```
. search concordance correlation
```

Equivalently, you could select **Help > Search**. Either way, you will learn about *sg84_3* and you can even click to install it.

If you want to search for additions over the net, i.e., the SJ and archive sites and user sites, type

```
. net search concordance correlation
```

or select **Help > Search**, and this time click *Search net resources*, rather than the default "*Search documentation and FAQs*".

28.4.4   Updating additions by users

After you have installed some user-written features, you should periodically check whether any updates or bug fixes area available for those commands. You can do this with the `adoupdate` command. Simply type `adoupdate` to see if any updates are available, and if they are, type `adoupdate, update` to obtain the updates. See [R] **adoupdate** for more details.

28.5   Making your own download site

There are two reasons you may wish to create your own download site:

1. You have datasets and the like, you want to share them with colleagues, and you want to make it easier for colleagues to download the files.

2. You have written Stata programs, etc., that you wish to share with the Stata user community.

Making a download site is easy; the full instructions are found in [R] **net**.

At the beginning of this chapter, we pretended that you had a dataset you wanted to share with colleagues. We said you just had to copy the dataset onto your server and then let your colleagues know the dataset is there.

Let's now pretend that you had two datasets, `ds1.dta` and `ds2.dta`, and you wanted your colleagues to be able to learn about and fetch the datasets by using the `net` command or by pulling down **Help** and selecting **SJ and User-written Programs**.

First, you would copy the datasets to your home page just as before. Then you would create three more files, one to describe your site named stata.toc and two more to describe each "package" you want to provide:

```
─────────────────────────────────────────────────── begin stata.toc ───────
v 3
d My name and affiliation (or whatever other title I choose)
d Datasets for the PAR study
p ds1 The base dataset
p ds2 The detail dataset
─────────────────────────────────────────────────── end stata.toc ───────
```

```
─────────────────────────────────────────────────── begin ds1.pkg ───────
v 3
d ds1.   The base dataset
d My name or whatever else I wanted to put
d This dataset contains the baseline values for ...
d Distribution-Date: 26sep2007
p ds1.dta
─────────────────────────────────────────────────── end ds1.pkg ───────
```

```
─────────────────────────────────────────────────── begin ds2.pkg ───────
v 3
d ds1.   The detail dataset
d My name or whatever else I wanted to put
d This dataset contains the follow-up information ...
d Distribution-Date: 26sep2007
p ds2.dta
─────────────────────────────────────────────────── end ds2.pkg ───────
```

The Distribution_Date line in the description should be changed whenever you change your package. This line is used by adoupdate to determine if a user who has installed your package needs to update it.

Here is what users would see when they went to your site:

```
. net from http://www.myuni.edu/hande/~aparker

http://www.myuni.edu/hande/~aparker
My name and whatever else I wanted to put

Datasets for the PAR study
PACKAGES you could -net describe-:
    ds1            The base dataset
    ds2            The detail dataset

. net describe ds1

package ds1 from http://www.myuni.edu/hande/~aparker

TITLE
      ds1.   The base dataset
DESCRIPTION/AUTHOR(S)
      My name and whatever else I wanted to put
      This dataset contains the baseline values for ...
      Distribution-Date: 26sep2007
ANCILLARY FILES                                     (type net get ds1)
      ds1.dta
```

```
. net get ds1
checking ds1 consistency and verifying not already installed...
copying into current directory...
      copying  ds1.dta
ancillary files successfully copied.

 . ─
```

See [R] **net**.

Subject and author index

This is the subject and author index for the *User's Guide*. You may also want to consult the combined subject index (and the combined author index) in the *Quick Reference and Index*. The combined index indexes the *Getting Started* manuals and all the reference manuals except the *Mata Reference Manual*.

Semicolons set off the most important entries from the rest. Sometimes no entry will be set off with semicolons, meaning that all entries are equally important.

! (not), *see* logical operators
!= (not equal), *see* relational operators
& (and), *see* logical operators
* abbreviation character, *see* abbreviations
– abbreviation character, *see* abbreviations
< (less than), *see* relational operators
<= (less than or equal), *see* relational operators
== (equality), *see* relational operators
> (greater than), *see* relational operators
>= (greater than or equal), *see* relational operators
? abbreviation characters, *see* abbreviations
| (or), *see* logical operators
˜ (not), *see* logical operators
˜ abbreviation character, *see* abbreviations
˜= (not equal), *see* relational operators

A

.a, .b, ..., .z, *see* missing values
abbreviations, [U] **11.2 Abbreviation rules**;
  [U] **11.1.1 varlist**, [U] **11.4 varlists**
aborting command execution, [U] **9 The Break key**,
  [U] **10 Keyboard use**
Access, Microsoft, reading data from, [U] **21.4 Transfer programs**
addition operator, *see* arithmetic operators
.ado filename suffix, [U] **11.6 File-naming conventions**
ado-files, [U] **3.5 The Stata Journal**, [U] **17 Ado-files**,
  [U] **18.11 Ado-files**
  downloading, *see* files, downloading
  installing, [U] **17.6 How do I install an addition?**
  location, [U] **17.5 Where does Stata look for ado-files?**
  long lines, [U] **18.11.2 Comments and long lines in ado-files**
  official, [U] **28 Using the Internet to keep up to date**
adopath command, [U] **17.5 Where does Stata look for ado-files?**
adosize, [U] **18.11 Ado-files**
Afifi, A. A., [U] **20.20 References**
algebraic expressions, functions, and operators,
  [U] **13 Functions and expressions**,
  [U] **13.3 Functions**
_all, [U] **11.1.1 varlist**

alphanumeric variables, *see* string variables
analytic weights, [U] **11.1.6 weight**,
  [U] **20.18.2 Analytic weights**
and operator, [U] **13.2.4 Logical operators**
Angrist, J. D., [U] **20.20 References**
append command, [U] **22 Combining datasets**
appending data, [U] **22 Combining datasets**
arithmetic operators, [U] **13.2.1 Arithmetic operators**
Author Support Program, [U] **3.8.2 For authors**
auto.dta, [U] **1.2.2 Example datasets**
autocode() function, [U] **25.1.2 Converting continuous variables to categorical variables**
[aweight=*exp*] modifier, [U] **11.1.6 weight**,
  [U] **20.18.2 Analytic weights**
Azen, S. P., [U] **20.20 References**

B

_b[], [U] **13.5 Accessing coefficients and standard errors**
BASE directory, [U] **17.5 Where does Stata look for ado-files?**
base level, [U] **11.4.3 Factor variables**
Baum, C. F., [U] **11.7 References**, [U] **16.5 References**,
  [U] **18.13 References**, [U] **20.20 References**
Belsley, D. A., [U] **18.13 References**
Binder, D. A., [U] **20.20 References**
biyearly() function, [U] **25 Working with categorical data and factor variables**
Break key, [U] **9 The Break key**, [U] **16.1.4 Error handling in do-files**
built-in variables, [U] **11.3 Naming conventions**,
  [U] **13.4 System variables (_variables)**
by-groups, [U] **11.5 by varlist: construct**
by *varlist*: prefix, [U] **11.5 by varlist: construct**,
  [U] **13.7 Explicit subscripting**, [U] **27.2 The by construct**
byte (storage type), [U] **12.2.2 Numeric storage types**

C

categorical variables, [U] **25.1.2 Converting continuous variables to categorical variables**
Chambers, J. M., [U] **1.4 References**
char command, [U] **12.8 Characteristics**
character data, *see* string variables
characteristics, [U] **12.8 Characteristics**,
  [U] **18.3.6 Extended macro functions**,
  [U] **18.3.13 Referring to characteristics**
clear option, [U] **11.2 Abbreviation rules**
Cleveland, W. S., [U] **1.4 References**
cmdlog command, [U] **15 Saving and printing output—log files**
_coef[], [U] **13.5 Accessing coefficients and standard errors**
coefficients (from estimation),
  accessing, [U] **13.5 Accessing coefficients and standard errors**